DAWN OF
ZOOLOGY

DAWN OF
ZOOLOGY

by Willy Ley

PRENTICE-HALL, Inc., Englewood Cliffs, N.J.

Dawn of Zoology
by Willy Ley

Library of Congress Catalog Card Number: 68-13648

Printed in the United States of America

T

Prentice-Hall International, Inc., London
Prentice-Hall of Australia, Pty. Ltd., Sydney
Prentice-Hall of Canada, Ltd., Toronto
Prentice-Hall of India Private Ltd., New Delhi
Prentice-Hall of Japan, Inc., Tokyo

Contents

List of Works by Willy Ley

Rockets, Missiles, and Men in Space
Engineers' Dreams
Willy Ley's Exotic Zoology
Watchers of the Skies, an Informal History of Astronomy
The Conquest of Space (with paintings by Chesley Bonestell)

TRANSLATIONS:
Otto Hahn: a Scientific Autobiography

COLLABORATIONS:
The Exploration of Mars (with Wernher von Braun and
    Chesley Bonestell)
Lands Beyond (with L. Sprague de Camp)

Introduction

CONTEMPORARY readers may be excused if they have been assuming that Willy Ley is two men who happen to have the same name, and that, recently, the most active of the two has been a rocket expert who, before the war, was among the earliest German experimenters in space science and in America outlined the mathematics of a Mars Project years before the construction of a rocket that could achieve escape velocity.

Actually, Mr. Ley's first professional training was in paleontology and he took up rockets as a hobby. Nowadays, I suppose, he should be called a rocket expert who continues paleontology and zoology as a hobby. Several of his very popular books have dealt with unsolved problems, zoological myths, or, as he prefers to call the subject, "Romantic Zoology." Perhaps psychologists could make something of the fact that he seems always to have been interested in either the past or the future rather than the present. Readers of this work can avoid all such problems by forgetting that Mr. Ley is a rocketeer and considering him only as a student of the development of zoology.

His story begins with Tiglath-Pileser—a mighty hunter to whom one of the Pharaohs sent an alligator and a hippopotamus as gifts. It continues down through Darwin and gives extended treatment to such major figures as Aristotle, Pliny, "Physiologus" and Gesner.

Included are many tidbits, such as the fact that the first known zoo was in ancient China; that Gesner's doctoral thesis boldly challenged Aristotle in contending that the brain, not the heart, is the seat of conscious activity; and that John Ray became the first real biologist in England because he was expelled for political reasons from his college fellowship.

Mr. Ley avoids the too familiar thesis that all the sciences grew out of the pseudo-sciences—chemistry out of alchemy; astronomy out of astrology; zoology out of myth, fable and the search for moral meaning in natural phenomena. Hunters, breeders of domestic animals, physicians seeking remedies and even monks obsessed with "and the moral of that is" may have made some contributions. But the desire to satisfy curiosity which had no ulterior purpose is the real father of zoology. His book will illustrate how such curiosity operated and how it often went astray before it achieved a correct answer.

—Joseph Wood Krutch

DAWN OF
ZOOLOGY

chapter one

The Urus.

Man the Hunter

Darnach sluog Sivrit sciere
einen Wisent und einen Elch
Starker Ure viere
und einen grimmen Scelch.

THESE lines from the *Nibelungenlied* when rendered in a more recent Germanic language—English, that is—look like this:

Thereafter Siegfried killed
a wisent and an elk
And then four sturdy uri
and one ferocious shelk.

The lines refer to the final fatal hunt in the forests of the Vosges mountains before Hagen von Tronje's spear pierced the vulnerable spot on Siegfried's back where a linden tree leaf had prevented Fafnir's blood from protecting the skin. The purpose is to depict Siegfried as the mighty hunter; almost incidentally they also reveal how rich these forests were in game at the time of Siegfried. And the very fact that the names of the animals are largely unfamiliar to practically everybody except professional zoologists shows how much Europe has changed in not much more than a millennium.

3

The wisent of the *Nibelungenlied* is the European bison, which still survives under strict protection. The elk is the animal more commonly called moose in the United States. The urus is—or rather was—a large short-haired form of wild cattle that became extinct in 1627. Shelk, a word now obsolete, meant a male horse, in this case a wild one.

The *Nibelungenlied,* in the form we now have, was written down not earlier than A.D. 980 and not later than 1200, but the events described were then about a half a millennium in the past. This fact accounts for some historical inaccuracies. For example, during the final battle in "King Etzel's" palace a hero called Dietrich von Bern is present—he is the historical Theodoric of Verona, while Etzel is Attila, the ruler of the Huns. But the historical Attila died in A.D. 453 while Theodoric was not born until 454. And Attila invaded the domains of King Gunther (known to history as Gundahar) in A.D. 436. The "time of Siegfried" (who is tentatively identified with a lord named Segerius) is then the early part of the fifth century, at which time these animals lived in the forests of the Vosges mountains. But around the year 1000, when the *Nibelungenlied* was written down, they still lived there, though probably in somewhat reduced numbers.

The meat of all the animals mentioned in the *Nibelungenlied* was still served regularly to the monks of the monastery of St. Gallen in Switzerland around the year 1000, as evidenced by the *Codex benedictionum ad mensas,* written about that year by Ekkehard, the *Magister scholarum* of the monastery. They also ate, according to Ekkehard: "bear, beaver, deer, and ibex"—Switzerland must have been full of game then.

In 1100 B.C., Tiglath-Pileser I, the king of Assyria, had enlarged his empire by extending it into the domains of the older Hittite empire and by defeating Marduk-nadin-akhē, king of Babylonia. The inscriptions on monuments he had erected brag verbosely about his political and military exploits, but they also make sure that the world would know about his prowess as a mighty hunter:

> Wild oxen [uri again], large and devastating ones, he killed at Arazig, the city, that lies near the land of Chatti and at the foot of the Lebanon mountains; live young of the wild oxen he caught, whole herds of them he brought together. . . . Elephants he killed with his bow, live elephants he caught and brought to his city of Assur . . . 120 lions he killed in his youthful abundance of courage and strength and 800 lions he killed from his chariot in the open field. . . .

The differences are interesting. Siegfried, in his forested mountains, hunts afoot and with his spear and sword and the chief purpose was to provide the kitchen with meat. The king of Assyria hunted mainly for sport, using arrows as weapons and apparently doing most of his hunting from a horse-drawn open war chariot.

Assyrian lion hunt, from an Assyrian frieze. The hunting was done with bow and arrow by the king (Tiglath-Pileser?) from a war chariot driven by somebody else. The dagger-bearing warriors on foot evidently administered the *coup de grâce*.

Let us turn the clock back another eight thousand years and return to northern Europe. The glaciers of the last stage of the Ice Age had then only recently withdrawn. The areas that had been chilled for millennia by the load of a thousand feet or more of compacted snow had changed into wide open fertile plains. They were plains because the forests had not yet had time to move northward in a solid phalanx of wooden pillars. But the plant-eating animals did not need to search for food. It grew all around them in abundance.

The men who hunted them were, in all probability, our direct ancestors; all, or nearly all, Neanderthalers had disappeared. The animals hunted included wild horses, several types of deer and stags, the still-living type of moose and a now extinct larger version of moose, reindeer and uri, and bears.

Man, in northern Europe just after the Ice Age, was not a numerous animal, but a casual observer from another planet would have seen quickly that Man was on the road to mastery. Any schoolboy knows that this mastery is due to the greater size, ability, and efficiency of the human brain, to that of other animals. That is true as far as it goes, but the ability to remember sights and smells and situations and to act upon such memories and conclusions drawn from them is not enough.

The body must have the means to act, to "implement the plan," as Sir Winston Churchill used to say, and Man's available implementation is not too good. The human body is completely unarmored and not well armed. Humans have astonishing endurance of legs and lungs and they have powerful hands. But they lack hard hoofs with which to kick, their fingernails are too weak for rending, and their teeth are not strong—we know positively that even then people suffered from cavities and abscessed roots.

It is quite possible that a kind of physical accident was as important as the superior brain—namely, the ability to throw things. The apes, as far as one can find out without living among them, do not seem to take advantage of this ability, but many monkeys do. Among my childhood memories is one of a baboon cage in the Zoological Garden of Berlin with a large sign warning the public: "This animal is in the habit of throwing pebbles. Be on guard."

Nobody warned the animals of the post-glacial epoch. Man, the being who could not only think but also hurt and kill from a distance, became master.

If a master is strong and reasonable—that is, if he is willing to give something in return for service—the servant does not lead a bad life. All that is needed is his willingness to be a servant—or else his inability to understand the relative positions. Since Man was obviously able to do something for willing servants, and since he grew bright enough to understand *his* part of the relative positions, he found servants.

There is a kind of general agreement between zoologists and anthropologists—and they don't agree too often, perhaps because their respective fields touch in only a few places—that the dog was the first animal to be domesticated. As events are usually imagined, canines of a smallish type first became camp followers, in the most literal meaning of this word. A hunter's life is one of famines and feasts. If the hunting is poor, the tribe goes hungry. If the hunting is good, there is too much to eat. As a result potential food is discarded. Who is going to chew on a tough and lean leg if there is a nice red liver and fat-encrusted kidneys? Even some of the things the hunter himself likes to eat will be left around, because after eating as much as he can the hunter simply falls asleep. There is then food for dogs. They don't have to hunt themselves any more. All that is required is patience. The brain of a dog is certainly good enough to learn such a set of facts very quickly.

There is no history of the sequence in which the various domesticated animals became domesticated. And it was probably not the same in various areas of the world. But for Europe north of the Alps one can make a good guess about the second animal to become domesticated. If the dog was the first, the second place most likely belongs to the pig. The reasons are the same, assuming that humans, in the meantime, had started making permanent, or at least seasonal camps.

At a camp that stayed in one place for several months, the picture must have been something like this: In good weather the males of the tribe go out and hunt, while the females and the children gather edible things that do not run away—plants, birds' eggs, grubs. Every item of food also becomes, in part, an item of discard. Heaps of discarded but still partly edible matter pile up near the camp. In places where the tribes did not move for generations, the heaps grew into mounds, the famous kitchen middens of northern Europe. Such mounds of debris containing edible matter would also attract animals other than dogs. Pigs are the most likely, along with some kinds of birds.*

Early man was certainly interested in pigs, and pig enclosures to keep them from running away may have been the earliest stables built.

Whether sheep or goats or horses or cattle were next on the list is impossible to say, but by the year 2000 B.C. all of these were domesticated. In different areas other animals were added to the list, as for example the camel in the lands of the Near East. By that time the Indians already had tame elephants and, very probably, also tame cheetahs which they used in hunting as northerners used dogs.

In Egypt some types of animals which we no longer consider domesticated were listed as such. Among the possessions of a rich Egyptian

* Birds attracted to the refuse heaps had two advantages: they were highly mobile and hard to hit, and most of them were too small to make killing them worthwhile. In all those ancient kitchen-midden sites (using the term in its widest sense as camp debris of any sort) bird bones are extremely scarce.

Wild boar, as pictured in the work of Aldrovandi.

of about the year 2000 B.C., 1,135 gazelles and 2,552 antelopes of several types are listed. Whether they were domesticated in our sense will remain an open question. The same goes for the "battle lions" of Amenhotep II and Rameses the Great. They kept fairly large numbers of lions, presumably quite tame because of regular feeding hours, which attacked the enemy in battle.

The association between Man and the larger animals both in peace and war dates back a long time, but it was a strictly utilitarian association. The cattle breeders no doubt knew all the practical aspects of their activity and took care to learn what they could, for the more a breeder knows about his animals the more likely he is to be successful. And Amenhotep's keepers of the battle lions also must have known a great deal about lions, their moods and temperaments. They probably knew more than they ever told their master, assuming that the master deigned to ask about the animals.

But what they knew amounted to simple tricks of the trade, comparable say to the awareness of an apprentice electrician that copper wires must be scraped shiny before they are twisted together to make an electrical connection.

Zoology did not begin with the hunters, who only knew what they hunted, nor with the breeders, who only knew what they bred. The prehistory of zoology began with something entirely different—the discovery that there were curiosities.

Tiglath-Pileser I, he who was concerned about his reputation as a great hunter, one day received an interesting present from the ruler of Egypt. The pharaoh sent him a large crocodile, a "donkey of the waters" (hippopotamus), and a few strange fishes from the sea. We do not know what Tiglath-Pileser did with the animals, but since the Egyptian ruler sent them as a royal present he presumably had been informed that neither the crocodile nor the hippopotamus was native to Tiglath-Pileser's realm.

Tiglath-Pileser's successor of about six generations later, Assur-nasir-pal, who ruled from 884 to 859 B.C., went a step further. After some preliminary bragging about his prowess and success as a hunter, ". . . 30 mighty elephants I killed, 257 enormous wild oxen I killed from my open chariot with arrows, 370 strong lions I killed with lances as if they were birds in a cage," he continued in a different vein: ". . . 50 young lions I took, [brought them] to the city of Kalach and to my palace, put them into a house and showed them. I let them bear young in large numbers; living lynxes I caught with my hands, herds of wild oxen, elephants, lions, ostriches, *pagu* (?),* wild asses, gazelles, antelopes, wild dogs, panthers, *sikurru* (?),* animals of the desert and of the mountains I brought to my city and let the peoples of my lands view them."

This was the first zoological garden outside of China, where a Park of Intelligence had been decreed by Emperor Wu Wang in about the year 1150 B.C. It is not known whether this Park of Intelligence was open to the public or whether it existed for the edification of the Imperial officials only. Nor do we know for how long it was maintained. The records show that the park established by Assur-nasir-pal still existed two hundred years after its founding but had sharply declined in quality. By 670 B.C. it contained only horses, camels, donkeys, goats, cattle,

* These animals have not been identified.

mules, sheep, stags, gazelles, hares, and birds. In short, it was hardly more than a collection of the currently domesticated animals.

But even a poor zoological park still evokes some curiosity, and Aristotle, a few centuries later, remarked quite correctly that science begins with wondering.

Other Greeks before Aristotle had wondered about various aspects of the earth and especially of the heavens. Aristotle extended his very considerable intellectual curiosity to animals. He studied animals for the sake of knowledge that his contemporaries probably deemed "useless" and that was, as a matter of fact, useless in his time.

Since nobody before Aristotle had even tried to be systematic in relation to animals, the older zoological knowledge comes from odd corners. The oldest literary source containing any zoological information is probably the famous *Papyrus Ebers* of about 1500 B.C. It is one of the medical papyri, containing, according to George Sarton,[1] 877 recipes (12 of which are spells) in 2,289 lines of script. Zoological matters are mentioned only by way of example or comparison, but whoever wrote the papyrus knew that tadpoles turn into frogs, that larvae turn into flies, and that a beetle—the sacred scarab, of course—begins life as a grub.

The next source is only slightly more recent than the *Papyrus Ebers*. It is an inscription in the temple of Der el-Bahri near Thebes, built on order of Hat-shepsut, Queen of Egypt. It tells of an expedition to the "Land of Punt" made by order of the Queen. The date of the expedition must have been around 1493 B.C., and the Land of Punt was the area on both sides of the Bab el-Mandeb, the strait at the southern end of the Red Sea. Animals mentioned in the inscription are: dog-headed monkeys, long-tailed monkeys, swift dogs (most translations say greyhounds, but they were not the greyhounds of today), and leopards. (The last are not mentioned as live animals; the text speaks of leopard skins.) A picture of the ship, in the same temple, yields some more zoological information. Several marine creatures are shown under the keel of the ship: three different fishes, an octopus, and a large lobsterlike crab without large pincers, like the *langouste* of the Mediterranean.

The next source is again nautical, namely the joint Israeli-Phoenician expedition to Ophir, in which the military skill of King Solomon's soldiers was combined with the Phoenicians' knowledge of the sea. The expedition returned victorious, ". . . bringing gold, and silver, ivory, and apes, and peacocks" (I Kings, 10:22). Gold, silver, ivory, and apes could indicate Africa but the peacocks pointed to Asia, and just because of those peacocks Ophir has been placed in a very large number of highly unlikely areas by various commentators. However, the east coast of Africa always seemed the most likely place and the discrepancy strongly suggested that something was wrong with the Biblical text. Most commentators tried to find a way out by saying that the word "peacocks" may have been used for ostriches, which would make the whole thing safely African.* But in the days of Solomon, the ostrich roamed in areas much closer to Palestine than it does now and would hardly have been considered a great curiosity. The whole story remained a mystery until the theologian Reinhold Niebuhr suggested a miswriting of only *one* Hebrew letter. Peacocks, in the original text, is *thukkijim,* but the word *sukkijim* means slaves. That an expedition to the African east coast—the area of Somaliland—should return with gold, silver, ivory, monkeys, and slaves is quite logical.

Homer—say around 800 B.C.—talks mostly about well-known domesticated animals but imparts a little information in the process. He is the first to mention mules, and he states that the breeding of mules was started at the shores of the Black Sea. Penelope kept tame geese on the grounds of her palace and liked to watch them—the earliest mention of a domesticated bird. The famous story (*Iliad,* Book III) about the annual battle between the cranes and the pygmies of Africa has gone through all the permutations possible in the course of history. During antiquity it was simply believed. From the time of the Renaissance until about a hundred years ago it was taken to be pure symbolism (but of what?), since there were no pygmies. When pygmies were discovered during the years 1863–65 by Paul Belloni du Chaillu the astonishment was great. Pygmies did exist, but how could Homer have known about them? In any case, Homer, it was assumed, had made a mistake in his geography; he had placed his pygmies in the area of the swamps of the Upper Nile—that is to say, near the African east coast—while Du Chaillu's actual pygmies lived near the west coast. But in 1870 Georg August Schweinfurth discovered pygmies in just the area where Homer had said they lived, beyond the Nile swamps. Very soon afterward it

---

* One recent commentator decided that the so-called Congo peacock must have been meant, but the Congo peacock (*Afropavo congensis*) lacks the peacock's sumptuous tail and the trained eye of a zoologist is needed to recognize it as a peacock. Moreover it does not occur along the east coast of Africa.

Peacocks, from *Hortus sanitatis*, 1491.

was established (by way of sculptures and inscriptions) that the Egyptians had known about the pygmies for a long time. Homer invented neither the pygmies nor the cranes flying down from the north. He only invented the battle between them.

In 525 B.C. Hanno the Carthaginian made a naval expedition southward along Africa's west coast. His farthest point south was the Cameroon mountains, and the zoological discovery of the expedition was the chimpanzee.

Whether Hanno intended to sail around Africa is doubtful. His voyage was part of a concerted effort to explore the seas to the north and to the south of the Pillars of Hercules; Hanno went southward; his brother Himilko went north.

Hanno's own report is known—Himilko's is lost—and it is a most unusually terse report, so terse and colorless that somebody guessed later that Hanno was frugal with words because the report was to be engraved on a temple wall and this wall could only accommodate an inscription of a certain length. Of course we don't actually know that this was the reason. All we have is a Greek translation of the report and of that translation we have only one copy, made during the tenth century and labeled *Codex Heidelbergensis* 398. The end seems to be missing—the final sentences are those quoted below—but even that is not certain.

The report, or at least the Greek version, consists of eighteen numbered paragraphs. Paragraph 10 says that the ships passed a wide river which was inhabited by crocodiles and hippopotami. Earlier statements about the progress of the voyage make it clear that this river must be the Senegal. Paragraphs 15–17 tell of passing a shoreline where rivers of fire from an active volcano flowed into the sea. Having passed the area of volcanic activity, Hanno's ships reached a bay and then, as paragraph 18 of the report says:

> At the other end of the bay there is an island, similar to the one mentioned earlier. On the island there was a lake and another island in the lake; this island was inhabited by forest people. There were many females with shaggy pelts; our interpreters called them *gorilloi*. We pursued the males but failed to catch one for they all ran away, climbing steep hills and defending themselves by throwing stones. We caught three females, but they bit and scratched and would not follow us. We killed them and brought their skins to Carthage. We did not go any farther because we ran short of provisions.

The Greek translator probably used the word *gorilloi,* which is not a Greek word, as an approximation to the word used by Hanno. Needless to say, it has caused confusion ever since the report was first published, at Basel in 1533. The animal encountered by Hanno's men can only have been the chimpanzee. The real gorilla lives much further inland, and a report of an encounter with a group of gorillas would have read differently, even if it had been written for engraving on a temple wall. But the result of the use of this term was that for centuries the chimpanzee was referred to as "gorilla," while occasional stories about the actual gorilla were firmly disbelieved. The confusion was not cleared up until Du Chaillu discovered the true gorilla a century ago.

A similar pattern of misinterpretation (or, in this case, noninterpretation) for lack of knowledge has to do with a Persian bas-relief at Persepolis. The overall theme of the friezes is a festive occasion when

Portion of a frieze at Persepolis, showing an okapi being brought as a present for Xerxes the Great (*ca.* 475 B.C.).

delegations from many nations brought presents to the Persian king Xerxes the Great. Xerxes died in 465 B.C. The bas-relief might have been made while he was still alive, in any event soon after his death. One of the groups shown consists of four people, a Persian usher showing the way to three men with Negroid features. The first of the three Negroes, evidently the head of the delegation, does not carry anything.

The second carries a closed vessel. The third carries an elephant tusk and leads an animal. It was only with the discovery of the okapi at the beginning of the current century that the animal being led on the frieze of Persepolis was identified.

The name of Xenophon appears in every history of military matters but is missing in virtually every history of zoology. While Xenophon did not make any zoological discoveries, his writings certainly deserve to be mentioned, since they contain information that cannot be found elsewhere. Xenophon wrote a short book known to Greek scholars as the *Kynegetikos,* a treatise on hunting with special emphasis on hunting hares, something Xenophon apparently liked to do himself. This treatise also has a section on breeding dogs, the first such discussion in any language.

The famous *Anabasis* contains, at one point, a zoological surprise. In 401 B.C. Xenophon had joined an army of Greek mercenaries which Cyrus the Lesser (also called Cyrus the Younger; both terms are used to distinguish him from Cyrus the Great, the founder of the Persian Empire) led against his brother and sovereign Artaxerxes. Battle was joined at Kunaxa and the result a debacle in which Cyrus himself was killed. The defeated army was left alone to find its way home if it could. The march of the Ten Thousand, as it is usually called, was led by Xenophon, who had been elected leader. The story of this military expedition, to the point where Trebizond was finally reached in 399 B.C., was told by Xenophon in the three books of the *Anabasis.** Section V of Book I begins as follows:

> Thence he [Cyrus] marched through Arabia, keeping the Euphrates on the right. . . . In this region the ground was an unbroken plain, as level as the sea, and full of wormwood; and whatever else there was on the plain by way of shrub or reed was always fragrant, like spices; trees there were none, but wild animals of all sorts, vast numbers of wild asses and many ostriches, besides bustards and gazelles. These animals were sometimes chased by the horsemen. As for the asses, whenever one chased them, they would run on ahead and stop—for they ran much faster than the horses—and then, when the horses came near, they would do the same thing again, and it was impossible to catch them unless the horsemen posted themselves at intervals and hunted them in relays. The

---

* The word *anabasis* might be translated as "climbing up," which was the Greek way of saying "moving away from the sea." Strictly speaking the title fits Book I only, for the other two are about getting back to the sea.

Ostrich, from Gesner. The unnamed artist apparently had seen an ostrich but drew the picture from memory, with only one type of feathers over a generally correct outline.

flesh of those that were captured was like venison, but more tender. But no ostrich was captured by anyone, and any horseman who chased one speedily desisted; for it would distance him at once in its flight, not merely plying its feet, but hoisting its wings and using them like a sail. The bustards, on the other hand, can be caught if one is quick in starting them up, for they fly only a short distance, like partridges, and soon tire; and their flesh was delicious.

It is known, because of surviving cups made of the shells of ostrich eggs, as well as from monuments, that ostriches occurred in Mesopotamia in ancient times. But if Xenophon's work had not survived we would not know that they were still fairly common in Asia Minor as late as 400 B.C. We do not know just when they disappeared from there nor can anybody think of a reason why they disappeared, for the region has not undergone any important climatic changes since that time.

The book about the Persian wars is the somewhat earlier *History* of Herodotus of Halikarnassos who lived from 484–425 B.C. Like Xenophon's book it is mainly concerned with history and military history and pays attention to natural history only occasionally. But Herodotus was a careful observer and a good reporter. He always tried to be fair-minded and accurate, and usually succeeded.

His remarks about zoological matters are usually found in his descriptions of what people did. He reported, for example, that the Egyptians used large brooders for hatching eggs. These consisted of large chambers of masonry that were kept at the proper temperature and in which thousands of eggs were spread about. A slave, who could not leave because the entrance had been sealed, had the duty of turning all the eggs at regular intervals. When the chicks had hatched he gave a prearranged signal; the entrance was then unsealed and he could come out. One of my teachers, in relating the story to his pupils, never failed to point out with much emotion that this was a prime example of "man's inhumanity to man." Since nobody in the class had ever been to Egypt nobody could tell him that the interior of that brooder was not much warmer than the outside. The slave in question, being used to heat, might even have considered it an easy job, compared to the other tasks that may have been demanded of him if he hadn't been sealed off.

Herodotus often mentioned what animals could be found where:

> . . . the remainder of Lybia towards the west is far fuller of wild beasts
> . . . this is the tract in which huge serpents are found, and the lions, the

elephants, the bears,* the aspicks and the horned asses (?). . . . Among the wanderers [in the eastern part] are none of these, but quite other animals; as antelopes, gazelles, buffaloes and asses, not of the horned sort, but of a kind which does not need to drink; also oryxes, whose horns are used for the curved side of citherns and whose size is about that of the ox; foxes, hyenas, porcupines, wild rams, *dictyes* (?), jackals, panthers, *boryes* (lizards?), land-crocodiles (monitor lizards), about three cubits in length, very like lizards [in shape], ostriches and little snakes, each with a single horn. All these animals are found here, and likewise those belonging to other countries, except the stag and the wild-boar; but neither stag nor wild-boar are found in any part of Lybia. There are, however, three sorts of mice in these parts; the first are called two-footed [jerboas]; the next, zegeries, which is a Lybian word meaning "hills"; and the third urchins. Weasels are also found. . . .

While Herodotus was a careful reporter, he did not do much investigating of his own. He himself said repeatedly: "If this be true, I know not; I but write what is said." Apparently he did not think it necessary to investigate stories about animals in detail; he may have felt that while somebody might lie when it came to politics or to finance, nobody would say something untrue about such a relatively unimportant thing as the animals of a region. The result was that Herodotus is responsible for quite a number of ridiculous stories, most of which were firmly believed for centuries to come.

The following are the peculiarities of the crocodile: During the four winter months they eat nothing; they are four-footed, and live indifferently on land or in the water. The female lays and hatches her eggs ashore, passing the greater portion of the day on dry land, but at night retiring to the river, the water of which is warmer than the night air and the dew. Of all known animals this is the one which from the smallest size grows to be the greatest: for the egg of the crocodile is but little bigger than that of the goose, and the younger crocodile is in proportion to the egg; yet when it is full grown, the animal measures frequently seventeen cubits and even more. It has the eyes of a pig, teeth large and tusk-like, of a size proportioned to its frame; unlike any other animal it is without a tongue; it cannot move its under jaw, and in this respect too it is singular, being the only animal in the world which moves the upper jaw but not the under. It has strong claws and a scaly skin, impenetrable

* George Rawlinson's translation, which I am using, is correct, but the mention of bears is a puzzle since no bears are known from Africa.

upon the back. In the water it is blind, but on land it is very keen of sight. As it lives chiefly in the river, it has the inside of its mouth constantly covered with leeches; hence it happens that, while all the other birds and beasts avoid it, with the trochilus it lives in peace, since it owes much to that bird: for the crocodile, when he leaves the water and comes out upon the land, is in the habit of lying with his mouth wide open, facing the western breeze: at such times the trochilus goes into his mouth and devours the leeches. This benefits the crocodile, who is pleased, and takes care not to hurt the trochilus.*

The description of the hippopotamus reads: "It is a quadruped, cloven-footed, with hoofs like an ox, and a flat nose. It has the mane and tail of a horse, huge tusks which are very conspicuous, and a voice like a horse's neigh. In size it equals the biggest oxen, and its skin is so tough that when dried it is made into javelins." Here only mane, tail, and neigh are wrong. Herodotus was partly going by the animal's Greek name, derived from *hippos,* meaning horse, and *potamos,* meaning river.

"As the Greeks are well acquainted with the shape of the camel," Herodotus wrote, "I shall not trouble to describe it; but I shall mention what seems to have escaped their notice. The camel has in its hind legs four thigh bones and four knee joints." This "fact" continues to escape our notice to this day.

Equally mysterious is the description of the lion's birth:

> The lioness . . . which is one of the strongest and boldest of brutes, brings forth young but once in her lifetime, and then a single cub; she cannot possibly conceive again, since she loses her womb at the same time that she drops her young. The reason of this is, that as soon as the cub begins to stir inside the dam, his claws, which are sharper than those of any other animal, scratch the womb; as the time goes on, and he grows bigger, he tears it ever more and more; so that at last, when the birth comes, there is not a morsel in the whole womb that is sound.

He has a similar story to tell about the viper:

> If [vipers] increased as fast as their nature would allow, impossible were it for man to maintain himself upon the earth. Accordingly it is

---

* Sounds impressive, but of course as in all other animals it is the crocodile's lower jaw that is movable, it does have a tongue, its sight is as good under water as on land, and the bird that walks into the crocodile's open jaws is the black-backed plover.

The two kinds of camels, as pictured in the works of Aldrovandi.

found that when the male and female come together, at the very moment of impregnation, the female seizes the male by the neck, and having once fastened, cannot be brought to leave go till she has bit the neck through entirely. And so the male perishes; but after a while he is revenged upon the female by means of the young, which, while still unborn, gnaw a passage through the womb, and then through the belly of their mother, and so make their entrance into the world. Contrariwise other snakes, which are harmless, lay eggs, and hatch a vast number of young.

Both stories sound as if Herodotus had carelessly asked a native to tell him about the lives of lions and vipers, maybe even going so far as to promise a coin in return for the favor. Then, of course, for the sake of the coin, and also to please the visiting foreigner, Arabic imagination went to work.

The next fabulous story seems to be based more on a misunderstanding than on a deliberate attempt to deceive. Persian informers told Herodotus that the "Indians"—meaning anybody to the east or north of the borders of Persia—obtain their gold from a desert where "there live among the sand great ants, in size somewhat less than dogs, but bigger than foxes. ... Those ants make their dwellings under ground, and like the Greek ants, which they very much resemble in shape, throw up sand heaps as they burrow ... the sand which they throw up is full of gold." There is a burrowing animal in the Asiatic deserts, the bobak, which is a burrowing rodent, and in some places there is also gold in the ground. So far the whole thing may be based on a mistranslation, but the subsequent story—that the gold hunters go into the desert riding a female camel and accompanied by two males which fall behind when the ants pursue them and are sacrificed while the faster running female escapes with its rider (and the gold)—is again the result of much imagination on the part of the storyteller.

But Herodotus was not completely gullible. He doubted certain stories about the geography of what was to him the "far north" (the lands around the North Sea) but has to conclude:

> Nevertheless, tin and amber do certainly come to us from the ends of the earth. The northern parts of Europe are very much richer in gold than any other region: but how it is produced I have no certain knowledge. The story runs, that the one-eyed Arimaspi purloin it from the griffins; but here too I am incredulous, and cannot persuade myself that there is a race of men born with one eye, who in all else resemble the rest of mankind.

Here is Herodotus's story about the "winged serpents," based on his personal investigation:

> I went once to a certain place in Arabia, almost exactly opposite the city of Buto, to make inquiries concerning the winged serpents. On my arrival I saw the backbones and ribs of serpents in such numbers as it is impossible to describe: of the ribs there were a multitude of heaps, some great, some small, some middle-sized. The place where the bones lie is at the entrance of a narrow gorge between steep mountains, which there open upon a spacious plain communicating with the great plain of Egypt. The story goes that with the spring the winged snakes come flying from Arabia towards Egypt, but are met in this gorge by the birds called ibises, who forbid their entrance and destroy them all. The Arabians assert, and the Egyptians also admit, that it is on account of the service thus rendered that the Egyptians hold the ibis in so much reverence.

At first glance this looks like a story invented to explain why the ibis was sacred, and to some extent that explanation is correct. But just what was it that Herodotus saw? The answer is somewhat surprising. From the description of the gorge and from the distances of the place from known places mentioned elsewhere by Herodotus, the gorge has to be in the Mokattam mountains. And in the spring, that is, after the rainy season, fossil bones in large numbers are uncovered there. They happen to be the bones of extinct mammals, not of serpents. Neither Herodotus nor any of his contemporaries could have known that.

But the bones are there, "some great, some small, some middle-sized."

chapter two

Aristotle

Man the Thinker

ARISTOTLE, the pupil of Plato, was born in 384 B.C. in northern Greece in the city of Stageira. Later Latin-writing authors could never agree whether to transcribe the original Greek letters as Stagira or as Stagyra. Both forms are still in use, so that Aristotle is referred to as "the Stagirite" or "the Stagyrite," but no matter how the name of the city is spelled, the boy did not stay there for very long. A few years later his father, Nikomachos, was appointed physician to Amyntas II, King of Macedonia, and the family naturally moved to the residence of the King. When Aristotle reached the age of 17 his father sent him to Athens to complete his education and he was received into the Academy that Plato had founded two decades earlier. The aging Plato, in his early sixties at the time of Aristotle's arrival, was greatly pleased with his new pupil, younger than he by nearly 44 years, but one who grasped concepts so quickly that Plato sometimes said that Aristotle must be "a reader of the mind."

Young Aristotle was precocious, brilliant, and energetic, and while precocity naturally has to come to an end with advancing years, brilliance of mind and virtually unlimited energy remained with him until he succumbed to an unspecified illness on the island of Euboea in 322 B.C.

Teacher and pupil, Plato and Aristotle, dominated all philosophy for a long time, beginning a few centuries after their deaths until well into the seventeenth century. "Dominated" must not be construed to mean "jointly." Historically their domination of all educated thought followed the same sequence as their physical lives. From, say, A.D. 200 until about 1200 the term "the Philosopher," pronounced in awe with an audible capital, meant Plato. After that it meant Aristotle. The process was simply that the teachings of one replaced the teachings of the other— a large-scale repetition of the process that had taken place in Aristotle's mind.

Young Aristotle, of course, had absorbed Plato's ideas for a few years and must have been a full-fledged Platonist for the same length of time. Strangely enough, his writings from his "platonic period" are lost, but any attempt to "explain" this loss (for example, as a deliberate suppression of his youthful works by the older and different Aristotle) runs into so many logical difficulties that the result has to be zero. These writings must have become the victims of an unknown historical accident. Just for how long Aristotle remained a Platonist is not known either. He spent two decades in Athens, but the customary conclusion that he remained Plato's devoted pupil all the time is plainly wrong. No doubt he went to the Academy from time to time to see his old master and to chat with other "members" (all highly informal) of the Academy closer to his own age. But that does not mean, or even imply, that he agreed with Plato or with the other pupils any longer.

That he had already moved away from Plato is self-evident; according to Diogenes Laërtios * the old Plato complained that "Aristotle spurns me as colts kick out at the mother who bore them." The differences in outlook and attitude probably began to show as soon as Aristotle felt sure that he completely understood Plato's teachings.

Plato tried to be what might be called a "pure" philosopher, who, having formed a set of opinions, spent his life defending them. To him the "truth" consisted of immortal ideas, and the material world was unimportant, a mere shadow of these ideas. Kings, in order to be kings, should be philosophers and rule accordingly. Plato, in expounding his opinions, and by being the daily oracle of the Academy, probably grew more and more adamant. The Germans—not the Greeks—have a word for it, *Greisentrotz*. The term is untranslatable; the first part of it means

---

* Diogenes Laërtios is also the only source for an incomplete description of Aristotle's appearance: "spoke with a lisp . . . , his calves were slender, his eyes small and he was conspicuous by his attire, his rings and the cut of his hair."

"old man" (with a hint of possible senility), the second part is best expressed by the not very literary term "mulishness"—the rigid insistence on being right *because* of greater age.

Aristotle—always keep in mind the difference of 44 years in age—looked at things differently. As a boy he had been exposed to court life in Macedonia and must have realized that politics was a hard-headed business which might be influenced by philosophical ideas but could not be subordinated to them. Even more important, Aristotle's father had been a physician and experience with sick or injured people at least teaches one thing: find out the facts before you act. Plato's attitude disregarded facts, if necessary, and could very easily grow into a refusal to learn facts. Aristotle began to pay more and more attention to facts, and he grew into a "natural" philosopher.

It is usually said that Aristotle was greatly disappointed when Plato, on his deathbed, designated his nephew Speusippos as his successor as head of the Academy. Aristotle may well have considered himself the natural successor—he would be in our eyes, too. But just as a candidate for president of the United States must choose a running mate from his own party, Plato had to designate somebody who agreed with him. In any event Aristotle and his friend Xenokrates left Athens, accepting an invitation from Hermeias, a former fellow pupil who had grown very rich in the meantime, to come to Assos, a place on what is now the Turkish mainland.

While there, Aristotle made a new friend, Theophrastos, and married Pythias, the niece of Hermeias. The time was spent in studying, debating, and teaching, for Hermeias had founded a branch of the Academy. Quite often Aristotle and Theophrastos sailed across the strait to the island of Mytilēnē (now Lesbos) where Theophrastos had been born. The sails were not just for relaxation; Aristotle was too restless for that. The shores of Mytilēnē teamed with littoral sea life. Aristotle collected, dissected, and studied sea creatures—he seems to have been the only man who has actually watched the copulation of the Mediterranean octopus—and presumably made endless notes.

In the meantime Amyntas had died and had been succeeded as King of Macedonia by his son Philip. Philip had a son of his own, named Alexander, who became known to history as Alexander the Great. But at the time in question Alexander was a boy of 12 and his father wanted a tutor for him. The son of Philip's father's personal physician had

Marine worms, from Gesner, vol. IV, after Rondelet.

acquired a reputation as a philosopher and was expected to be both able and willing to become the tutor of the successor to the throne. The invitation was sent out "in the second year of the 109th Olympiad, when Phytodotus was Archon of Athens"—that is, in 342 B.C. Tutoring the young man—precocious, brilliant, and energetic—forced Aristotle to formulate and to tighten his own ideas. Tutoring began with Homer's *Iliad,* and philosophy, logic, and related subjects followed. One may have doubts as to whether Alexander was a "good" pupil—though he carried a copy of the *Iliad* with him on all his campaigns—but it is certain that he was a grateful pupil for as long as he lived. When Alexander became King, Aristotle stayed with him for a few years as counselor and friend.

In 335 B.C., while Alexander was fighting rebellions and other little wars, Aristotle went to Athens to start an academy of his own: the Lyceum.[1] There he lectured, taught, and wrote until 323 B.C., when his benefactor Alexander died in Babylon. Many Athenians had been opposed to Alexander, and his death left Aristotle in an awkward position. Consequently he resigned the leadership of the Lyceum (his friend Theophrastos became his successor) and left for Euboea, where he died only a few months later.

According to a classical tradition that does not need to be doubted Aristotle's manuscripts passed to one Neleos, the son of one of his friends, and were simply forgotten until they were rediscovered in a basement in the year 80 B.C.[2]

Somebody wrote a few decades ago that the life of Aristotle after his death has many of the elements of a tragedy, meaning that the people who proudly called themselves "Aristotelians" a millennium later did the opposite of what Aristotle would have expected or wanted them to do. Aristotle had always tried first to amass information, in many cases from his personal observations; to find common characteristics and then to attempt an explanation. The "Aristotelians" of a later date decided that

Mediterranean octopus, from Gesner, vol. IV, after Rondelet.

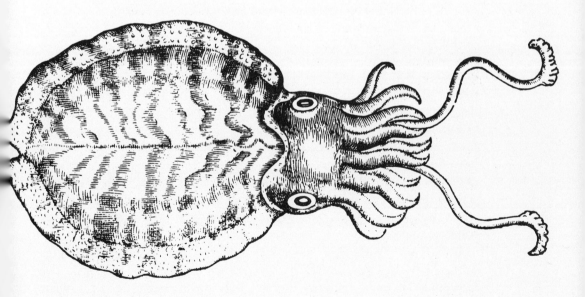

the master's work contained all the information there was. One might hold lengthy discussions on the meaning of passages that had been obscured by time and poor copyists, one might dispute endlessly just which animal or bird was meant in a given passage, but most Aristotelians did not feel it necessary to add anything new. And, of course, one could never contradict anything Aristotle had said, even if it was by no means certain that it had actually been Aristotle who had said so. Somewhere Aristotle had said that the mayfly has four legs, hence mayflies had four legs, though anybody could catch a mayfly and find out in three seconds that it has six.

A late masterpiece of such behavior was a book by a German naturalist who called himself Jacobus Thomasius. It was published in 1659 and had the title *De visu Talparum,* "On the Sense of Vision in the Mole." If a treatise with this title were published today one would expect a record of observations on this topic and a report on experiments with moles of various kinds to find out just how well they do see under different conditions. Not so Magister Thomasius. His book is a complete collection of everything that had ever been said about the mole's ability (or inability) to see, and no conclusion is reached.

Small wonder that the pioneers of science of the sixteenth century and after ridiculed learned cud-chewing of this kind. They not only ridiculed it because it did not add to the store of knowledge, they had to fight it hard because it got in their way. In a manner of speaking the pioneers had to fight Aristotle who had been a pioneer himself. Of course he had made a number of mistakes. He had, for example, denied that plants had sexual organs, with the result that the discovery of the sexuality of plants was delayed until 1694. And Aristotle, for reasons that can no longer be traced, had said that the heart was the seat of intelligence and that the function of the brain was merely to "cool" the heart. And while Aristotle had seen that the veins and the arteries duplicated each other he had mistakenly declared that the veins contained blood while the arteries contained blood and air. The stubborn adherence of "learned" men to what was written delayed the discovery of the circulation of blood until 1628.

But it was in the field of astronomy that Aristotle's mistakes had produced the results most incredible to us. He had said, probably still very much under the influence of Plato at the time, that the heavenly bodies consisted of a fifth, and pure element that could not be found on earth. When Father Christoph Scheiner, in 1611, reported to his ecclesiastical superior Busaeus that he had discovered spots on the sun he was told that the spots must be a flaw in his instrument, or else his eyes, probably because of overwork, had produced such spots. Nothing like that could be found in Aristotle, Busaeus stated; therefore it could not be true. However, it was hardly Aristotle's fault that later scholars took his every word to be an eternal truth. If he could have lived on indefinitely he would probably have rewritten his own books quite cheerfully every century or so.

Aristotle was the first zoologist as we understand the term, in that he studied animals *as animals* and not just as something to be hunted or, perhaps, to be domesticated. But his works were not zoological books as our time knows them. A modern reader who takes a printed edition of Aristotle and tries to look up what he knew, say, about the camel, is bound to be disappointed. The arrangement of the books is based upon different considerations. Aristotle wanted to find characteristics that could be used to establish natural groups—anybody can see that the birds are one natural group and the fishes another one. But while such obvious distinctions must have been noticed before him, he still had to make his own trail: "I found no basis prepared, no models to copy," he wrote. "Mine is the first step and therefore a small one, though worked out with much thought and hard labor. You, my readers or hearers of my lectures, if you think I have done as much as can fairly be expected of an initial start . . . will acknowledge what I have achieved and will pardon what I have left for others to accomplish."

His scheme was based on a major subdivision. Animals either had blood, or else they did not. Blood, to Aristotle, was a red-colored sticky liquid; it did not occur to him—as it did to Pliny the Elder only a few centuries later—that the "bloodless" animals may have another body fluid taking the place of blood. Having made the major subdivision into blood-bearing and bloodless animals, Aristotle arrived at the following scheme:

A. Blood-bearing animals

1. Four-footed animals that bring forth their young alive—the mammals of our terminology
2. Birds
3. Four-footed animals that lay eggs, for example, lizards, salamanders, and frogs—that is, most of the reptiles and amphibians of our terminology
4. Whales and their allies—animals which Aristotle thought breathed both air and water
5. Fishes

B. Bloodless animals

1. Cephalopods—the common octopus of the Mediterranean and its allies
2. Weak-shelled animals—meaning crabs, crayfish, etc.
3. Insects, which class included the spiders, scorpions, and centipedes
4. Hard-shelled animals, for example, oysters and clams
5. Plant animals, for example, sea urchins, jellyfishes, and so forth, which Aristotle considered to be intermediate between true animals and plants

The list, in the form given here, does not appear anywhere in Aristotle's writings. His writings contain such statements as: "Four-footed animals that produce live young have hair; four-footed animals that lay eggs have scales." Later commentators abstracted such generalizations and arranged them into the list; it is what would have resulted if Aristotle had condensed his statements into a tabular form.

Looking at Aristotle's generalizations with the eyes of a twentieth-century zoologist (compare the modern classification of the animals [3]), one can only agree with his own remarks: he should be praised for what he did accomplish and pardoned for what he could not do. His generalizations about the "blood-bearers" suffers from his having used a poor yardstick, namely the number of limbs. If Aristotle had looked at the skeleton instead and had paid more attention to the presence or absence of lungs he might have realized that a dolphin was only a changed "four-footed bearer of live young."

His ideas about the marine invertebrates were necessarily farther astray than those about the larger "blood-bearers," even though he seems to have studied marine invertebrates with much zeal. For him to have realized that the free-swimming rapacious octopus, with its large eyes and rapid movements, belonged to the same general type as the blind and motionless clams would be asking too much. And Aristotle, being used to the obvious bilateral symmetry of "right" and "left" that can be seen in every mammal, bird, lizard, and fish, could hardly be expected to understand that there is another kind of arrangement, the five-pointed "symmetry" of the sea stars and their relatives. The classification of the marine invertebrates was not improved until Baron Georges de Cuvier, at the end of the eighteenth century, invented his three groups of "radiates," "mollusks," and "articulates."

Aristotle's descriptions of the parts of animals are quite often elaborate. It is logical to assume that his description was elaborate when it was

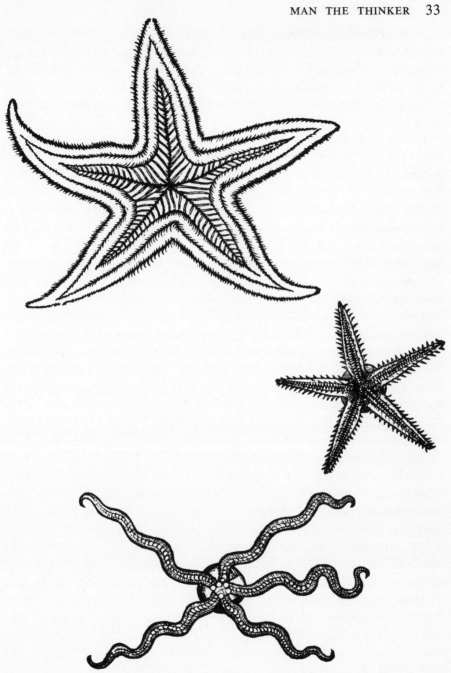

Various sea stars from the Mediterranean, from Gesner, vol. IV, after Rondelet.

based upon personal observation and short and casual when he relied on written sources or even oral reports. That snakes should be so similar to lizards in practically every detail seems to have surprised him. "Take away the feet of a lizard and you have a snake, for they are so similar," he wrote at one point. But he drew no conclusions from this similarity, merely voiced his surprise.

The species he described number about 520 (plus a few that cannot be identified) and the vast majority of them are animals that could then be found in Greece or in the waters around the Greek islands. The fact that Aristotle described mainly local faunal elements has a bearing on the oft-repeated assertion that Alexander the Great during his campaigns had exotic animals sent back to his former tutor. But if Alexander had sent him a crocodile, for example, Aristotle would not have repeated Herodotus' assertion that its upper jaw is hinged; a five-minute examination would have shown that Herodotus had been mistaken. He must never have examined a lion, either, though he may have seen one; otherwise he could not have said that the lion had no cervical vertebrae but a single long bone. His statement, in another place, that a lion's bones are so hard that they produce sparks when struck with iron is a slightly different matter. If somebody told him that this was the case Aristotle had no real reason to doubt it; he probably just remembered it as an interesting fact. Aristotle was an indefatigable collector of facts, including spurious ones. He felt that the larger the number of facts, the better the generalizations that could be drawn from them—an idea that befits the man who invented formal logic.

Just how much material in Aristotle's zoological writings is based on older works is impossible to say. He did use the History of Herodotus, but he may also have used a few works we don't know existed. Unlike Pliny the Elder, Aristotle rarely quoted others by name, which is one reason for the assertion that his works were not written to be read by others but are more in the nature of extended lecture notes for his own use.

While Alexander probably did not send specimens back to Athens, Aristotle did get reports about strange animals from Alexander's headquarters. These reports may have been written on Alexander's orders, but they can just as well be the result of personal correspondence between savants who had things to tell to each other. Aristotle's own grandnephew Kallisthenes was with Alexander, as was the geographer Onesikritos and a philosopher named Pyrron. One of them, or all three, supplied Aristotle with information about a very remarkable beast, the Indian elephant.

Aristotle's writings contain a great deal of information about elephants. There is a description of how the animal uses its trunk, another about the use of tame elephants to capture wild ones, and a fair amount of anatomical detail. There is in fact so much that a retired French officer, Colonel Pierre Armandi, concluded not quite a century ago that Aristotle must have seen an elephant. But the date of the first elephants in Greece falls quite a number of years after the deaths of both Alexander and Aristotle. Hence, Colonel Armandi concluded, Alexander must have sent a live Indian elephant to his former teacher. This deduction failed to work out. The arrival of an elephant in Athens would have been mentioned

Elephant, from Gesner, vol. I. This drawing must be remotely based on a picture of an African elephant, as evidenced by the large ears. But both the tip of trunk and the feet are wrong.

by quite a number of different people. And Aristotle's description is wrong in anatomical detail, which makes it clear that he never saw an elephant.*

Among the "Minor Works" of Aristotle is a small book which bears the Greek title *Peri Thaymaisōn Akoysmatōn,* or, in Latin *De Mirabilibus auscultationibus;* the English version is "On Marvellous Things Heard." The editors of the Loeb Classical Library presented this book with a stern warning:

> This curious collection of "marvels" reads like the jottings from a diary. All authorities are agreed that it is not the work of Aristotle, but it is included in this volume as it forms part of the *corpus* which has come down to us; most Aristotelian scholars believe that it emanated from the Peripatetic School. Some of the notes are puerile, but some on the other hand are evidently the fruit of direct and accurate observation.

I do not know why the Aristotelian scholars are agreed that it is not the work of Aristotle. If their opinion is based on fine points of classical Greek grammar, I am not competent to judge it. But if it is based on the grounds that some of the 178 items are puerile, I don't agree. Aristotle might well have jotted down a few silly stories to aid his memory. I have filed many clippings that are evidently the result of applied stupidity, in order to remember them. Even Beethoven and Wagner wrote some things that are unworthy of them.

Here are a few examples from Aristotle:

> They say that the cuckoos in Helice, when they are going to lay eggs, do not make a nest, but lay them in the nests of doves or pigeons, and do not sit, nor hatch, nor bring up their young; but when the young bird is born and has grown big, it casts out of the nest those with whom it has so far lived. [Perfectly correct.]
>
> In Egypt they say there are sandpipers that fly into the mouths of crocodiles and pick their teeth, picking out the small pieces of flesh that adhere to them with their beaks; the crocodiles like this and do them no harm. [Correct.]
>
> They say that Celtic tin melts much more easily than lead. [It does.]
>
> Among the Indians in the part called Keras, they say that there are small fish which wander about on dry land, and then run back again into the river. [True, if this means the fish *Periophthalmus,* as it probably does.]

---

* But Colonel Armandi's idea gave rise to a nice historical novel by L. Sprague de Camp, called *An Elephant for Aristotle* (New York: Doubleday, 1963), which deals with the tribulations of the poor officer who had been ordered to get the huge beast across a thousand miles of trackless country to Athens.

Of course many items are either wrong or trivial, and often both. For example:

> The goats in Cephallenia apparently do not drink like other quadrupeds, but every day turn their faces to the sea, open their mouths, and inhale the air.
>
> They say that the tortoises when they have eaten a snake eat marjoram on top, and that if they do not find any they die quickly.
>
> In Cyprus they say that mice eat iron.
>
> The strait between Sicily and Italy grows bigger and smaller according to the moon.
>
> The bee appears to herald the winter solstice by walking to his work.
>
> They say that the hedgehog can go without food for a year.

This is a selection from one of the disputed works. But if it is disputed only because a large number of the items are nonsense, let us recall that Aristotle also talked nonsense about the "four elements" of fire, water, air and earth, which he did not invent, but defended. Or think of his concept that everything had to be either cold and dry, or cold and moist, or warm and dry, or warm and moist.

I prefer to think of Aristotle as he really was, sailing across the Mediterranean at sunrise, with lines from Homer about "Eos, the rosy-fingered goddess of dawn" and the "wine-dark sea" on his lips, and with the hope that, at the shores of Mitylēnē, a form of littoral life which he would catch and dissect would teach him true understanding.

European hedgehog, from Gesner. The hedgehog is a surviving type of the early mammals generally called insectivores. It is not related to the porcupine, which is a far more modern form, namely a rodent.

chapter three

Cajus Plinius Secundus, or Pliny the Elder.

Man the Collector

PLINY the Elder lived a busy life; he wanted it that way. Born in what is now Como in northern Italy, then named Novum Comum, in A.D. 23, he had the good luck to live when his country was at the maximum of its power and glory, somewhat like an Englishman born in 1840 or a Frenchman born a century before that.

The early parts of Pliny's life are known in bare outline only. He went to Rome at an early age. Of his schooling we only know that he attended the lectures of grammarian Apion. For some time he practiced law and then joined the military service. While attached to the military he was successively in Germany, Gaul, and Spain. In Germany the legate Pomponius Secundus made him commander of a troop of cavalry and in Gaul he was *procurator* (overseer) under Vespasian, who later became emperor. Pliny was on intimate terms with Vespasian forever after and the close friendship also extended to Vespasian's son and successor Titus whom Pliny, in writing, called *jucundissimus,* an untranslatable term which is at once affectionate, familiar, and respectful. At one time before he reached the age of 30, Pliny was in Africa; neither the date nor the reason for the trip are known. At the age of 29 or 30 he returned to Rome.

He soon had various kinds of official duties and finally Vespasian appointed him *praefect* of the Roman fleet at Misenum at the Sinus Cumamus (Bay of Naples). During all the time not allocated to military and other duties he studied, read, and wrote. He never mounted a horse to go somewhere but rode in a carriage because this enabled him to read while in transit. As his nephew Pliny the Younger reported, "After a meal, if he had any leisure to spare, he would lie down in the sunshine, while some book was read to him, he himself making notes and extracts in the meantime. . . .

"I remember," Pliny the Younger continued, "on one occasion, a friend of his interrupting the reader, who had given the wrong pronunciation to some words, and making him go over them again. 'You understood him, didn't you?' said my uncle. 'Yes,' said the other. 'Why, then, did you make him go over it again? Through this interruption of yours we have lost more than ten lines.' "

Pliny the Elder did not originate the saying that no amount of money can buy back lost time, but, as this example shows, he might well have. A traditional description of Pliny's appearance at the age of about fifty is that he was far-sighted, balding, with thin arms and legs and a large potbelly. I heard this description for the first time when I was in high school. But to this day, except for his corpulence, mentioned by his nephew, I have been unable to find a classical source for it.

In A.D. 79 Pliny, in his capacity as naval commander, was stationed at Misenum, when Mount Vesuvius erupted. What happened then was beautifully described by Pliny the Younger in a letter to his friend Tacitus, the historian:

> On the ninth day before the calends of September [August 24], at about the seventh hour [1 P.M.] my mother observed the appearance of a cloud of unusual size and shape, mentioned it to him. After reclining in the sun he had taken his cold bath; he had then again lain down and, after a slight repast, applied himself to his studies. Immediately upon hearing this, he called for his shoes, and ascended a spot from which he could more easily observe this remarkable phenomenon. The cloud was to be seen gradually rising upwards; though from this great distance it was uncertain from which of the mountains it arose; it was afterwards ascertained to be Vesuvius. . . . To a man so eager as he was in the pursuit of knowledge this appeared to be a most singular phenomenon, and one that deserved to be viewed more closely; accordingly he gave orders for a light Liburnian vessel to be got ready, and left it at my option to accompany him. To this, however, I made answer that I should prefer continuing my studies; and as it happened he himself had given me something to write. Taking his tablets with him, he left the house. The sailors stationed at Retina, alarmed at the imminence of the danger—for the village lay at the foot of the mountain and the sole

escape was by sea—sent to entreat his assistance in rescuing them from this frightful peril. Upon this he instantly changed his plans and what he had already begun from a desire for knowledge, he determined to carry out as a matter of duty. He had the galleys put to sea at once and went on board himself, with the intention of rendering assistance not only to Retina, but to other places as well. . . . The ashes were now falling fast upon the vessels, hotter and more and more thickly the nearer they approached the shore; showers of pumice too, intermingled with black stones . . . the sea suddenly retreated from the shore, where the debris of the mountain rendered landing quite impossible. After hesitating for a moment whether or not to turn back upon the pilot strongly advising him to do so, "Fortune favors the bold," he said, "conduct me to Pomponianus." Pomponianus was then at Stabiae, a place that lay on the other side of the bay . . . the wind was extremely favorable to this passage, and my uncle, soon arriving at Stabiae,* embraced his anxious friend and did his best to restore his courage; and the better to reassure him by evidence of his own sense of their safety, he requested the servants to conduct him to the bath. After bathing he took his place at table, and dined, and that too in high spirits, or at all events, what equally shows his strength of mind, with every outward appearance of being so. In the meantime vast sheets of flame and large bodies of fire were seen arising from Mt. Vesuvius. . . .

Pliny, still determined to be a good example, said that these were just abandoned villages burning, had himself conducted to a guest room, and actually fell asleep. Servants detailed to watch at the door of his chamber heard him snore. But the eruption grew in fury and the ground began to shake, so that finally Pomponianus dared to have his guest (and military superior) awakened. They decided to leave the house that might collapse any moment but were worried about the steady rain of pumice and lapilli. Pliny the Younger continues in his report to Tacitus:

Taking the precaution of placing pillows on their heads, they tied them on with towels, by way of protection against the falling stones and ashes. It was now day in other places, though here it was still night, more dark and more profound than any ordinary night; torches, however, and various lights in some measure served to dispel the gloom. It was then determined to make for the shore, and to ascertain whether the sea would now admit of their embarking; it was found to be still too stormy and too boisterous to allow of their making the attempt. Upon this my uncle lay down upon a sail that had been spread for him, and more than once asked for some cold water, which he drank; very soon, however,

* Now Castellamare.

they were alarmed by the flames and the sulphurous smell which announced their approach, upon which the others at once took to flight, while my uncle arose leaning upon two of the servants for support. Upon making this effort, he instantly fell to the ground; the dense vapor having, I imagine, stopped the respiration and suffocated him; for his chest was naturally weak and contracted, and often troubled with violent palpitations. When daylight was at last restored, the third day after the closing one of his existence, his body was found untouched and without a wound; there was no change perceived in the clothes, and its appearance was rather that of a person asleep than of a corpse.

Pliny the Younger inherited 160 books of notes, known as the *electorum commentarii* ("annotated selections") of which nobody seems to have made much use. As regards the earlier writings of Pliny, his nephew is again the only complete source. Soon after his uncle's death he received a request to enumerate his writings and in his reply listed them as follows:

1. *De iaculatione equestri* (On Throwing the Javelin from Horseback). "His first composition, written while he was in command of a troop of horses."
2. *De vita Pomponi Secundi duo* (Life of Pomponius Secundus, in 2 books). "These books he composed as a tribute which was justly due to the memory of his deceased friend."
3. *Bellorum Germaniae viginti* (German Wars in 20 books). "This he had begun while serving in Germany, having been admonished to do so in a dream; for in his sleep he thought that the figure of Drusus Nero stood by him . . . entreating him to rescue his memory from the injustice of oblivion."
4. *Studiosi tres* (The Student, in 3 books). "In these he has given instructions for the training of the orator, from the cradle to his entrance into public life."
5. *Dubii Sermonis octo* (Dubious Language, in 8 books). "Written during the last years of the reign of Nero, a period in which every kind of study, in any way free-spoken or even of elevated style, would have been rendered dangerous by the tyranny that was exercised."
6. *A Fine Aufidi Bassi triginta unus* (Continuation of the History of Aufidius Bassus, in 31 books).
7. *Historia naturalis* (Natural History, 37 books). "A work remarkable for its comprehensiveness and erudition, and not less varied than Nature herself."

Pliny the Elder's works are lost, except for fragments of 5, and for 7—the *Historia naturalis*—preserved in its entirety.[2]

For many centuries, until new books on animals were written during the latter part of the sixteenth century, Pliny's work was regarded as one of the important books on animals that had survived from antiquity. Later authors quoted from Pliny's *Natural History* when they wanted to make a point. Or they quoted by saying that "Pliny already knew that . . ." or else they confronted Pliny's statement with that of other authors. That Pliny had been a great man was something they did not even have to mention, and nobody specifically criticized him. True criticism—in both directions—did not come along until the nineteenth century. In 1827 a Belgian, A. L. A. Fée, wrote a special eulogy about *Pline le Naturaliste* and not long afterward, the Baron de Cuvier, in his *Histoire des sciences naturelles,* also praised him. But the German zoologist J. Victor Carus, in his *History of Zoology* (published in Munich in 1872) waxed sharply critical.

> If one reads the eulogy of Fée or Cuvier's description of his merits, one may be led to believe that he [Pliny the Elder] was a man of genius who saw the whole of human knowledge, who opened new vistas everywhere, who sorted everything properly, and whose zoological work gave a definite form to this branch of science. To his contemporaries . . . it must have been impressive how he, a Roman knight, often immersed in military and government affairs, under the steady pressure of public service, finally even fleet admiral, could not only harbor the idea of writing an encyclopedia of human knowledge but even succeeded in carrying it out. But how anyone, in our time, could say that the loss of his writings would be an irremediable loss is hard to understand. . . . As regards zoology his work is nothing but an uncritical and unreliable compilation. He often cites Aristotle but also misunderstands him often and does not value him any higher than any other writer. Stories about fabulous animals which Aristotle rejected, Pliny accepted again without expressing any doubt. Of course his Natural History proves that in his time more animals were known than during the time of Aristotle (four centuries separate the two) but his descriptions are incomplete and not good enough to be useful.

The strange fact is that both sides are to a large extent right. In its time, and for centuries to come, the *Historia naturalis* was an indispensable book, but to a zoologist who had mastered virtually everything that had been learned during the intervening eighteen hundred years it was a performance which could have been better even in its own time.

The first "book," evidently written last, consists of the dedication to the Emperor Titus, a general preface, and a table of contents for the whole work, with lists of the authors consulted, the authors being arranged in order of frequency of use.[3]

Book II is devoted to a description of "the world" and in our eyes seems a strange mixture of subjects, since it deals with the sun, the moon, the planets, and the stars, then proceeds to a discussion of lightning, the four elements, winds, the shape of the earth, the causes of the seasons, rivers and springs, and so forth. The sequence was based on the opinion of Aristotle that there could be no changes in the sky and that any observed changes, therefore, had to be atmospheric phenomena. But while the reason was Aristotelian, Pliny set a pattern that could be found in popular books until about a century ago, namely that of considering the universe as consisting of "the eternal stars" on the one hand and the changeable earth on the other—with the result that the unchanging sky was described in a hurried or even slightly bored manner, as something one had to get out of the way in order to turn to the interesting things.

Since book II had dealt with the earth in general terms, books III to VI are devoted to details of geography and ethnography. The treatment is neither critical nor very scientific, but it contains a large amount of incidental information that is interesting. Books VII to XI are the zoological books. Books XII to XIX are on botany and its practical aspects like forestry, agriculture, and horticulture. Books XX to XXVII are still botanical, but about the medicinal uses of plants. Books XXVIII to XXXII continue the medical trend, with the medicinal value of animals. Book XXXIII is about precious metals, book XXXIV about bronze and its uses, book XXXV about painting, book XXXVI about stone and its use for building and sculpture, and the last book, XXXVII, is about precious stones.

The zoological section—here too Pliny set a pattern—begins with Man

> . . . for whose sake all other things appear to have been produced by Nature,* though, on the other hand, with so great and so severe penalties for the enjoyment of her bounteous gifts, that it is far from easy to determine whether she has proved to him a kind parent, or a merciless step-mother. In the first place she obliges him alone, of all animated beings, to clothe himself with the spoils of the others; while, to all the rest, she has given various kinds of coverings, such as shells, crusts, spines,

---

* In still another persistent pattern, Pliny expected everything to be either directly useful to Man or, at the very least, to teach a moral lesson, an idea which coincided with the attitude of the first book of the Bible and may have helped to make Pliny's work acceptable to the Church in later centuries.

hides, furs, bristles, hair, down, feathers, scales and fleeces. The very trunks of the trees even, she has protected against the effects of heat and cold by a bark. . . . Man alone, at the very moment of his birth cast naked upon the naked earth, does she abandon to cries, to lamentation, to tears. . . . But as for laughter, why, by Hercules!—to laugh, if but for an instant only, has never been granted to man before the fortieth day from his birth. . . .

But the gloom is short-lived; there are too many wonderful things to tell. He marveled at the enormous diversity of languages, asked rhetorically, "Who could ever believe in the existence of the Ethiopians [meaning black-skinned people in general] who had not first seen them?" and insisted that Nature had surpassed art, for human countenances, "although composed of but some ten parts or little more, are so fashioned that among so many thousands of men, there are no two in existence who cannot be distinguished from one another." Having just said that all people look different even if similar (presumably within a given nation or area), he proceeded to those races that did look different.

In a place . . . known by the name of Geskleithron, the Arimaspi are said to exist, a nation remarkable for having but one eye and that placed in the middle of the forehead. This race is said to carry on a perpetual warfare with the griffins . . . for the gold which they dig out of the mines and which these wild beasts retain and keep watch over with a singular degree of cupidity, while the Arimaspi are equally desirous to get possession of it. There is a country called Abarimon . . . the inhabitants of which are a savage race, whose feet are turned backwards relative to their legs: they possess wonderful velocity and wander about indiscriminately with the wild beasts. . . . [In northern Africa] are found, as we learn from Calliphanes, the nation of the Androgyni, a people who unite the two sexes in the same individual, and alternately perform the functions of each. Aristotle also states that the right breast is that of a male, the left that of a female. . . . On many of the mountains there is a tribe of men who have the heads of dogs, and clothe themselves with the skins of wild beasts. Instead of speaking they bark; and, furnished with claws, they live by hunting and catching birds. According to the story, as given by Ctesias, the number of these people is more than 120,000. The same author tells us that there is a certain race in India, of which the females are pregnant once only in the course of their lives, and that the hair of the children becomes white the instant they are born. He speaks also of another race of men who are known as Monoculi, who have only one leg, but are able to leap with surprising agility. The same people are also called Sciapodae, because they are in the habit of lying

One-eyed people of the East, from a printed edition of the "Travels" of John de Mandeville.

on their backs, and protect themselves from the sun by the shade of their feet. These people, he says, dwell not far from the Troglodytae, to the west of whom again there is a tribe who are without necks and have eyes in their shoulders.*

At the very extremity of India, on the eastern side, near the source of the river Ganges, there is the nation of the Astomi, a people who have no mouths; their bodies are rough and hairy, and they cover themselves with down plucked from the leaves of trees. These people subsist only by

* If all this reminds you of *Othello* (Act I, scene 3)
   Rough quarries, rocks and hills whose heads touch heaven,
   It was my hint to speak—such was the process;
   And of the cannibals that each other eat,
   The Anthropophagi, and men whose heads
   Do grow beneath their shoulders . . .
the similarities are not accidental. Pliny was Shakespeare's source.

breathing and by the odors which they inhale through the nostrils. They support themselves upon neither meat nor drink; when they go upon a long journey they only carry with them various odoriferous roots and flowers, and wild apples, so that they not be without something to smell at. But an odor which is a little more powerful than usual easily destroys them.

Pliny did not invent a single one of these strange races (later on, in Europe, they were collectively referred to as "wonder-people"); he just produced the collection from which a few samples have been presented just now. But by writing down this collection he influenced literature for many centuries to come. Having the strange races out of the way, he returned to normal human beings, but still on the trail of the unusual and remarkable. "Marvellous Births" is the next item, then follows a chapter on unusual duration of pregnancy, on "Monstrous Births," instances of striking resemblance of people who are not related, remarkable circumstances connected with menstrual discharge, and examples of unusual size, including one Gabbaras, "brought from Arabia by the emperor Claudius" as the tallest man of his time, giving his height as the equivalent of 9 feet 4 inches. He continues with stories of precocious children, stories about remarkable strength, about remarkable genius, and so forth, none of it having anything to do with either zoology or anthropology. Only one rather charming passage from the chapter on long-lived persons shall be quoted: "Xenophon, in his Periplus, gives to the king of the island Lutmii six hundred years, and, as though in that instance he had lied too sparingly, to his son eight hundred." But Pliny added that such figures might be based on misunderstandings: "For some nations reckon the summer as one year and the winter as another, others again consider each of the four seasons a year . . . the Egyptians calculate by the moon, and hence it is that some individuals among them are said to have lived as many as one thousand years."

Book VIII of the *Historia naturalis* is about the land animals and Pliny began with the elephant because it is the largest. He also thought that it was the most intelligent of all animals: ". . . it understands the language of its country, it obeys commands, and it remembers all the duties which it has been taught. It is sensible alike of the pleasures of love and glory and, to a degree that is rare even among men, possesses notions of honesty, prudence and equity; it has a religious respect also for the stars and a veneration for the sun and the moon." No doubt proud owners of elephants bragged about their big pets to travelers from the western country in language some dog owners use to this day.

There is a discussion of the "antipathy of the elephant and the dragon." Pliny, who had been talked into the belief that India produced the biggest trees, the tallest grass (bamboo), and the healthiest people, also thought that the Indian elephant was larger than any other kind of elephant. And India, naturally, also produced the largest dragons: ". . . of so enormous a size as easily to envelop the elephant with its folds and encircle them with its coils. The contest is equally fatal to both; the elephant, vanquished, falls to the earth and by its weight crushes the dragon which is entwined around it." While the tale is a fable it shows that the Romans used their word for dragon (*draco*) with the meaning "giant serpent." Pliny then went on to say that the dragons of Ethiopia are smaller than the Indian dragons but still have a length of 20 cubits (about 30 feet). Pliny believed this without hesitation, and on occasion it can be true. But he was surprised to find that King Juba said that the African dragons have crests, and though he obviously had doubts he could not resist telling the story that these dragons are sometimes found near the African coast, "four or five of them twisted and interlaced together . . . setting sail with their heads erect, they are borne along upon the waves to find better sources of nourishment in Arabia."

Since the arrangement of the animals is by diminishing size, Pliny had to jump around geographically. After finishing with the big serpents— surprisingly he talked about "boas" in Italy—he said that Germany did not have many animals, "though it has some very fine kinds of wild oxen: the bison which has a mane, and the urus, possessed of remarkable strength and swiftness. To these the vulgar, in their ignorance, have given the name of bubalus [buffalo] whereas that animal is really produced in Africa. . . ." [4]

The geography of the north was still rather confused in Pliny's time. Scandinavia, for example, was thought to be an island, for the simple reason that the best way to reach it was by ship. Of an animal *achlis,* on that "island," Pliny said that "it is not unlike the elk, but has no joints in the hind leg. Hence," he continued, "it never lies down but reclines against a tree when it sleeps; it can only be taken by previously cutting into the tree, and thus laying a trap for it, as otherwise it would escape through its swiftness." The animal *achlis* is the same as the *alces* (elk) with which Pliny compared it; the story about its lack of joints had been told earlier by a much greater Roman, Gaius Julius Caesar himself. Of course the moose has the same kinds of joints in its legs as all its relatives have. But having watched European moose in the open—knowing about Pliny's tale at the time—I noticed that slowly walking moose appear to be stiff-legged; they move almost like a cat walking away from something in disdain. The story of the jointlessness was probably an attempt to explain what had been seen. An alternative explanation is that Germanic interpreters and traders tried to find out just how much a Roman would believe.

Pliny then proceeded to the lion of which he had many stories to tell. One amusing one concerns the lioness, reported to be promiscuous, for which Pliny offered an excuse. Since Africa is so hot the animals have to rely for water on only a few rivers and since that means that there are many different animals close together, some promiscuity is bound to occur. The offspring of a male panther and a straying lioness, he gravely reported, is the leopard. Actually lions and panthers cannot crossbreed, and besides, the panther and the leopard are one and the same animal, though the name panther is customarily used for the black variety of the leopard. After having told his lion stories, Pliny proceeded to the tiger, then to the two kinds of camels and the *cameleopard,* the giraffe.

Giraffe, as pictured in the work of Aldrovandi.

Pliny apparently did not follow any special scheme of arrangement, except for starting with the largest animal, but there is a tendency to group animals by the geographical areas where they occur, with tropical Africa and tropical Asia usually considered a unit. So his next animal is the rhinoceros:

> At the same games [those of Pompeius Magnus where African monkeys were first shown] the rhinoceros was also exhibited, an animal which has a single horn projecting from its nose; it has been frequently seen since then. This, too, is a natural born enemy of the elephant. It prepares itself for the combat by sharpening its horn on the rocks; and in fight directs it chiefly against the belly of its adversary, which it knows to be the softest part. The two animals are of about equal length, but the legs of the rhinoceros are much the shorter.

Arabic writers later elaborated on the enmity between elephant and rhinoceros in the best *Thousand and One Nights* style: the elephant, having its belly slit open by the sharpened horn, drops dead and, in falling, kills the rhinoceros; then the Roc comes and picks up both to carry them to its island as food for its own young.

After the story of the rhinoceros there are several pages of utter confusion; nothing can be identified, even remotely, with actually existing animals. There is:

> ... the sphinx which has brown hair and two mammae on the breast ... horses with wings and armed with horns which are called pegasi.[5]... There are oxen, some with one horn and others with three, and the leucocrotta, a wild beast of extraordinary swiftness, the size of the wild ass, with the legs of a stag, the neck, tail, and breast of a lion, the head of a badger, a cloven hoof, the mouth slit up as far as the ears, and one continuous bone instead of teeth; it is said, too, that this animal can imitate the human voice. . . . Ctesias [6] informs us that among these same Ethiopians there is an animal which he calls the mantichora; it has a triple row of teeth which fit each other like those of a comb, the face and ears of a man, and azure eyes, is of the color of blood, has the body of a lion, and a tail ending in a sting like that of a scorpion. Its voice resembles the union of the sound of the flute and the trumpet; it is of excessive swiftness and is particularly fond of human flesh.

Then Pliny came to the unicorn:

> The Orsaean Indians hunt ... a very fierce animal called the monoceros which has the head of the stag, the feet of the elephant, and the tail of the boar, while the rest of the body is like that of the horse;

it makes a deep lowing noise and has a single black horn which projects from the middle of its forehead, two cubits in length. This animal, it is said, cannot be taken alive.

The basilisk is next, described as having the shape of a snake but moving in a different manner.

It destroys all shrubs, not only by its contact, but those even that it has breathed upon; it burns up all the grass too, and breaks the stones, so tremendous is its noxious influence. It was formerly a general belief that if a man on horseback killed one of these animals with a spear, the poison would run up the weapon and kill, not only the rider, but the horse as well. To this dreadful monster the effluvium of the weasel is fatal . . . it has pleased nature that there should be nothing without its antidote.

After this plethora of fabulous beasts, things settle down with wolves, snakes, "scincus" (monitor), hippopotamus and hyena. While Pliny agreed with Aristotle that the hyena's body did not combine both sexes, he had another story to tell about it:

. . . it imitates the human voice among the stalls of the shepherds; and while there, learns the name of some one of them and then calls him away and devours him. It is said also that it can imitate [the sound of] a man vomiting and that, in this way, it attracts the dogs and then falls upon them. It is the only animal that digs up graves in order to obtain the bodies of the dead.

The union of a male hyena with a lioness, he says, produces the corocotta which, like the leucocrotta, can also imitate the human voice.

After the discussion of the stag, Pliny states, correctly and with a little surprise, that Africa does not produce any stags, but it produces a far greater wonder, namely the chameleon, "the only animal that receives nourishment neither by meat nor drink, nor anything else, but from the air alone." Of the bear Pliny knew that it can walk upright and that it will climb down a tree "backward," as he put it, meaning that the bear descends a trunk the way a man would walk down a ladder. Of course bears were used in the "games" and Pliny noted that Domitius Ahenobarbus brought one hundred Numidian bears and a hundred Ethiopian hunters to the circus. But Pliny wrote: "I am surprised to find the word Numidian added, seeing that it is well known that there are no bears in Africa." The absence of any member of the bear tribe in Africa is actually a major zoological riddle—from what is now known about animal migrations of prehuman times one should expect to find bears in Africa. But there aren't any anywhere on that large continent.

The discussion of the bears is followed by one about the mice of Pontus and they are followed by the hedgehog, beginning with the words: "Hedgehogs also lay up food for the winter, rolling themselves on apples as they lie on the ground, they pierce one with their quills, and then take up another in the mouth, and so carry them into the hollows of trees." The European hedgehog, about the size of a small rabbit, belongs to the so-called insectivores in the modern scheme of classification but it is omnivorous in its habits. In the open it will eat a few earthworms if it can get them, devour a garden snail, and then look for some wild strawberries, but its attention might be diverted by a passing beetle. It is easily tamed but somewhat annoying as a pet because it will sleep all day hidden behind some furniture and be quite active after the sun goes down. A tame one will share in the family's meals, preferring meat scraps and fresh fruit, usually shunning starchy food, though a man I know told me that his tame hedgehog was fond of chocolate pudding with raisins, and will see to it that there are no mice in the house. But the very story told by Pliny, that it will carry fallen apples to its lair by spiking them on its quills, is still hotly debated today among European nature lovers and zoologists. Photographs showing a hedgehog with two small unripe apples and some dry leaves on its quills were waved aside as having been rigged for the purpose. Of course it would not be difficult to put an apple or two on the spines of a tame hedgehog and then photograph it in the garden while it is still carrying its burden. On the other hand the story was around when I was a small child of preschool age (my grandfather told it to me), and it was around in the days of Pliny the Elder. It has been told for many generations in northern Italy, Austria, Switzerland, France, Germany, Poland, and northwestern Russia—in short, I feel inclined to believe that Pliny was told the truth by his informants. The position of the opposition is, of course, that Pliny started a long-lived myth.

Pliny's next chapter dealt with the lynx and included the story that its urine hardened into a precious stone and that the lynx "envies us the possession of its urine and therefore buries it in the earth." To this John Bostok, M.D., one of the translators, added the footnote: "It is not unusual for animals to cover their excrements with earth, probably from the fact of their being annoyed by its unpleasant odor." A neat Victorian sentiment, unfortunately marred by the fact that it misses the mark by about a mile; the reason some animals cover up their excrements is that they are trying to avoid giving their presence away to predators.

The last section of Pliny's book on terrestrial animals is devoted to domestic animals: dogs, horses, asses, mules, sheep, goats, and so forth, ending with monkeys and hares; with a general chapter in which he wondered why certain animals fail to exist in certain places.

Book IX, about the fishes, begins with the question of why the inhabitants of the ocean are so much larger than those of the land. Of course the true answer, which is in the realm of engineering and deals with the square-cube law, the support of weight by fluids and so on, eluded him. He concluded that it must be because the animals of the ocean have a superabundance of moisture, implying that the limited size of walking and especially of flying animals is the result of the restricted amount of moisture available to them.

Dolphin, from the appendix of Gesner, vol. IV; no source credited there.

Following his inclination to believe that the biggest of everything is in existence in India, he places the largest water-dwelling creatures in the Indian Ocean. They are the *balaena*, "four jugera in extent" (an area measuring 960 by 480 feet) and the *pristis*, 300 feet long. We don't know just what fish went under the name of *pristis*—though it was a favorite name for Roman ships—but the word *balaena* seems to have been used as a general term for any of the large whales, most of which, on occasion, must have made an appearance in the Mediterranean. The "eel" of the Ganges river was reported to be close to 300 feet in length, too. The largest "fish" of the Gallic Ocean * is the *physeter* (Greek for "blower"). The name makes it likely that one of the large whales is meant.

Pliny then cited instances of very large bones, used in the construction

* The part of the Atlantic bordering the west coast of France.

of houses and gates; obviously these were the ribs and jaws of whales. As for the question of respiration, he noted that *balaenae* and dolphins have lungs and inhale and exhale air. As regards fishes with gills, Pliny noted that Aristotle has convinced many that they do not exhale and inhale, but he did not wish "to conceal the fact that I for one do not by any means at once subscribe to this opinion, for it is very possible, if such be the will of Nature, that there may be other organs fitted for the purpose of respiration, and acting in the place of lungs; just as in many animals a different liquid altogether takes the place of blood."

Of course Pliny had lots of stories to tell about dolphins, all of which were dismissed half a century ago as poetic imagination. Now that we have learned that dolphins have intelligence these stories no longer sound so impossible, with some slight allowance for mistakes in reporting the events and the inevitable exaggeration that accompanies repeated retelling of the same story. Here is one of Pliny's dolphin stories:

> At Hippo Diarhytus [the island of Caria] on the coast of Africa, a dolphin used to receive his food from the hands of various persons, present himself for their caresses, sport about among the swimmers and carry them on his back. On being rubbed with unguents by Flavianus, the then proconsul of Africa, he was lulled to sleep, as it appeared, by the sensation of an odor so new to him, and floated about just as though he had been dead. For some months after this he carefully avoided all intercourse with man, just as though he had received some affront or other; but at the end of that time he returned, and afforded just the same wonderful scenes as before. At last, the vexations that were caused them by having to entertain so many influential men who came to see this sight compelled the people of Hippo to put the animal to death.

Halfway through the book, Pliny took stock of what was known: "There are seventy-four species of fishes, exclusive of those that are covered with crusts; the kinds of which are thirty in number." The ones "covered with crusts" include the crabs as well as sea urchins, sea stars, and so forth, the crustaceans and the echinoderms of modern terminology, with a few clams thrown in. Pliny said that he would describe only the most remarkable of them. His idea of what is remarkable turns out to be what one would have expected from his general attitude: the remarkable fish were those of the largest size (for example, the tuna) and those of direct utility. But he has heard of a truly remarkable fish, the one now known as a periophthalmus, which is in the habit of making excursions onto land. The book closes with a chapter on "the antipathies and sympathies that exist between aquatic animals."

Book X, about the birds, naturally begins with the ostrich. "This bird exceeds in height a man sitting on horseback and can surpass him in swiftness, as wings have been given to aid it in running; in other respects ostriches cannot be considered as birds, and do not raise themselves from the earth." Pliny had been told that an ostrich can digest anything they swallow (unfortunately not true, as zoo keepers have found out) and that it hides its head in the belief that it is then invisible. "Their eggs are priced on account of their large size, and are employed as vessels for certain purposes, while the feathers of the wing and tail are used as ornaments for the crest and the helmet of the warrior."

After telling the well known phoenix story he recorded that the phoenix took its flight from Arabia into Egypt at the time of the consulship of Quintus Plautius and Sextus Papinius. "This bird was brought to Rome in the censorship of the Emperor Claudius . . . and it was exposed to public view in the Comitium. This fact is attested by the public Annals, but there is no one that doubts that it was a fictitious phoenix only." Earlier in the chapter Pliny had said about the phoenix, "I am not quite sure that its existence is not all a fable."

Eagles are discussed next, then vultures, hawks, cuckoos, crows, ravens, and horned owls. The chapter on the peacock shows once more that Pliny was by no means as uncritical as later authors made him out to be:

> When it hears itself praised, this bird spreads out its gorgeous colors, and especially if the sun happens to be shining at the time, because then they are seen in all their radiance and to better advantage. At the same time, spreading out its tail in the form of a shell, it throws the reflection upon the other feathers which shine all the more brilliantly . . . manifesting great delight in having them admired by the spectator. The peacock loses its tail every year at the fall of the leaf, and a new one shoots forth in its place at the flower season: between these periods the bird is abashed and moping and seeks retired spots. The peacock lives twenty-five years and begins to show its colors in the third. By some authors it is stated that the bird is not only a vain creature, but of a spiteful dispositon also, just in the same way that they have attributed bashfulness to the goose. [The word translated as "bashfulness" is *verecundia,* which can also be translated as "modesty."] The characteristics, however, which they have thus ascribed to these birds appear to me to be utterly unfounded.

The rooster, which follows after the peacock, "knows how to distinguish the stars and marks the different periods of the day, every three hours, by his note." In his description of the goose there is an unexpected side issue: just who discovered the preparation of the goose liver? Pliny cannot be certain—it was either Scipio Metellus or the knight Seius—but he does know that Messalinus Cotta, the son of the orator Messala, should be credited with the invention of the dish consisting of roasted goose's feet cooked as a ragout with roosters' combs as the other main ingredient—a dish most people probably can do without.

After discussing cranes, storks and swans, swallows and pigeons, Pliny devoted a chapter to the different types of flight. "Some birds," he said, "expand their wings, and, poising themselves in the air, only move them from time to time; others move them more frequently but then only at the extremities . . . some fly with the greater part of the wings kept close to the side . . . the heavier birds can fly only after taking a run, or else by commencing their flight from an elevated spot."

Among "foreign birds" the pelican is mentioned, as is the flamingo (under the name of *phoenicopterus*) and a "new bird" (*nova avis*) which has recently been introduced into Italy and bears only that name (it is believed that the gray partridge is meant). Alpine birds mentioned are the *lagopus* (the "hare's foot," meaning the snow partridge) and the *pyrrhocorax,* the Alpine crow.[7]

After the death of Pliny the Roman Empire produced only one more writer who wrote about animals at length. He was Claudius Aelianus, who in the past has been confused occasionally with a writer called Aelianus Tacticus; the latter, as is strongly indicated by this designation, wrote on military matters. Claudius Aelianus, born about A.D. 170 at Praeneste, was a Roman who, as he said himself, had never left the Italian peninsula and had never been aboard a ship, but who mastered the Attic version of classical Greek to such an extent that he was described as "honey-tongued." He was much in demand as an orator, speaking in Greek, needless to say. He also wrote in Greek, yet his work on animals is usually referred to under its Latin title *De natura animalium*. In his later years he belonged to a circle of learned men—Galenos, Oppianus, and Philostratos were among them—whom Empress Julia Domna had gathered around her. He never married and died A.D. *ca.* 230, sixty-odd years of age.

Though some other works of his have survived, his fame is based on *De natura animalium*. This should not be referred to as a zoological work, unless it is clearly understood that "zoological" is merely supposed to mean "about animals." It contains little direct zoological description, though on occasion personal observations are mentioned. The book is a miscellany of statements about animals, true, false, miraculous, and ridiculous, arranged in no perceptible order, often redundant and repetitious, and based on hearsay and Greek authors. Roman authors are never even mentioned, though it is logical to assume that Pliny's *Historia naturalis,* by way of example, was responsible for this work.[8]

The author most frequently mentioned by Aelianus is, to nobody's surprise, Aristotle. But though Aristotle's name appears at least half a hundred times it may be said that it is taken in vain, for it is certain that Aelianus had not read the works of Aristotle but quoted his opinions from excerpts made by Aristophanes of Byzantium. Homer is mentioned quite often too. Aelianus' English translator, A. F. Scholfield says that it was "a mannerism with the scholars of Alexandria to cite Homer whenever it was possible, and Aelian follows the fashion, less (it would seem) with the aim of establishing some fact of natural history than of proving Homer's knowledge of the science." This may have been a mannerism, but it is a fact that Homer's statements about animals and plants were quite trustworthy.[9]

Only a few of the seventeen books of Aelianus deserve mention.

In a display of complete arbitrariness the first section of Book I is about the shearwaters of the island of Diomedea. These birds neither harm nor approach barbarians but welcome visitors from Greece with outstretched wings, as if they wished to embrace them. The second section deals with a fish, the third with another fish; then we have a story of a man with whom animals fell in love; this is followed by the assertion that "the jackal is most friendly disposed to man." After that there are stories of bees and then fishes again—everything is jumbled up ("to make it more interesting reading," Aelianus explained in an epilogue) in the wildest possible manner. Of course all classical mythology is hauled in, as long as an animal figures somewhere in the story. Aside from that, there are such interesting "facts" as the following: Ants will stay in their homes all day long every first day of the month. Ring doves put sprigs of the bay tree into their nests as a protection against sorcery. If a man wants to provoke a quarrel at a dinner party all he need do is to drop a stone that has been bitten by a dog into the wine vessel. The bee-eater (bird) flies backward. The liver of a mouse grows an extra lobe every day as long as the moon is waxing; when it starts waning the liver lobes disappear one every day. Men and dogs are the only creatures that belch. The sea-scolopendra bursts when a scorpion spits in its face. The screaming of cranes brings on showers. If a man cuts through the bone of a lion, fire bursts forth. It is a characteristic of animals to fall in love not only with their own kind, but even with those that bear no relation to them as long as they are beautiful.

I did not actually count, but a reading of the whole work—at a sitting —gave me the impression that the dog is the animal most often mentioned. But the second place probably goes to the elephant, about which Aelianus kept digging up "facts" and stories. One of them is especially interesting [10]:

> At the foot of Atlas (this mountan is celebrated by historians and also by poets) there are marvellous pasture-lands and forests of the deepest, whose dense foliage is like that of groves all shady and over-arched. And that, you know, is where elephants are said to resort in old age when heavy with years. And Nature leads them as it were to a colony, giving them rest at last and providing them with a desired anchorage and harbor, so to speak, where they can live out the rest of their life. And they have a spring of drinking water . . . and an agreement with the barbarians in those parts that they shall not be hunted. . . . A certain king was eager to kill some of them on account of the splendor and size of their tusks . . . he dispatched three hundred men to shoot this sacred herd. And all equipped they accomplished their journey with the utmost speed, and were actually nearing the spot when a pestilence suddenly seized them . . . all died save only one, and he returned and rendered to him who had sent them a full account. . . .

This is the earliest version of the famous and mysterious "graveyards of the elephants" which persisted into the early portion of the current century.

Book XVI contains a few items unmentioned or hardly mentioned before Aelianus. Apparently more news from India kept trickling in. He relates that in India there is an animal somewhat like the land-crocodile in appearance. "The scales that cover it are so rough and of such close texture, that when flayed they perform the functions of a file. They will even cut through bronze and eat their way through iron." The name given is *phattage;* the pangolin is meant. There is reference to a herbivorous animal of India that is twice the size of a horse, with a pitch-black bushy tail, "each hair attains a length of two cubits" (3 feet) and is very fine. The yak is meant.

Finally, there is Aelian's version of the unicorn story, which was to lead to endless zoological discussions and literary exercises of all kinds.

In these regions (the interior of India) there is said to exist a one-horned beast which they call *Kartazonos*. It is the size of a full-grown horse, has the mane of a horse, reddish hair and is very swift of foot. Its feet are, like those of the elephant, not articulated and it has the tail of a pig. Between its eyebrows it has a horn growing out; it is not smooth but has spirals of quite natural growth, and is black in color. This horn is also said to be exceedingly sharp. And I am told that the creature has the most discordant and powerful voice of all animals. When other animals approach, it does not object but is gentle; with its own kind however it is inclined to be quarrelsome. And they say that not only do the males instinctively butt and fight one another, but that they display the same temper towards the females. . . . It likes lonely grazing-grounds where it roams in solitude, but at the mating season, when it associates with the female, it becomes gentle and the two even graze side by side. Later, when the season has passed and the female is pregnant, the male Kartazonos reverts to its savage and solitary state.

This, of course, is a description of the Indian rhinoceros, as is even shown by the name.* But the Kartazonos evolved into the unicorn, even though its prototype became reasonably well known in the European west.

---

* The Grecian version *kartazonos* is probably derived from the Persian *kargadan,* which, in turn, comes from Sanskrit *Khadgadanta,* an expanded version of *Khadga,* meaning "one-horned animal," the Sanskrit term for the rhinoceros.

chapter four

Man the Allegorizer

THE *Historia naturalis* of Pliny the Elder may be full of mistakes, myths, and outright fairytales, and anybody who wants to pick flaws in Aelianus has an easy life: all he needs is a copy of the book and some general zoological knowledge of the twentieth century. But both Pliny and Aelianus did the best they could. They may have transmitted myths, but it was not their intention to do so.

But while Aelianus was still working on his manuscript, another book was written somewhere in the Greek-speaking world, probably in Alexandria. Ostensibly it was a book about animals but it paid no—or only accidental—attention to their natural history. It told fables, it concocted parables, it even invented animals if the intended allegory could not be attached to something actually living. The book sounds as if its author had consciously applied Pliny's attitude: if the animal was not useful as food or as a medical remedy, then at least it should teach a moral lesson. And the lessons were, in each case, those of Christian theology, designed to give spiritual strength to the faithful and to warn sinners.

That book was the "Physiologus," one of the greatest literary successes of all time. Innumerable manuscript copies must have been made of the Greek original, innumerable manuscript copies of the Latin translation, and translations into at least a dozen other languages are known. Its appeal was so widespread that it could even take a temporary frowning by the Church in its stride. And some of the stories told are part and parcel of European folklore to this day.

The Greek word *physiologos*—first used by Aristotle—means "somebody who knows nature." The modern term "naturalist" comes closest to it, but the original word was understood to embrace natural philosophy as well. But the "naturalist" of the title is sometimes treated as a real person in the text with the use of the words: "Physiologus says about this animal . . ." Referring to an author by his occupation rather than by his name was occasionally done, much as if a book of medical advice for the household were to be called "By the Doctor."

The logical conclusion to be drawn from this is, of course, that the "physiologus" of the title was such a well-known person in his time that his name was not needed. Later copiers consequently looked for a famous person in antiquity who might have been the author.[1]

Dialogue between the Unicorn and the Monk, from *Dialogus creaturarum*.

The Greek Physiologus deals with about forty animals—real and mythical; one plant, "the tree Peridexion that grows in India"; and six stones. These are not all gems, though diamond and pearl are among them; those not gems are the magnet, the "burning stones," and the "Indian stone." The sequence of the animals does not follow any pattern or system, except that the lion, as king of the beasts, always comes first.

Let us now open the Physiologus, beginning with the lion. The lion, it says, has three characteristics: (1) it erases its footprints with its tail so that the hunters cannot follow it. This signifies the incarnation of the Lord, a secret which is unknown even to the powers of heaven (and those of the devil, later versions add). (2) When the lion sleeps, its eyes stay awake—that is, they are open. In that manner the body of Christ slept after the crucifixion, but his divine part was awake at the right hand of the Father. (3) The lioness gives birth to a dead lion, but on the third day its father comes and breathes into its face, thereby bringing it to life. This signifies the Resurrection on the third day.

The lizard, the second animal of the Greek version, becomes blind in its old age. Then it seeks a wall facing the east and extends its head through a crack. The rays of the rising sun cause it to regain its eyesight. Man, if his heart has become blind, should look to Christ, who is the Sun of Justice, for help.

As for the *nyktikorax* (the word can only be translated as "night-raven"; of course there is no actual bird with which it can be identified), it loves darkness better than it loves light. This signifies the Lord who loved the heathen that were enshrouded in darkness more than the Jews who had heard the prophecies but had rejected Him.

The phoenix, says Physiologus, lives in India or Arabia. Every five hundred years it flies to the Lebanon mountains, fills its wings with fragrant herbs, and then flies to Heliopolis to the Temple of the Sun where it burns itself. But on the following day the ashes produce a small worm, which becomes a small bird on the second day and a full-grown phoenix on the third. The phoenix then flies back to its own country. The phoenix is a symbol of Christ who returned from the dead on the third day. The two wings full of fragrant herbs mean the Old and New Testament, full of divine wisdom.[2]

The lines about the hoopoe are without religious allegory. The young birds, when they see that their parents are too old to fly or even to see, pull out their feathers and lick their eyes and take them under their wings and nurse them until the plumage has renewed itself and their sight returns because of this rejuvenation. But if an unintelligent bird loves his parents so much, how much more is it the duty of children to love their parents. (The story shows inadvertently how mysterious the molting of birds, as well as the shedding of the skin by snakes and lizards, must have been to the ancients.)

We now come to the *myrmekoleon,* the ant-lion. The ant-lion is familiar to the modern reader—it is the larva of an insect which sits at the bottom of a small funnel in loose sand, catching ants that come near. That is the ant-lion of the modern natural history books, but the one of the Physiologus is much more literal. The *myrmekoleon* is the result of

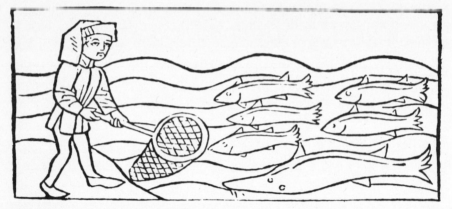

Dialogue between the Fishes and the Fisherman, from *Dialogus creaturarum,* a late Latin version of the Physiologus, printed in the Netherlands.

an unnatural union between a lion and an ant, but it does not live long, for there is no suitable food for it. The nature of one parent prevents it from eating meat, the nature of the other prevents it from eating plants or seeds. Thus must perish all who are of two hearts and who try to serve both the Lord and the devil.

As for the *hydrus,* it is the enemy of the crocodile. When it sees a crocodile sleeping with its mouth open, the *hydrus* covers itself with mud so as to be slippery. Then it enters the mouth of the crocodile, permits itself to be swallowed, and then tears up the crocodile's intestines. Thus Christ donned the body of a mortal, descended into hell, and conquered both death and the devil.

If the salamander enters a fire, the fire will become extinguished. Thus the just are in no danger, just as the three men in the fiery furnace were unscathed.

Let us look at just two more examples, the *serra* and the ostrich, the latter being usually the last animal of the Physiologus.

The *serra,** Physiologus says, is a marine animal with large wings. When it sees ships sailing in the sea it tries to swim with them, but it soon tires, folds up its wings, and then drifts back to the place where it was before. The ships are the saints who suffer the vicissitudes of life like those of a sailing voyage and then reach port in heaven. But the animal symbolizes those who try to emulate them but soon begin to slacken and return to their secular pleasures.

---

* There is no clue to what animal is meant; the Latin word *serra* means "saw" (the tool) and the Greek word *priōn,* used in the original, has the same meaning. A fish named *pristis* in Aristotle's writings has nothing to do with the story; it merely has a similar Greek name. But it is possible that the story about the *serra* was inspired by dolphins, which will play around a vessel for some time and then fall astern when they are tired of the game.

The ostrich looks to the sky to see when the time comes to lay its eggs, for it will not lay until the Pleiades have risen, at the time the heat is greatest. It lays its eggs in the sand and covers them with sand, but then it goes away and forgets about them; they will be hatched by the heat of the sun. But if the ostrich knows his Time how much more should Man know it: we must look to heaven, forget material things, and follow Christ.

The sermonizing of the Physiologus must have struck the right note, because the work had nothing else to recommend it. As far as the "facts" are concerned it is without value and it certainly is not a literary or poetic masterpiece. But its numerous translations prove that it had a universal appeal in its time.[3] Late in the career of the Physiologus, after A.D. 1100, it was changed.

The reason was that it was anonymous. It was "masterless property" and nobody who had ideas about improvements or additions ever felt in the least restrained. If a copyist had a work with a glistening name on the first page, say Aristotle, or Plato, or Origines, he would be careful with every word and if at some point he felt moved to make an addition, he would say so. Numerous manuscripts contain copyists' remarks, saying in effect "This is what the master has written, though I don't understand its meaning." But the anonymous Physiologus imposed no restrictions resulting from reverence. If a writer thought it would be an interesting literary exercise to render the book in rhymed verse, or hexameters, or whatever, he went ahead and did so.

One such example is the Physiologus of Bishop Theobald, who is believed to have been the abbot of the Abbey of Monte Cassino 1022–1035. While there, it is assumed, he translated parts of the book into Latin "in verses of different meter." It is, of course, possible that he did not do any translating but used a Latin version. While the date of the

Dialogue between a black and a white bird, from *Dialogus creaturarum*.

Latin translation of the Physiologus is not known, there can be no doubt that one existed in the time of Bishop Theobald. Nobody has ever argued that the bishop's verses were good literature. He just did the best he could with a worthwhile purpose in mind, the purpose being that it is easier to remember verse—even bad verse—than prose. Theobald's Physiologus is a drastically shortened version, containing only twelve animals, with the lion first and the panther last.[4]

By the time printing was invented, the Physiologus was no longer fashionable and the fact that Bishop Theobald's version was printed in Cologne in 1492 is also probably due to its poetic guise; the printer evidently considered it an example of religious poetry. It is a very small book, with an introduction in prose followed by the twelve poems, each of which has an explanatory postscript in prose, probably for the convenience of priests who might wish to use one of the poems as the theme for a sermon. The whole covers only fifteen printed pages.

Here is the opening poem on the lion.[5]

De Leone

Tres leo naturas et tres habet inde figuras
Quas ego Christe tibi bis seno carmine scripsi
Altera divini memorant animalia libri
De quibus apposui, que rursus mystica novi
Temptans diversis si possum scribere metris
Et numerum solidum complent animalia solum
Nam leo stans fortis super alta cacumina montis
Qualicunque via vallis descendit ad ima
Si venatorem per naris sentit odorem
Cauda cuncta linit, quae pes vestigia figit
Quatenus inde suum non posset cernere lustrum
Natus non vigilat dum sol se tertio girat
Sed rugitum dans pater eius resuscitat ipsum
Tunc quasi viviscit et sensus quinque capiscit
Et quotiens dormit nunquam sua lumina claudit
Sic tibi (qui celsi resides in culmine coeli)
Cum libuit tandem terrenam visere partem
Ut genus humanum relevares crimine lapsum
Non penitus notum fuit ulli demoniorum
Viscera Mariae tibi Christe fuere cubile
Et qui te genuit triduum post surgere fecit
Cum mortis vindex mortum crucis ipse subires
In nos custodes qui nullo tempore dormis
Pervigil ut pastor ne demat de grege raptor

Concerning the Lion
(as translated by Alan Wood Rendell)

Natures three of lions are found with mystical meaning.
These I have written to Thee, O Christ, in metrical verses.
Writings divine tell the tales of other creatures of Nature,
Of which poems I have made, and again with a mystical meaning,
Writing of them, if I can, in verses of different meter,
These living creatures alone complete the full count of their number.
Stands in his might the Lion, on the highest peak of the mountain,
By whatsoever road he descends to the depth of the valley,
If through his sense of smell he perceives the approach of a hunter,
He rubs out with his tail all the marks which his feet may have printed,
So that none most skilled can tell what road he has travelled.
Cubs, new born, live not till the sun three courses has finished,
Then with a roar the Lion arouses his cub from his slumbers,
When he begins to live, and gains all five of his senses,
Now whenever he sleeps his eyelids never are closed.
Thus to Thee, Christ, who dwellest above the height of the heavens,
When to the earth Thou cam'st at Thy will at the end of the ages,
That Thou mightest redeem all men, now in wickedness fallen,
It was not known at the time, to any one of the Demons,
That for Thee, Christ, Thy bed should be the womb of the Virgin,
That Thy Father would cause Thee to rise at the end of the third day,
And Thyself wouldest undergo death though of death the Avenger,
Thou of us man the Guard, whose eye never closeth in slumber,
Shepherd, Thou guardest Thy flock evermore from assault of the Demons.

Another metrical version of the Physiologus, probably written in the mid-twelfth century, is the Anglo-Norman of Philippe de Thaun, who was also the author of a poetic work called the *Livre des Creatures*. This cannot be dated but its first six lines tell a little about the author:

> *Philippe de Thaun ad fait une rasun*
>> (Philippe de Thaun had made a discourse)
> *Pur pruveires guarnir de la lei maintenir*
>> (to furnish priests [information] to maintain the law)
> *A sun uncle l'enveiet, quae amender la deiet*
>> (He sent it to his uncle who ought to amend it)
> *Si rien i ad mesdit ne en fait ne en escrit*
>> (If there is anything in it said ill in matter or in writing)
> *A Unfrei de Thaun, le chapelain Yhun* *
>> (to Humphrey of Thaun, the chaplain of Yhun) *
> *E seneschal lu rei, icho vus dir par mei.*
>> (and seneschal of the king, I tell you in passing.)

To modern readers the title *Livre des Creatures* is highly misleading, for the book has nothing to do with animals on earth. Its "creatures" are the twelve signs of the zodiac, most of which are animals. The whole book is an explanation of the calendar, of the solstices, and so forth, explaining also why the months and the days of the week bear the names they do. According to the historian Thomas Wright [6] Philippe de Thaun's source for this book was a book called *De Compoto,* written in 980 by Helpericus, a monk of St. Gallen in Switzerland, the monastery with the interesting menu mentioned in Chapter One.

Philippe's rather long version of the Physiologus consists of 36 different items (plus, in the last few pages, a section on precious stones that is so jumbled that it cannot be broken down well), of which 10 are birds and 2 are plants, the plants being the traditional tree Peridexion and the magic mandrake, complete with the story that it screams when pulled from the earth. That story is the one alluded to by Shakespeare in *Romeo and Juliet:*

> And shriek like mandrakes torn out of the earth,
> That living mortals, hearing them, run mad.

though Shakespeare no doubt used a much later source. The treatment of the animals mentioned is more or less that of the older Physiologus;

---

* Unfortunately we do not know where "Yhun" is or was; at another point the poet says that his name is derived from Than Manor, located three leagues from Caen, Normandy.

Mandrakes on the title page of the *Grete Herball,* 1526.

one of the changes is that *Formicaleun* (ant-lion) is no longer the impossible hybrid, but the insect we know and which Philippe probably knew from personal observation, too.

Here is the section on the *Idrus* (or *hidrus,* or *hydrus* or *hydros*) with translation. Readers who know French are advised to read the Norman slowly and aloud, paying no attention to the spelling but keeping in mind that the "u" probably sounded as French "ou" sounds now, when so treated the text suddenly turns out to be much simpler than it appears at first glance.

Cr Be Aspide.

A Sample from the Bestiary of Philippe de Thaun.

IDRUS est beste e nage d'un estrange curage;
A colovere est semblance, en isle est conversable;
& Phisologus içeo dit, que ydrus
Volenters est en idles, mult pareet cocodrilles,
Par engin li quert mort quant buche uverte dort,
Quant l'ad aparceud, met sai en la palud,
Quant se est enboée e del limun luée,
Quant pot escolurger e sa buche mucher,
Dunc vent à cocodrille là u il dort en le idle,
En la buche se met petit e petitet,—
Or oez, quel merveille! li cocodrille s'esveille,
& itant par par est glut que tut vif le stranglut;
Idrus el cors li entre, la buele de sa ventre
Li trenche, e depart, si l'ocit par tel art,
Puis s'en ist vif del cors, sa buele en get hors.
Ceo est allegorie, grand chose signefie.
Le ydrus en verté nus signefie Dé:
Dés pur redemptiun prist incarnatiun,
Ke devint en pudnete, e puldre en boete,
De boe vint limun, e de char quir avum;
Dés de char fud vestud, dunt Satan fud vencud,
Qu'en eie acuntant par altre tel semblant?
Dés devenquid Diable par semblant cuvenable.
COCODRILLE signifie diable en ceste vie;
Quant buche uverte dort, dunc mustre enferm e mort;
Enfern ert en repos buche uverte nent clos. . . .

Aspis snake from the *Libellus de Natura Animalium,* reprinted in a facsimile
edition by D. R. Hillman & Sons, Ltd., © Wm. Dawson & Sons, Ltd., 1958.

Translation by Thomas Wright, Esq. (1841)

Idrus is a beast and swims with a strange force;
it resembles a snake, it lives in an island;
And Physiologus says, that the ydrus
willingly is in an island, it hates much the crocodile,
by cunning it seeks his death when he sleeps with his mouth open,
when it has perceived him, it puts itself in the fen,
when it is covered with mud and slime,
when it can strain and cover its mouth,
then it comes to the crocodile where he sleeps in the isle,
puts itself in his mouth by little and little,
now hear, what a wonder! the crocodile awakes,
and is so greedy that he swallows it all alive;
idrus enters into his body, the bowel of his belly
it cuts, and separates, and slays him by this means,
then issues alive from his body, and throws out his bowels.
This is the allegory which signifies a great thing.
The idrus in truth signifies God:
God for our redemption took incarnation,
which became in dust, and dust into mud,
of mud came slime, and of flesh we have skin;
God was clothed with flesh, whereby Satan was vanquished,
why should I go on telling it by another similitude?
God vanquished the Devil by a fit similitude.
Crocodile signified the Devil in this life;
when he sleeps with his mouth open, then he represents hell and death;
hell rests with mouth open, not closed. . . .

While the Physiologus of Philippe de Thaun is in the Norman French that was spoken in England, *Le bestiaire divin* of Guillaume (called Guillaume Clerk de Normandie) of the year 1210 is in the Norman French of northern France of that period. Since the later *Physiologi* seem to have been written for the delectation of the nobility rather than for the edification of the clergy, Richard de Fournival took an almost logical step with his *Bestiaire d'amour,* which converted the once devout book into courtly poetry where the gentleman tells his lady love that she should be like the turtle doves, only to receive the reply that she would much prefer to emulate the aspis snake and to cover both her ears so that she would not be enchanted by his powerful words.

Philippe de Thaun's Physiologus is no longer just a translation, versified, but interpolates opinions and statements from other works, mainly from St. Isidore of Seville.

Literate people of the tenth century and later usually had three books that told them about the world of nature. One was the Physiologus; the others were the works of Isidore and the "Geography" of Solinus. Solinus was a Roman grammarian of the third century A.D.; he may have written other works but only the "Geography" has survived. Compared to the other books already in existence in the third century his is a poor and unimportant compilation; moreover, at least two thirds of it are plainly cribbed from Pliny's *Historia naturalis.* But it did have a few advantages: it was short, it did not indulge in polemics, and it did not delay the reader by quoting opposing authorities; it did not want to be learned, it wanted to be read. Also it was in Latin, the language that literate people of the early Middle Ages could read—usually they were not familiar with classical Greek, or with Arabic which, most of the time, was also "the language of the enemy."

Thus Solinus's work must be mentioned, not because of its value, but because of its many readers. Its geographical contents were poor; its remarks on animals are either unilluminating or wrong and sometimes even both.

But the book was read, and quoted. And it received a new lease on life when it was published by Thomas Hacket of London in 1587 in an English translation by Arthur Golding, with the title *The excellent and pleasant work of Iulius Solinus Polyhistor.* Reading it one can find out that the chameleon lives on air only, but one cannot find a reason for this assertion. The marvelous races—the "wonder-people," as Conrat von Megenberg called them a millennium after Solinus—have somewhat increased in number. There are the *Hippopodes* which, though "shaped in all points like men down to the insteps, have feete like horses"—this could easily have been the mistake of a man accustomed to sandals who saw tightly fitting boots for the first time.

Then there are the *Phanesians,* dwelling somewhere at the Black Sea, "whose eares are of such an unmeasurable syse, that they couer the rest of theyr bodyes with them, and neede no other apparrell to clothe theyr limbes with." I wonder whether Nikolai Gogol, in conceiving his demon Viy, with eyelids so long and heavy that somebody had to hold them up for him if he wanted to see, had the *Phanesians* in mind, or whether he knew about them at all.

While Solinus had written to be read, St. Isidore—or Isidorus Hispalensis—wrote to preserve knowledge. Isidore lived from A.D. 560 to 636 and was archbishop of Seville from about 600 until the end of his life. His book *De natura rerum* was dedicated to Sisebut, king of the Visigoths; this was followed by a much longer work usually called the *Etymologiarum.* An important feature of the book is that it explains the origin of classical words to the readers (making countless blunders in the process). Archbishop Isidore seems to have assumed, and probably with good reason too, that his potential readers could just barely read and had to have everything explained to them.[7] St. Isidore has been called (by Montalambert) *le dernier savent du monde ancien,* a designation which might just be defensible on chronological grounds. But Isidore is no longer a classical writer. His Latin is corrupt, with all the earmarks of a language that has been learned and not practiced much. Classical terms are often used wrongly; the treatment is often abbreviated to such a point as to become meaningless; often obvious guesses take the place of cross checks. St. Isidore tried to put down what was known—the sections of his book range from grammar and rhetoric (I and II), via mathematics and laws (IV and V) to stones and metals (XVI) to ships (XIX) and domestic tools (XX). Section XII is about animals and this is subdivided into eight chapters: (I) Flocks, herds and beasts of burden, (II) wild beasts, (III) small creatures, (IV) serpents, (V) worms, (VI) fishes, (VII) birds, and (VIII) small flying creatures.

Here are a few samples:

> A sheep is a domesticated animal with soft wool, harmless and calm in disposition.
> [The cat] *musio* is so called because it is a foe to mice (*muribus*). Common people call it cat (*cattus*) because it catches. Others say be-

The house cat, from Gesner's vol. I.

cause it sees (*catat*). For it has such sharp sight that it overcomes the darkness of the night by the brightness of its eye.

Tuna (*thynni*) have a Greek name. They appear in spring time. They come in from the right side and go out on the left. They are supposed to do this because they see more keenly with the right eye than with the left.

Birds (*aves*) are so called because they have no definite roads (*viae*) but speed hither and thither through pathless ways (*avia*).

These, it must be emphasized, are some of the better examples, cases in which a translation—which often sounds like a bad joke—is possible at all.

That the classical satyrs, described as goat-footed and with horns, but without mention of sex, are listed among the strange races of men is not surprising under the circumstances. But after mentioning the *Sciapodes* with their single large foot, Isidore listed the *Antipodes*—so called because their feet are backward!

Such is the work of the "last of the savants of the ancient world."

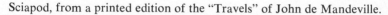

Sciapod, from a printed edition of the "Travels" of John de Mandeville.

Headless man, one of the "wonder-people" supposed to live in either Asia or Africa; from a printed version of the "Travels" of John de Mandeville.

Man the Cleric

SOMEBODY—at some time during the Second World War—bemoaned the fact that "most people want their history simple enough to be written on the back of a postage stamp." I agree with the complaint but I have to add that this phenomenon is not so recent. Some people have always wanted it that way, and condensed statements about events in the past, simplified into mere labels, have even been taught in the schools.

The term Dark Ages is such a label, covering European history for one millennium, from about A.D. 500 to about 1500. Everybody "knows" that no advances of any kind were made during these ten centuries, that learning was held to be without value and was discouraged and even actively suppressed. Everybody knows that the few people who traveled, with Marco Polo as the prime example, were not even believed when they returned (probably true in this case). Everybody knows that a man with a new idea, like Christopher Columbus, had to fight superstitions and wrong geographical beliefs. (Actually Columbus had to contend chiefly with a nearly empty official treasury—a condition that has failed to vanish along with the Dark Ages.)

The Dark Ages began with a phenomenon unique in history. It has the German name of *Völkerwanderung,* or Great Migration. The Huns, coming out of Asia, invaded Europe and by this act set off a large-scale chain reaction. The Visigoths, under their king Alaric, crossed the Alps and swarmed into Italy, seizing Rome in A.D. 410. The Vandals, displaced from the eastern part of Germany, moved across France into Spain and did not even stop there. Under their king Gaiseric they went into North Africa and in 439 set up a kingdom at the site of ancient Carthage. The Saxons, also displaced, invaded Great Britain, where the Roman legions had pulled out in 410. In 451 the Huns under Attila were finally defeated at Chalons and turned back, producing a temporary vacuum in the eastern portions of Europe that led to new invasions. The invasion of northern Italy by the Langobardi (or Lombards) in 568 is usually considered the last spasm of the *Völkerwanderung*. After all this there naturally followed a period of exhaustion during which most of the now stationary tribes were converted to Christianity. The Saxons, those who had stayed in continental Europe as well as those who had gone to England, resisted conversion for a long time.

The rule of Charlemagne brought some stability, and if Charlemagne had been able to rule for two or three centuries that stability would have been maintained. But he was mortal too, and after his death in 814 more unrest followed, caused in a large measure by onslaughts of the Magyars from the east, and by extensive raids by the Danes from the north. The Magyars were decisively beaten in 933 and again in 955, but there was not much rejoicing in the Christian camp, this time for a superstitious reason. The year 1000 was less than half a century away and many Christians were convinced that this year would mark the end of the world. The Pope, the French scholar Gerbert who ruled under the name of Sylvester II and who was greatly interested in mathematics and astronomy, did his best to discourage this belief, but the fateful year of 1000 had to pass before people listened. The turning point took place under Sylvester's rule, which lasted only until 1003. The world had not come to an end and the Pope's example showed that learning and piety could be combined.

But in popular parlance the Dark Ages are considered to have lasted another five centuries. Actually, many advances had quietly taken place even during the troubled period from 500 to 1000. For example, the stirrup had been introduced, a most important innovation at a time when a man depended on his horse. The zero had been imported into the western world from India by an Arab mathematician, making possible a simple system of writing, and of manipulating, numbers. It is by no means far-fetched to say that the magnificence of later medieval cathedrals is largely due to the fact that the Mohammedan Muhammad ibn-Mūsa al-Khārizmi recognized the superiority of the number system of India.

Similarly, during the "Dark" Ages the magnetic compass was invented, either in Scandinavia or in England, leading to more daring navigation at sea. The strong acids, nitric acid and sulfuric acid, were first prepared during that period, probably by Arabs; in any event Arabic works are the earliest written sources about these. And very soon after, alcohol was distilled from wine—reputedly by Christian monks in Italy. A new metal, zinc, and with it a new alloy, brass, appeared sporadically. Without the strong acids and without alcohol we would have no chemical industry, and the lack of brass would have changed the face of all other industry. Two other discoveries or inventions of the "Dark" Ages are plaster of Paris and gunpowder, the first of the explosives.*

Finally, the thirteenth century alone produced a whole catalogue of glittering names. Listed in order of their dates of birth they are:

Albertus Magnus of Cologne	(1193?–1280)
Vincent of Beauvais	(birth date unknown, died in 1264)
Thomas of Cantimpré	(1210–1275?)
Roger Bacon	(1214–1294)
St. Thomas Aquinas	(1225–1274)
Bartholomaeus Anglicus	(13th century, dates unknown)
Dante Alighieri	(1265–1321)

With the exception of Dante they were all clerics, and three of them— Albertus of Cologne, Vincent of Beauvais, and Thomas of Cantimpré— became important for the history of zoology. But chronologically they were preceded by two highly unusual personalities: a nun and an emperor.

The nun was Hildegardis de Pinguia (Bingen) who lived from 1098 to 1179, while the emperor was Frederick II, Holy Roman Emperor, King of Sicily, and King of Jerusalem, whose life span covered the period 1194–1250 and who may or may not have known of Hildegard.

The old castle of Böckelheim, overlooking the Nahe river in West Germany, has two claims to fame. One is that Heinrich IV, King of the Germans, conquered in battle and taken prisoner by his own sons, was imprisoned in that castle in 1105. The other is that Hildebert, the man in charge of the castle—*Vogt* was his title—had fathered a daughter about seven years earlier. She was to become the famous Hildegard who, in the words of George Sarton, "was a woman of great learning and vision; an

---

* I intentionally omit mentioning dates and names, since each one of these is the subject of scholarly controversies for which there is no room in this book. But that all these inventions, innovations, and discoveries took place during the "Dark" Ages is indisputable.

St. Hildegard of Bingen. She is shown on the lookout of her nunnery; below, the monk Volmar is transcribing her writings.

encyclopedic mind of the mystical type; the earliest medical writer of Germany, and one of the most influential personalities among the Christians of her time. She carried on an extensive correspondence with St. Bernard of Clairvaux, with four popes, five emperors and kings, and with many prelates."

Whether the child Hildegard was actually present when King Heinrich IV was delivered into her father's custody is not known from documentary sources, though it is quite likely. But it is a masterpiece of amateur psychology at its most amateurish to say, as has been said, that the sight of the king in irons shaped the child's destiny by "making her realize that secular glory is a fleeting sham." It is not known whether the king was actually encumbered by shackles on that occasion, and even if so that was not an unusual sight in 1105. And while there can be no doubt that Hildegard was neurotic all her life, it was, one is tempted to say, one of those "useful" neuroses, resulting in great memory-sharpening sensitivity. On the one hand she was given to visions, on the other she was an indefatigable observer and memorizer.

At the age of eight she was sent to the convent on the Disibodenberg nearby, where the sister of Count Meginhard von Spanheim, Jutta by name, was Sister Superior. We don't know much about Hildegard's upbringing. She was more than forty years of age before she could write a letter in Latin without help. Her visions she noted down in "simple language"—meaning an uncomplicated Latin—which was then transcribed by others, mainly the monk Volmar. She spoke German normally, but she seems to have known of the works of untranslated Latin-writing authors fairly early in her life. Were the nuns tutored in German by monks who had Latin works in front of them? This seems the only reasonable explanation and this assumption also explains a kind of unevenness, linguistically speaking, in Hildegard's own works. This linguistic unevenness has caused doubts about the authenticity of her works. But living in a bilingual area does not mean that everybody living there has a *complete* vocabulary in both tongues. Doubts based on the use of German words in Latin manuscripts are meaningless here; they only show that one language was spoken and the other written. By now the works of St. Hildegard are accepted as authentic, though they may contain some later interpolations.

Hildegard of Bingen is generally called St. Hildegard, though she was not officially canonized. The general feeling among Catholic historians, practically all clerics themselves, seems to be that the canonization failed to take place for external reasons—the deaths of witnesses, general

political unrest, and dissension in the church itself. Father Erich Was-
mann, S.J., incidentally a renowned zoologist himself, always referred to
her as St. Hildegard, and so did Cardinal Pitra who must have been well
informed about the details of the case. One decisive point in her life was
the founding of a new convent in 1147. Since it took the name of the
mountain, Rupertsberg, on which it stood, there has been some hair-
splitting about the question of whether Hildegard was the "abbess of the
Rupertsberg" or only the Sister Superior of the convent. Most Catholic
writers refer to her as the abbess, which she certainly was in fact if not
in title. It is noteworthy that she insisted that her nuns should come to
service well washed, with clean garments and "festively adorned" (with
flowers?) because a service should be pleasing in every respect.

Her works fall into several categories: the *Scivias* or books of visions,
dating from the period 1141–1150; the *Liber divinodum* (sometime between 1163 and 1170), dealing with cosmology and anatomy and trying to draw parallels, and finally the *Physica* and the *Causae et curae,*
which some historians consider separate if related works, and many think
should be regarded as two parts of one book. The *Physica* deals with
botany and zoology, while the *Causae et curae* is a medical work.[1]

As the title of the last work indicates, St. Hildegard was as much concerned with the causes of disease as with their cures, and it was her
opinion that much sickness is caused by eating certain foods. So far, so
good, but her lists of "harmful" foods certainly sound surprising to a
modern reader. Lentils she condemned outright, but not on moral
grounds that might derive from the Biblical story of Jacob and Esau.*
She simply said that they should not be eaten; the same goes for raw fruit
of any kind. Fruit, if somebody wants to eat it, should be boiled first.
She especially warns against the eating of strawberries (she may have
been allergic to them), or of fresh fruit in general. Her chapter on mush-
rooms is one loud and long condemnation, with a few medical hints, all
mistaken. As for eggs, they are a fine food when fried in butter; eaten raw
or hard-boiled they are harmful. The eggs of geese and ducks are harmful
in any shape. As for meat, that of bears, horses, pigs, and lambs is bad.
The only meat that is not harmful comes from cud-chewing animals, but
even here one must be careful not to eat it while it is too hot. Fresh water
is weakening, but the weakening quality of water is useful when mixed
with wine, for wine is "too strong." After all this, what she has to say about
beer comes as something of a surprise. Beer is the best drink ever invented; it is wholesome and good for all ages, except very small children,

---

* The lentil stew of the original became "pottage" in the King James version.

because the water in the beer has been "cleansed by the power of fire," and it is good and nourishing because it is really the "juice" of grain.

As regards remedies derived from herbs, St. Hildegard mentioned chiefly plants that still grow in the area where she lived. The general attitude is the classical one expressed by the phrase *similia similibus curantur,* a simple motto, meaning that the resemblance of a part of a plant to an organ of the body indicates curative powers—for example, that a plant with heart-shaped leaves might be good for heart trouble if you know how to use it. In addition to mirroring this classical opinion, St. Hildegard's chapters on herbs are a happy hunting ground for specialists. Some of the things she said had been learned by monks tending the herb gardens of monasteries; others are derived from the knowledge of old women dabbling in medicine; some are Germanic folklore of pre-Christian times, while some are old folklore overlaid with Christian ideas: "The fern is a plant the devil avoids and it has certain powers which are reminiscent of those of the sun, because it brings light into darkness. The fern disperses fantasies and therefore evil spirits don't love it. Where it grows the devil can rarely carry out his designs, contrariwise the plant will not grow near a house where the devil resides. But where it grows lightning will not strike and a field protected by ferns will rarely be struck by hail." While the devil flees ferns, they cannot protect their wearer against insanity, for insanity is *not* possession by the devil.

The *Physica,* after chapters dealing with stones and with trees, begins with the fishes and the chapter on the fishes begins with the whale. This deviation from the older scheme has a reason: St. Hildegard followed the Book of Genesis, in which the plants are the first living things to be created, to be followed on the fourth day by the creatures of the waters, with the whale mentioned first. Of course a whale was known to St. Hildegard by hearsay only, hence it is not surprising that she ascribed great "virtue" to it: if a person wore a belt and shoes fashioned of whale skin he would be protected from all disease.

The remarks about fishes, especially the freshwater fishes shows great familiarity with them on the one hand—every cloister had its fish ponds —and some curious ideas on the other. Fishes are generally healthy because "they are nourished by herbs." (In reality vegetable food is a rather minor item in the diet of fishes.) Some strange stories filtered into the description, as for example the one about the origin of the eel, which was and is an important food fish in that area. "In the days before there were eels a male pike saw a water snake lay its eggs in the water. The pike drove away the water snake and discharged its semen over the eggs and the snake was afraid of the pike and did not dare to come near. Thus the eel originated from the eggs of the water snake and the semen of the pike." But she then stressed that "nowadays" things are different and the eel generates its own young.

Still following Genesis, the birds are treated next and again St. Hildegard tells some strange stories. The peacocks, for example, originated by the crossing of some birds with certain small ground-dwelling animals, and even now the male peacock, "which has loose manners," occasionally crossbreeds with ground animals. The resulting young resemble their mother in shape, but show some of the coloration of the father. The crow originated because a magpie stole eggs of the raven and hatched them. One gets the feeling that St. Hildegard wanted to account in this manner for the existence of animals not specifically mentioned in Genesis. My reason for thinking this is that she accounts for the existence of poisonous animals by their creation after Adam and Eve were cast out of the paradise. "After the soil had absorbed Abel's blood . . . new fire blazed out from hell and soon God willed that a kind of fog came out of broiling hell and spread over the earth and where this fog moistened the ground poisonous, bad, and death-dealing creatures were born." These died during the Flood, but the Flood dispersed their dead bodies all over the earth and where they came to rest and decayed new creatures of the same kind came out of the corruption.

In the section on mammals it is evident that St. Hildegard knew the Physiologus, or at least a few stories from it. The latter is the more likely, since the traces are few; for example, the story that the lion brings its cubs to life by its roar, or, in the section on birds, that the turtle dove loves solitude. One rather definite influence of the Physiologus is the story of the unicorn which, in St. Hildegard's work, acquires (probably for the first time) the version that then became standard fare in later books. The older writers had stressed its speed, which prevented it being caught. Aelian added that the unicorn is friendly with other animals but often fights with others of its own kind, even with the females. But when the female is pregnant the male unicorn is mild and gentle. This passage was misunderstood or twisted for moralizing purposes by the author of the Physiologus, who wrote: "The unicorn cannot be subdued by the hunters but can be caught by a virgin. This means that Christ, mightier than all the powers of heaven, descended into the womb of a virgin to acquire human shape."

St. Hildegard enlarged on this. There was, she wrote, a philosopher (her interpretation of the meaning of the word "physiologus"?) who was

Unicorn, as pictured in Ryff's translation of the zoological book of Albertus.

astonished that he could not think of a way of subduing or catching a unicorn. But one day he had several young girls accompany him into the forest and he noticed that a unicorn sat down a short distance away and looked at the girls avidly. The philosopher, stealthily approaching the unicorn from behind, succeeded in catching it while it was watching the girls. In concluding her story Hildegard, daughter of the *Vogt* of Castle Böckelheim, pointed out that only girls of noble birth could attract the unicorn, peasant girls could not possibly do this. Moreover even the noble ladies had to be young, slender of body, and with a pretty face.

St. Hildegard died in 1179 at the age of 81 years. She does not seem to have written much after 1170. During her lifetime she was of extraordinary influence in her area but she failed to exert any literary influence. Albertus Magnus does not even mention her, nor does Thomas of Cantimpré. On the other hand her unicorn story, presumably by word of mouth, spread far and wide. She was, no doubt, a "holy abbess" with the common people and the minor clergy, as well as the nobility of her time.

But the world of learned letters paid no attention to her until her writings were resurrected by churchmen in the nineteenth century, as part of ecclesiastical history.

The very combination of the words "the nun and the emperor" implies contrast, and contrast there was between the quiet but highly active nun and the equally active but most unquiet emperor.

Frederick II von Hohenstaufen,[2] grandson of Frederick Barbarossa, although he was Holy Roman Emperor and leader of the Fifth Crusade, managed to be on bad terms with the ruling popes. He is probably the only man who was excommunicated three times. His physical appearance, at the age of about 45, is described as short and stout, baldheaded and nearsighted, with a ruddy face, but with a friendly and pleasant countenance. As a military leader he was able, but not brilliant. As a statesman he was of good will (his favorite project was a union of Italy and of Germany), but not very effective. As a person he was generous and expansive—and was promptly accused of being given to orgies. He spoke six languages (Greek, German, French, Latin, Italian, and Arabic) and his major characteristic seems to have been an absolutely insatiable curiosity, embracing everything from astronomy to zoology, especially zoology. He traveled accompanied by his private menagerie.

> In November, 1231, he came to Ravenna "with many animals unknown to Italy: elephants, dromedaries, camels, panthers, gerfalcons, lions, leopards, and bearded owls." Five years later a similar procession passed through Parma. . . . The elephant, a present from the Sultan, stayed in Ghibelline Cremona, where he was put through his paces for the Earl of Cornwall and died thirteen years later "full of humours," amid the popular expectation that his bones would ultimately turn into ivory. In 1245 the monks of Santo Zeno at Verona, in extending their hospitality to the emperor, had to entertain with him an elephant, five leopards and twenty-four camels. The camels were used for transport and were even taken over the Alps, with monkeys and leopards, to the wonder of the untravelled Germans. Another marvel of the collection was a giraffe from the sultan, the first to appear in mediaeval Europe. Throughout runs the motive of ivory, apes and peacocks from the East, as old as Nineveh and Tyre and as new as the modern "Zoo," with the touch of the thirteenth century seen in the elephant which Matthew Paris thought rare enough to preserve in a special drawing in his history, and the lion which Villard de Honnecourt saw on his travels and carefully labelled in his sketchbook "drawn from life"! [3]

The Sultan in the foregoing quotation is al-Ashraf, Sultan of Damascus, who exchanged presents with Frederick. The Sultan sent a "planetarium," representing the motions of the planets, and Frederick in return sent a white bear (polar bear or albino?) and an albino peacock. One of the happy moments in Frederick's life was when he received an albino parrot from a ruler in Egypt.

Frederick, in 1224, founded the University of Naples, where St. Thomas Aquinas began his studies under an Irish master, Petrus de Hibernia. He laid down a course of study of medicine, surgery, and pharmacy, uniform for the whole kingdom of Sicily, with the provision that royal officers had to be present during the examinations. He wrote verses in Italian and encouraged local poets. Dante emphasized later that Italian poetry had started at Frederick's court. Members of the court included, at one time or another, the learned Michael Scotus (Michel, the Scot), who translated Arabic works, and an astrologer called Magister Theodore, who divided his time between casting horoscopes and making confections of sugar—then rare—and fresh violets.

A typical day in Frederick's life included checking on edicts, correcting a translation from the Arabic made by one of his scholars, dissecting a bird, and dictating letters to Moslem rulers. These letters are collectively known as the "Sicilian questions"—they consisted of lists of questions, about things which the emperor wanted to know "because my philosophers have no good answers to these questions." He repeatedly sent a diver—named Nicholas but called *ichthys* (the fish)—to the bottom of the Strait of Messina to tell him what lived down there. When a fisherman caught an exceptionally large pike, Frederick personally inserted an inscribed copper ring into its gills and set it free again to test how

The ring attached to a fish by Emperor Frederick. The Greek inscription begins with the words "I am the fish" and ends with the date "fifth day of October." The Greek letters inside the smaller circle give the year: 1230. The fish is reported to have been caught in 1497.

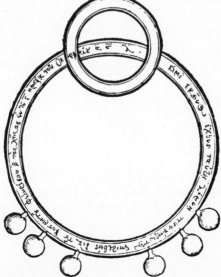

long large fishes might live. He tested the reports that eggs could be incubated by mere heat without a brooding hen. He had ostrich eggs brought to Apulia to find out whether they were actually hatched by the sun, instead of by their mother.

His philosophers argued over whether vultures find their prey by sight or by smell; Frederick sent vultures aloft with the eyes sealed. They failed to find food, but whether Frederick arrived at the correct generalization that birds completely lack any sense of smell is uncertain.

His extensive correspondence with non-Christian rulers made him suspect, his unusual experiments even more so, and his insistence on a weekly bath was probably due to un-Christian influences too. Still, when he finally died, the Italians mourned him, and the Germans, who had seen him but rarely, refused to believe the report: they said that Frederick had only retired to a cave inside a mountain and that he would come forth again when his people needed him most. (Later that legend was transferred to Frederick Barbarossa.)

Frederick's only book, *De arte venandi cum avibus* (The Art of Hunting with Birds), is probably due to the introduction of a Moslem invention. Falcons had been used for hunting in the West for quite some time. But even with a trained falcon the hunter had a problem: during the trip from the castle to the hunting grounds the birds must not be allowed to see anything, or else they might take off after some prey at the wrong time. The solution had been to pierce the bird's lower eyelid and to pull a thread through the hole, which was then tied over the bird's head. During the ride from the castle the bird, perching on the master's glove, was blinded by having its own eyelids pulled shut. At the hunting ground the thread was released and the falcon took to the air. The Mohammedans had replaced the thread by a hood. Frederick welcomed the innovation and introduced it to his domains.

Nothing much had been written about hunting with falcons, or about birds in general, so Frederick set out to fill the gap. He said himself that he had conceived the plan of the book thirty years before its completion. The year of completion is only generally known—after 1244 but before 1248. The book is dedicated to his son Manfred, who would have been twelve years old in 1244, about the age where young noblemen joined their elders in a hunt.

Frederick used Aristotle's outline *ubi oportuit* ("where it is opportune to do so") but quite often Aristotle was quoted for the purpose of being contradicted on the basis of practical experience. The book is that of a man who had observed birds, worked with them while hunting, killed them, and dissected them, during most of this life. The description of migrations began with a reference to Aristotle, but then took flight on its own. Frederick had seen migrating birds from Germany to Sicily and knew what he was talking about. After describing the traditional seven

One of the Emperor's falcons, from Gesner, vol. III.

"climes" of the northern hemisphere he calls all the climes from the third to the sixth *nostre regiones* (our regions). The whole work not only breathes independence; it is set down with the assurance of a man who is describing his own activities, bolstered by book-knowledge, *ubi oportuit.*

The whole work is subdivided into six books, and there are two families of manuscript. The first consists only of the first two books of *De arte venandi,* usually with additions by Manfred. The oldest extant manuscript is that of the Vatican Library, which is also richly illustrated. It is possible, though it can be neither proved nor disproved, that many of these illustrations are based on drawings by Frederick. It is known that he could draw, and that he designed the towers of Padua. The two-book version has been printed repeatedly,[4] but the six-book version exists in manuscripts only. Even the extant six-book manuscripts do not seem to be complete. Frederick, in one of the prefaces, refers to a section on the care of birds while they are molting. This section is unknown, and one might conclude that the busy emperor just did not get around to writing it. But Albertus Magnus of Cologne made use of the work by Frederick II, writing additions saying "because so many people would like to learn about these birds" and he quoted Frederick both about the care of hawks and about black falcons, a passage also missing in the manuscripts. One must therefore conclude that the original was somewhat larger than the manuscripts we now have.

However, the missing portions seem to have been minor, and the existing manuscripts give us a very good idea of the book. The first book begins with praise of falconry. Frederick made it clear that his desire was not for fame but simply to have better falcons than anybody else. A discussion of the anatomy of a bird follows, in which for the first time the shape of a bird's lungs and the shape of the breastbone are described and the fact that the larger bones are hollow is stated. Book II is practical; it discusses the raising, feeding, and training of falcons. Book III continues the practical advice, describing the various kinds of lures used and the training of dogs that are supposed to hunt in conjunction with the falcons. Book IV is devoted to the gerfalcon; the differences between it and the other species of falcons are discussed and the hunting of cranes with gerfalcons is described in detail. (At one time Frederick issued a decree to his officials in several provinces that all the cranes that could be rounded up had to be sent to one of the royal residences for the training of falcons.) Book V is also devoted to a special application of falconry; it describes the hunting of herons with the "sacred falcon." Book VI is specialized in a similar way; its theme is the hunting of waterfowl with the peregrine falcon.

Frederick's work, though strikingly "modern" in many respects, cannot be properly called a zoological work. The nearest equivalents of more recent times are the hunters' manuals of the late nineteenth century. While accurate in their zoological descriptions they were books of advice, just like Frederick's "Art of Hunting with Birds."

The great encyclopedias of the thirteenth century were different in attitude; their authors tried to bring together everything that was known. Considering the difficulties of acquiring knowledge from books before books were printed, one can feel only awe when looking at the volumes compiled by Albertus Magnus, by Thomas of Cantimpré, and by Vincent of Beauvais.[5]

Of these three men who, in writing encyclopedias, revived the study of zoology, Albertus of Cologne was the oldest; but the part of his work that deals with animals was not finished until much later than that of his one-time pupil, Thomas of Cantimpré.

Thomas was born at Leeuw St. Peter near Liège in what was then the duchy of Brabant which accounts for the fact that he is often called Thomasius Brabantinus or Thomas of Brabant. Cantimpré was the name of his cloister. He began his writing career at an early date, at first with ecclesiastical works. In his late thirties, he started on his main work, which, according to his own words, occupied him for fourteen or fifteen years. This was the book that interests us here, entitled *De natura rerum* (On Things of Nature). It was to consist of nineteen books, but there was no provision for a discussion of celestial phenomena in these nineteen books. He must have felt that this omission made his work incomplete and fortunately the astronomical treatise known as the Sphere of Sacrobosco [6] became available at the time, so Thomas added a paraphrase of the Sphere as his twentieth book.

Thomas did not follow the scheme which seems to have been in the mind of St. Hildegard of Bingen—that of using the order of the days of creation in Genesis as a guide to the sequence of things to be described. His first book is about Man, but not, as one might think, ethnographical. It deals mainly with human anatomy. The second book is about the soul; the third one is the *liber de monstruosis hominibus orientis*, the book of the monstrous people of the east, which follows Pliny closely. Books IV to IX are about animals, books X to XII about trees and plants. The remaining books deal with springs and their properties, gem stones, the seven metals, the seven "climes" (of the northern hemisphere), the seven planets, and finally Aristotle's four elements. The whole was an encyclopedia of all natural phenomena, the first to be written since Pliny the Elder.

Thomas avoided the allegorizing descriptions of the Physiologus as much as was possible, tried to suppress myths (except for the *monstruosis hominibus,* which were too colorful to discard), and, in general, tried to look at animals as animals, as natural phenomena to be described. Just the same, a great deal of space is devoted to their medicinal properties; after all, the animals had been created for the use of Man. Quite a number of "moral lessons" are included too. Thomas wrote for fellow clerics and they, in fact, constituted the overwhelming majority of his readers.

The arrangement of the animals in the various books is in alphabetical order of their Latin names. The generalizations are still based mainly on those of Aristotle. For example: all animals with two or four legs and those without legs (snakes) have blood; those with more than four legs do not have blood. All animals that have ears can move them, with the exception of Man; all animals that have eyelids close them when asleep, with the exception of the lion and the hare; * all four-legged animals that have horns lack upper incisors, and so forth. But while Thomas followed Aristotle and Pliny—he knew both from Latin translations from the Arabic as apparently he could not read Greek—he was not afraid to think for himself, if the occasion arose. The description of the monstrous humans made him ask whether they were descended from Adam. And if he failed to understand why an animal was built the way it was he did not hesitate to say that this must be an *improvidentia naturae,* a "carelessness of Nature."

Thomas was not a traveler; the extent of his travel is covered by the triangle Cologne, Paris, and Liège. Hence he had to make the best of descriptions of animals he had never seen, which led to such statements as that the scorpion, if he happens to see a *stellio* (?) will break out in cold sweat! Thomas would not have said anything like that about a dragonfly, which he knew, but a scorpion was a dweller in hot and distant deserts and he knew of no reason why it shouldn't perspire.

* The story that the European hare sleeps with its eyes open persists in European folklore to this day and has even been the subject of zoological essays. The fact is, of course, that the hare closes its eyes when asleep. The popular belief is probably due to a misinterpretation. If you come across a hare in a field it will remain motionless, carefully watching every move of the intruder without twitching a muscle. The lack of motion suggests that it is asleep—if not, it would run away, wouldn't it?—and therefore "it never closed its eyes, even when sleeping."

"Marine unicorn" and "marine cow." The "horn" of the marine unicorn shows clearly that it was modeled after the tusk of a narwhal.

The total number of four-footed animals mentioned is 110, with a few duplications; the number of birds listed is 114 (bats are among them). The book on sea monsters contains 57 names. The term "sea monsters" should be understood to mean unusual-looking water-dwelling creatures, for it contains the octopus, a marine turtle, a seal, the dolphin, and a few fabulous marine animals. The book on the fishes lists 85 names, but again the term is used loosely for marine creatures; it includes another octopus, various crabs, the pearl oyster, and something called *stella* (star) probably meaning a starfish. The book on snakes lists 44 names; it includes lizards, centipedes, the scorpion (with the story mentioned above), and the tarantula. The term *vermes* (worms) was obviously used to include everything that did not fit elsewhere; the book on "worms" (50 names) contains frogs, toads, grasshoppers, cicadas, bedbugs, bees, wasps, ants, and leeches.

It would be highly unjust to judge Thomas' work by later standards. He was the first of his time to make an attempt to describe the "things of nature," and especially the animals. In an epilogue he said that his inspiration had been a sentence in the works of St. Augustine, who said that it would be useful if somebody did just that.

Albertus Magnus, who was either ten or seventeen years older than Thomas, also wrote a book on animals. Because he was older and especially because Thomas as a young man had attended lectures given by Albertus in Cologne, it was assumed for a long time that the work of Thomas was, at least in part, based on that of Albertus. On the basis of this assumption it was certainly strange that Thomas, who always carefully mentioned his sources (even though he misspelled names on occasion), had never quoted from Albertus. The answer is that Albertus quoted from Thomas; Albertus had worked on his animal chapters on and off, for a number of decades and did not get them into final shape until late in his long life. Meanwhile Thomas had finished his book—around the year 1248—and it is quite probable that he saw to it that a copy of his work was sent to his former teacher.

As for Albertus Magnus, later called the *Doctor universalis,* but more commonly Albertus of Cologne, we know that he was born at Lauingen on the Danube in Bavarian Swabia, but there is disagreement about the year. Most old chronicles which mention the date at all say that it was in 1193 and German historians still defend this date. But most English reference books say that he was born around 1200. He joined the Order of the Dominicans in 1223. He had studied liberal arts in Padua; after joining the order, he went to Bologna to study theology. In 1230 he was sent to Cologne as instructor. But it was some time before he settled down. He taught in Strasbourg, Freiburg, Regensburg, and Hildesheim. In 1243 he returned to Cologne, but only two years later his order sent him to Paris; the University of Paris and the Dominicans did not see eye to eye and the Dominicans hoped to strengthen their position by having one of their most learned members on the scene. He returned to Cologne in 1248 and stayed there, though with interruptions, until 1260. In that year he became Bishop of Regensburg but after two years he resigned his post. By that time he was either 62 or 69 years of age and wanted to devote the remaining years of his life to the conclusion of his literary works. He retired to Cologne, where he died on November 15, 1280.

The work of Albertus differs from that of Thomas in intent though not too much in form. Thomas wanted to write an encyclopedia. Albertus was not, or only secondarily, interested in completeness; he had a general commentary in mind. To accomplish this he used several methods. He started with Aristotle—after all, he had translated all of Aristotle's works, including the spurious ones, into Latin for the convenience of the brothers who had not learned Greek—and then interpolated the comments of other writers—for example, the Arab ibn-Sīna (Avicenna) and Pliny.

But that was only the beginning. Albertus had traveled a great deal and seen many things; whenever he could describe something out of his own experience, he did so. For example, he described a flying fish from the Mediterranean very clearly and from his own observation, adding that the Italians call this fish the "swallow of the sea." It is interesting that his is the first book on animals that gives not only the Greek and Latin names, but the German names as well. This was probably because, in addition to his own observations, Albertus had a large store of stories from unknown contemporaries. As a practicing priest who traveled a great deal he met and talked with peasants, fishermen, soldiers, fowlers and hunters, and with other clerics of all ranks. Of course he also heard confession and it is quite obvious that many of his observations on the sex life of his contemporaries came to him via the confessional.

Many of the stories he heard were probably just omitted if he did not believe them, but if he had found that a story represented a widespread, if erroneous belief he would mention it, adding, "this is an absurdity."

Albertus Magnus

Thierbuch.
Alberti Magni / Von Art Natur
vnd Eygenschafft der Thierer / Als nemlich Von Vier füssigen/ Vögeln/ Fyschen / Schlangen oder kriechenden Thieren / Vnd von den kleinen gewürmen die man Insecta nennet / Durch Waltherum Ryff verteutscht.

Mit jhren Contrafactur Figuren.

Hierin findestu auch viel Artznei krancker Roß vnd anders haußutheß Auch wider die schedliche gifft der Schlangen vnd anderer gewürme.

Begnadet mit Keyserlicher freiheit in Syben Jar nit nach zutrucken.

Title page of the *Thierbuch Alberti Magni,* the only portion of his work to be translated into German. The translator was Walther Ryff. The animals are: eagle, lion, "marine fox," and "basilisk."

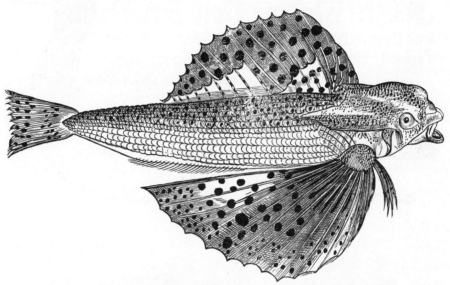

A Mediterranean flying fish, from Gesner, vol. IV (Gesner does not credit a source so this picture probably came to him directly and not via Belon or Rondelet).

He did not respect authority at all. "Pliny tells many things that are wrong," he would write. Of Solinus, whose "Geography" has been mentioned, and of Jorach (a Jewish scholar, place and time unknown, who must have written some kind of natural history), he said that they were "learned men who frequently lie." [7]

The remarks about Pliny's *Sciapodes* show clearly that Albertus put reasoning and common sense above tradition. The Sciapodes must be a fable, he declared, since people with a foot of such construction could not move about. Moreover, he added, it is not just a question of having only one leg and one foot—in order to make movement possible, the foot has to be lighter than the body it has to move. He also had absolutely no patience with the story of the tree-geese, the Hibernian geese which were supposed to grow on trees. That story had just found its way into books at the time. The earliest source is supposed to be a Danish historian, known as Saxo Grammaticus, who was probably born in 1150; the story was also told by the Irish writer Sylvester Giraldus, a contemporary of Saxo Grammaticus. Albertus said it was "nonsense," adding that he had seen the Irish geese copulate and lay eggs just like any other kind of geese.

The much-discussed "tree-goose," from Gesner, vol. IV.

He even criticized Aristotle but there tried to blame the copyists: "Aristotle says that in the case of waterfowl, for example wild ducks, the females are larger than the males; this must be a slip of the pen (*error literae*), since one can see that it is not so." Or, elsewhere, "Aristotle says that males will hatch from long and pointed bird eggs, while females come from rounded eggs, but this is wrong and is not the word of the Philosopher, but a mistake of the copyist. Avicenna says that round and small eggs produce roosters, and that hens come from long and pointed eggs; this agrees with my own experience with eggs. . . ."

He did not quite dare to dismiss the pegasus, the griffin, the unicorn, and the dragon, perhaps because he did not wish to be told that his work was incomplete because of these omissions. But in each case the mention begins with the words: "it is said." The phoenix is mentioned, but with the qualification: "as is written by those who write about mystic theology, instead of describing natural things." The basilisk is dismissed with the statement that this word refers to an alchemical elixir and does not mean an actual animal.

Albertus considered that species is determined by shape, and that the color is not important. The falcon of the warmer climes (meaning the Mediterranean countries) is darker than the falcon of the north, but this is due simply to the greater heat of the southern countries which penetrates the seed and makes it darker. In the cooler north the seed contains more moisture, hence it is more transparent and the offspring is lighter in color. Nor are color differences because of differences in temperature very rare, he continued. He had seen a white blackbird, which was no doubt white because it came from a cold country; its shape clearly showed it to be a blackbird. (What he had seen was, of course, an albino.) Similarly the squirrel that has a reddish fur along the Rhine is reddish with gray spots in Poland and completely gray in Russia. Actually these are different species, but since they look alike otherwise, Albertus believed that they bore out his contention. While this was logical, though mistaken, reasoning from the naturalist's point of view, another idea of his was more philosophical.

Albertus believed there were no large gaps between the major types of animals. He thought—it sounds like an early evolutionary idea, though it wasn't—that all the seeming gaps were bridged by intermediate forms. To him the moose was an animal "between horse and stag." The ostrich was "not so much a bird, but a link between the flying and the walking animals." Likewise the bat was a link between small animals like mice and small flying birds. Dolphins and whales on the one hand, and beavers and otters on the other, were links between land-dwelling and water-dwelling animals. The jellyfish were links between low animals and plants, and the sponges were quite close to the plants.

He proposed a system of ranks, based on the possession of a soul, but while he used the term as a theologian would, his "soul" is difficult to distinguish from intelligence. At the top of the scale there is Man, fully endowed with a soul. One step down there are the pygmies which are not human because they don't have a soul—in the sense of the human soul, that is. But the pygmies are above the next step, the monkeys. Another step down are all the four-legged animals, the step below them is occupied by the birds, and the step below the birds is occupied by the fishes. Below them are the cephalopods, below them the crabs—and thus it went, step by step, to the sponges. Below the sponges would be the plants, though Albertus did not actually say so.

The work of Albertus was rather original in many respects; it followed older examples and had the character of a compilation, but it was not founded on library research only. Many independent unwritten sources were added and Albertus tried to exercise critical judgment all the way through.[8]

The third of the encyclopedists of that unusual century was Vincent of Beauvais, or, Latinized, Vincentius Bellovacensis. Of his life and career virtually nothing is known, except that for a time he was "reader"—a step or two below "professor"—at the monastery of Royaumont in the vicinity of Paris. That he died in 1264 is generally accepted. As for the date of his birth there are several guesses, all based on different estimates of the number of years it must have taken him to write his work. This work was entitled *Speculum majus* (Great Mirror), and consisted of three parts, the *Speculum naturale* (Mirror of Nature), the *Speculum doctrinale,* and the *Speculum historiale.*[9] Of primary interest to us is the first part, the *Speculum naturale,* consisting of 32 books with 3,718 chapters—of course some of these "chapters" are only half a dozen lines long. Here we have a virtually complete collection of everything that had been said about the natural world—animals, plants, and stones—by Latin, Greek, Arabic, and Hebrew authors. The very volume of the quotations precluded criticism or weighing of evidence. Nor was this Vincent's goal; he simply wished to put together everything that could be gathered.

Vincent of Beauvais has been well summarized by the unnamed writer of the article about him in the Encyclopedia Britannica:

> Vincent has hardly any claim to be reckoned as an original writer. But it is difficult to speak too highly of his immense industry in collecting, classifying and arranging these three huge volumes of 80 books and 9,885 chapters. The undertaking to combine all human knowledge into a single whole was in itself a colossal one and could only have been born in a mind of no mean order. Indeed more than six centuries passed before the idea was again resuscitated; and even then it required a group of brilliant Frenchmen to do what the old Dominican did unaided.

While Thomas, Albertus, and Vincent wrote for educated men, especially fellow clergymen, still another cleric, a Franciscan who is known as Bartholomaeus Anglicus, set out to write an encyclopedia for "plain people" who needed no education beyond a reading knowledge of Latin to follow him. His work is also much shorter. The first printed edition comprises only 220 leaves, or 440 pages, large size. Nothing is known of Bartholomaeus' life except that he arrived in Paris around the year 1220, probably as a fairly young man and that he is known to have been in Magdeburg after 1230. His life span must have run from about 1200 to 1260, with a leeway of around five years at either end.

He called his book *De proprietatis rerum* (On the Properties of Things) and divided it into nineteen books having the following subjects: (I) God, (II) Angels and demons, (III) Psychology, the soul, (IV and V) Physiology, (VI) Family life and domestic management, (VII) Medicine, (VIII) The stars, astrology, (IX) Division of time, (X) The elements, matter, (XI) The air and meteorology, (XII) Flying creatures, (XIII) Fishes, dolphins, and whales, (XIV) Physical geography, (XV) Political geography, (XVI) Gems, minerals, and metals, (XVII) Trees and herbs, (XVIII) Animals, and, finally, (XIX) Color, odor, taste, food and drink, weights and measures, and musical instruments.

The books on animals and plants show that Bartholomaeus was much interested in these; many remarks indicate personal observations. But though this was a very successful book,[10] it did not advance science, except, perhaps, by stimulating the interest of readers. The science in Bartholomaeus' work was not always up to date, but it was presented in an interesting manner.

In about 1264 Jakob van Maerlant,[11] the "founder of Dutch-Flemish literature," decided to produce a book for those "who are annoyed by romances and tired of lies." He had a fine Latin manuscript, written by "van Coelne Broeder Alebrecht," meaning Albertus Magnus of Cologne. The title he gave to his translation was *Der Naturen Bloeme* (The Flower of Nature) and he spent five years putting the original into Dutch metric poetry. He did not live long enough to learn that the Latin manuscript he had translated was not Albertus' book, but Thomas of Cantimpré's *De natura rerum,* but in any case he made a remarkably precise translation of the original.

During the interval between the death of Jakob van Maerlant and the invention of printing another translation of the work of Thomas was made, by still another cleric, the canon of Ratisbon (Regensburg), Conrat von Megenberg, this time into German. A century had gone by since the writing of the original and Conrat von Megenberg felt justified in making changes, criticizing some parts, elucidating others, leaving out what he thought was mistaken, and so forth. In short, it was not a true translation, but a revision with an incidental change of language. In a way this translation was a "link"—using the word in the same sense in which Albertus Magnus used it—between the scholastic works of the thirteenth century and the new compilations of another famous Conrad, namely Conrad Gesner, another two hundred years later.*

We know the year of Conrat's birth (though not the date), because on the first page of his first book, written in Paris, he noted that he completed it in 1337, at the age of twenty-eight. Hence he was born in 1309. Another source states that he was a pupil at the Latin School in Erfurt, and at the age of twenty he arrived in Paris where he obtained his degree and wrote the book just mentioned, which dealt with the church in Germany. Immediately after its completion he left Paris and went via Germany to Vienna where he taught ecclesiastical history or Latin, probably both. At the age of thirty-three he became severely ill. His legs and his hands were paralyzed, and he was unable to walk and could not even eat without assistance. Then he dreamed that he was kneeling in prayer in the church of the Lower Minster in Regensburg, which he must have seen before. While praying at the grave of St. Erhard he saw an inscription (which did not exist in reality) stating that he would be helped. On awakening Conrat decided to follow the dream and had himself carried on board a Danube boat, upriver bound, with the city of Ulm as its final destination. While traveling Conrat dictated two Latin hymns and when he was carried ashore in Regensburg he requested that these hymns be sung while he was praying at the grave of St. Erhard. As he had firmly believed he would be, he was cured and as soon as he was able he showed his gratitude by writing the life history of St. Erhard.

In Regensburg he accepted the position of canon of the cathedral and acted temporarily as priest of the cathedral. In addition to his ecclesiastical duties he was also "counsellor in the services of the city" and in this capacity was sent in 1357 to Avignon where the Pope then resided. His mission was to obtain certain privileges for the city, which he did.

After settling in Regensburg, Conrat wrote a number of tracts in Latin, all of them dealing with church matters. At some point, however, he

---

* Because we have here two authors with the same first name writing on the same subject, I have spelled the first name of the canon of Regensburg with a final "t" to provide a distinction, my justification being that contemporary sources refer to him as Maister (Magister) Chuonrat von Megenberg.

must have decided that he would write in German. He had a large Latin manuscript at his disposal, consisting of twenty books by two different authors. The twentieth book was the *Sphaera mundi* of Sacrobosco, while the other nineteen "were collected from ancient authors by Maister Albertus Magnus"—actually Thomas of Cantimpré's *De natura rerum*. Conrat first translated the Sphere, without taking any liberties except for a rhymed preamble. He circulated the manuscript among interested people, who presumably praised it, since he then set out to render the main work into German, apparently completing it in 1349.[12]

In the course of the work, Conrat makes a number of references to his own name which are quite tantalizing, since he does not say enough to solve the mystery of what "Megenberg" means. The problem is that there is neither a family *nor* a place of that name. More than a hundred years ago, Dr. Franz Pfeiffer, in editing a reprint of Conrat's book, went through a large number of old Bavarian chronicles, trying to find the name. The closest he could come was to find the spellings of "Meyenberg" and "Meygenberg" for a village now spelled Mainberg, which is near the Main river, east of the city of Schweinfurt. A personal visit showed that there were ruins of an old castle near the village. Had this been the castle of Megenberg and was Conrat the last of a line of knights who had inhabited the castle? Nobody knows, but the way Conrat speaks about himself suggests it. The word itself furnishes no clue to its meaning.

Conrat's translation came to be known as the *Puoch der Natur* (The Book of Nature) and it immediately became very popular. At least 100 manuscript copies are known (the Library of Munich had no less than 17, and the Library of the University of Vienna had 9) and it has been printed more often than any other work of the period.[13]

The earliest printed edition, probably following the style of the manuscript copy, does not have a title page. The first page begins with the words: The Registry [meaning contents], and on the next line: "The book first speaks about Man, then of his skull . . ." etc., listing the chapters of the first book. Leaf No. 2 shows a woodcut, a naked man flanked by two robed doctors. Leaf No. 3 begins: "After that follows the Book of Nature which contains at first the nature of Man, after that the nature of the sky, the animals, the birds, the herbs, the stones," . . . etc. After the contents have been enumerated, it is stated that: "A highly learned man has collected and worked on this book for fifteen years, and has taken from the following teachers, poets, and experienced doctors of medicine, namely Augustinum, Ambrosium, Aristotilem, Basilium, Ysidorum, Plinium,

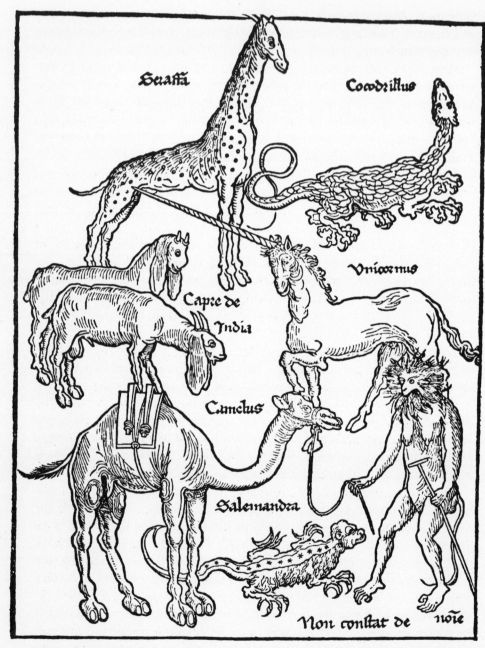

"Animals of the Holy Land." Originally in a travel book by George Breydenbach, but used as an illustration in the printed versions of Conrat von Megenberg's *Puoch der Natur;* first printed picture of a giraffe.

Galienum, Avicennam, etc., and many other magisters and teachers . . . which book Maister Chuonrat von Megenberg transferred from Latin into German."

Megenberg's independence becomes clear at the very beginning of the second book: "I now leave the order of the Latin book because it is here quite disorderly." His disapproval of the lack of orderliness led to a wholesale rearrangement, as can be seen from the comparison in the following table, in which the left-hand column lists the original order of Thomas' books, with roman numerals and the right-hand column gives Conrat's order with arabic numerals.

COMPARISON OF THE ARRANGEMENT OF SUBJECT MATTER

DE NATURA RERUM (Thomas of Cantimpré)	PUOCH DER NATUR (Conrat von Megenberg)
I. *de anatomia humani corporis*	1. Of Man and his nature (I)
II. *de anima*	2. Of the sky and the seven planets
III. *de monstruosis hominibus orientis*	(XVI, XVII, XVIII, XIX)
	3. Of animals:
IV. *de animalibus quadrupedibus*	A. First about those that walk
V. *de avibus*	the earth (IV)
VI. *de monstris marinis*	B. Of fowls in general (V)
VII. *de piscibus fluvialibus atque marinis*	C. Of marine marvels (VI)
	D. Of fishes (VII)
VIII. *de serpentibus*	E. Of snakes (VIII)
IX. *de vermibus*	F. Of worms (IX)
X. *de arboribus communibus*	4. A. Of trees (X)
XI. *de arboribus aromaticis*	B. Of savory trees (XI)
XII. *de herbis aromaticis et medicinalibus*	5. Of herbs (XII)
	6. Of noble gems (XIV)
XIII. *de fontibus*	7. Of jewels (metals) (XV)
XIV. *de lapidibus pretiosis*	8. Of marvelous springs (XIII)
XV. *de septem metallis*	Appendix (III)
XVI. *de septem regionibus*	
XVII. *de spera & septem planetis & eorum virtutibus*	
XVIII. *de passionibus aeris, fulfure, tonitruo & consimilibus*	
XIX. *de quatuor elementis*	

The roman numerals in parentheses show which book of Thomas's work was used for which chapter in Conrat's. Book II of Thomas has been suppressed and Conrat also intends to suppress Book III, the one on the monstrous men. But his friends must have told him that it should not be left out, so Conrat treated it as an appendix, saying that the Latin work has one more book, "this I shall add here for the sake of friendship." But while he adds it for friendship's sake he waxes critical at once:

> It is a question where the wonder-people, called *Monstruosi* in Latin, come from and whether they are of Adam's seed. My answer to this question is different from that given in the Latin book. There it is said that the wonder-people are not of Adam's seed, unless, as Adelinus said, they originated by unnatural acts of men who laid with animals. For there are wonder-people that are called Onocentauri, that are people from head to waist, but oxen below. Know that this is impossible for the seed of creatures that far apart will be mutually destructive and cannot produce anything alive. And if a living being should actually be produced in such manner it would die immediately. I, the Megenberger, hold the following opinion: there are two kinds of wonder-people, one kind with a soul and one without. I count among the first kind those which have a human soul but are physically faulted. The soul-less wonder-people may resemble the human shape somewhat ... the wonder-people with soul are of Adam's seed and faulted by his sins for I believe that, if the first man had not sinned, all people would have been born flawless.

The wonder-people with souls are those that are born of women but have deformities, such as one normal and one underdeveloped leg, or two heads, or similar malformations. Conrat blames the sperm for this (too much, or too powerful, or not enough, too weak), while malformations in animals are probably due to astrological influences. As for the soul-less wonder-people they are not human and their origin is unknown. After having stated these opinions, Conrat simply repeats the list compiled by Pliny, with some additions that, compared to the classical imagination, sound quite tame.

The first book, about the parts of the human body, follows Thomas (and, indirectly, Aristotle), with the addition of medical advice—what to do about a headache caused by exposure to the sun; an occasional superstition—a new mirror may become spotty because a menstruating woman looks at it; and personal opinions: "Learned men say that the

Bird-headed man, one of the "wonder-people," from a printed edition of the "Travels" of John de Mandeville.

eyebrows have the same purpose as a fence protecting a garden, but I think that Nature produced eyebrows to ornament the eyes. The prettiest are those that look as if they had been painted with a brush. The eyebrows of a man should be heavier. . . ."

The first 48 chapters of this book are devoted to explanations of how the various parts of the body function; the 48th chapter deals with childbirth. The long 49th chapter contains hints for determining the character of a person from his physical characteristics.

Chapter 50 talks about dreams. The main advice is that bad dreams of various kinds mean that something is wrong with the body and are an admonition to consult a doctor. "But some dreams reflect the thoughts we have when awake."

The second book is about the sky, the planets, sun, and moon, and meteorological phenomena. While the themes discussed in this book, which deviates more from the original than any other, have nothing to do with zoology, one item must be mentioned because of its historical importance. In the chapter on thunder and lightning Conrat explains that lightning is a vapor which is reflected back and forth between the "cold" clouds and the "fiery" upper atmosphere: "this repeats until the vapor is thrown down with the speed of a projectile fired from a gun." Thomas' original gave the same explanation, but with the comparison "like a dart shot from a crossbow," Conrat's change of simile not only proves that guns were invented during the century between original and translation but also that they had become well known by the year 1349.

Book 3, about animals, comprises roughly one half of the whole *Puoch der Natur*. Book 3, "of the animals that walk the earth," has 68 chapters. The animals are discussed in alphabetical order of their Latin names; hence the first animal to be discussed is the donkey (Latin *asinus*). As usual some medicinal "information" is interpolated, such as that stags never suffer from fever and that for this reason salves prepared with stag fat "soothe the heat of the sick." Moralizing has its place in Megenberg's book—in connection with the animal *cathus,* which smells very bad and which has flame come out of its mouth when it is angry, he says, "To us this animal is a symbol of zealous gossips and old women which blacken the honor of decent people with the fiery words that come from their mouths."

Of the weasel it is said that it is brave enough to kill snakes. The reason given is somewhat surprising in a book that often moralizes—the weasel hates snakes because they eat mice which are also the weasel's food. The story that the porcupine will shoot its quills at hunters and their dogs appears in Chapter 36, a story that is not just a fantasy but more in the nature of a misinterpretation. A porcupine, when cornered, will swish its quills around and since a few quills are usually loose, they may fly out and travel a distance of a few feet.

Chapter 39 deals with the *lamia,* probably meaning one of the larger monkeys, because it is said that it comes out of the forest at night, enters gardens, and breaks branches off trees with its powerful arms. "The animal is bad-tempered, but it does offer its milk to its young. But our prelates, bishops, and priests are far meaner still, for they do not offer their congregations the spiritual bread, the word of God, and are a hindrance to those who want to do so." The classical satyr appears under the name of *pilosus* (hairy) but is only mentioned, without stories of any kind.

Birds are discussed in 71 chapters, beginning with the eagle (Latin *aquila*) which is called the king of the birds. Second to be treated is the *arpia,* the classical harpy, of which it is said that it can be tamed and will then learn to speak.Then there is the famous tree-goose. Conrat just told this story as it came to him, without making any comments at all. Here is a translation of his version:

> Bachadis is . . . a bird that grows on a tree. The tree has many branches and the birds grow from these branches so that there is always a large number of them hanging down. The [grown] birds are smaller than geese and have feet like ducks, but are of the color of dark ashes. They hang by their beaks from the bark of the tree. They soon fall into

The puzzling bat, as drawn by Gesner's unnamed artist.

the water and continue to grow until they start to fly. Some people ate those birds, but Pope Innocent IV forbade the eating of the birds during a Lateran Council.[14]

Since Thomas had described the bat among the birds, Conrat did the same, but he pointed out that it did not have feathers anywhere, that it looked like a mouse, and that it gave birth to live young, "like a walking animal," and even suckled them. "It also has teeth, unlike any other bird," he stated, adding, "In India the bat grows larger than a pigeon and has teeth like a human."

The section on marine marvels consists of 20 chapters. The first is about an animal called *abides,* of which it is said that it grows up in the sea, but then goes on land and lives off the land. If it were not for the last remark one might guess that a seal of some kind was meant; one can only wonder what sequence of misunderstandings finally resulted in the animal *abides.* The whole section is furthest removed from reality. The *abides* is followed by another unclassifiable marvel named *achime,* followed by *barchora,* for which Conrat suggests the name of "hard-beak"—probably an octopus. Next comes the crocodile, then two more fanciful inventions, and then the *canis marinus,* the "sea dog," which is now the German word for seal. But the information given is not enough for identification; it is merely stated that the sea dogs hunt fish as land dogs hunt other animals but that they hiss and do not bark like land dogs. Next is the *draco maris,* the dragon of the sea, described as resembling the "real" dragon but without wings. Then comes the dolphin, with all the classical stories about it. Next comes the *equus fluminis* (water horse), which might just conceivably be the hippopotamus. There is a description of a "water cow" and of something called *giadius.* The name looks like the Latin word *gladius* (sword) but if the Atlantic swordfish is meant a lot of things have gone wrong. The chapter reads:

> Giadius means a sword trunk. [The German word *Rüssel,* here translated as "trunk," means an elephant's trunk.] Isidorus and Plinius report that it is a sea marvel, with a trunk as sharp as a sword. With this trunk it makes holes in ships and then pulls them under water. Its beak curves downward. Its claws are divided like a fork, its tail has knots and its teeth are curved like those of a wild boar. The legs are its most vulnerable area. Dishonest advocates are like this animal; at court they quietly make holes in the ships of justice and drown the people who have come with just claims. Oh, how little they think of what they will be told on Judgment Day!

From then on hearsay has the upper hand.

There is the *kilion* with internal organs on the wrong side of the body, the *ludolachra* with four wings (two attached to the head and two to the back) and the "sea monk" which lures people into the water to eat them. Then follow three classical creatures—the nereids, the sirens, and Scylla. After that comes *stinchus* which is said to live along the Nile, looking like a crocodile but of smaller size. Very likely *Varanus niloticus,* the Nile monitor lizard, is meant. The last one is *testeus,* probably a marine turtle.

The whole section is quite dry. Obviously Conrat did not feel at ease with the marine marvels because he did not know a single one of them. Elsewhere he had opinions and stated them. As, for example, when he quoted Pliny as saying that the feathers of an eagle could not be mixed with feathers of other birds, he added, "I don't believe that." Or when he has been told that a dying swan will push a feather into its brain: "This makes no sense and the writer has made a mistake." But in section C he only moralized and sermonized on a few occasions and the only criticism occurs in the chapter dealing with what is probably the hippopotamus, where the description is followed by a weak: "Make out of this what you wish."

In the section dealing with the fishes (29 chapters), he felt on firmer ground, to mix a metaphor. His language became crisper; he *knew* what he was writing about. When he described the eel—first chapter of this section because of the Latin name *anguilla*—he gave advice on the best way of cooking it. About the herring he knew that those caught near Scotland were bigger and better than those caught near the German shore. He did tell the story that whales are sometimes mistaken for islands by sailors because all the best authorities told it, but in the very next chapter he is at home again. This is on the crayfish, "which has a hard back like crocodiles and eight legs and two arms with 'scissors' instead of hands." He stated that the crayfish goes backward but took exception to the idea that it never "follows its face." "I have watched myself that a crayfish will walk forward, even though slowly."

The oyster "is a sea-fish of the tribe of the clams" and Conrat reported that crabs like to eat its flesh. He finds himself in full agreement: "The flesh, simmered with oil and onions, is a wonderful dish for Lent."

The last chapter is here translated in full for a reason that will become apparent very quickly:

> *Vipera marina* means a sea snake. It is a fairly small sea-fish, less than an ell in length. Above its eyes it carries a small horn on its head, small

but deadly with poison. A person who has been wounded by this horn is fatally poisoned and the fishermen are very careful. As soon as they have caught such a fish they decapitate it. But the rump is used because it is a fine dish.

The late German edition of Conrat's work has a footnote reading *"Petermännchen?"* This is the German name of a North Sea fish with the scientific name *Trachinus draco*. A British book, E. G. Boulenger's *World Natural History* gave the English name as weever. I have no reason to believe that Professor Boulenger ever read Conrat, but here is *his* section, written in 1938:

> The Weever Fish, whose name is derived from the old Anglo-Saxon word Wyvern, meaning a viper or dragon, has poisonous dorsal spines, and also a large poison spine on each gill cover. The fish, living as it does half buried in sand, may easily sting incautious waders, and the notice "Ware WEEVERS" may sometimes be seen displayed on piers, etc. The fish is good eating, and in France legislation compels removal of the spines before it is exposed for sale.

The next section deals with snakes in 37 chapters. Neither Thomas nor Conrat could have known much about snakes from personal observation, for in Europe north of the Alps only four or five species of snakes occur. The harmless common grass snake (*Natrix*) is the most numerous; and only one, the common viper or adder (*Vipera berus*), is poisonous, though even an untreated bite is rarely fatal to an adult.

The result of the lack of personal knowledge on the part of both Thomas and Conrat, in connection with the exaggerated stories of classical writers, is a wild hodgepodge, mitigated in places by a display of common sense. The introduction to section E claims that all snakes are poisonous, that all snakes eat animals and vegetable matter indiscriminately, that snakes drink little but love wine, that they regrow their eyes if they have been blinded, and that they flee when they encounter a pleasant smell. But in the middle of all this nonsense there is the correct statement that snake venom is harmless if it does not enter the bloodstream.

The basilisk must have been troublesome to Conrat. Albertus had rejected it as an animal, but Thomas had written about it, naming it (following precedent) the "king of all snakes"—hence the name, since Greek *basileus* means king. Conrat probably did not dare to omit the basilisk; besides his parishioners probably told him that they had seen a snake wearing a crown.* Following his original, he said that the basilisk can kill both by its glance and by its breath. Where a basilisk lives, trees and lesser plants die off, the air becomes so poisonous that birds cannot fly through it without dying, and even the hardest rock crumbles into dust when struck by the breath of the basilisk. Its shape is not described, though it is said that it is small and can, therefore, be overpowered by the weasel, which dies after the encounter. A dead basilisk has many uses, however, because if you burn a dead one to ashes and spread the ashes over a place no spider can spin its net there, no venomous animal of any kind can endure, and it also cannot be dirtied by bird droppings. The ash will impart a golden sheen to silver—this, of course, is the "basilisk" of the alchemists.

There follow several chapters on various snakes, none of which can be identified from the description until we come to the dragon. It is described as one of the largest animals on earth and of awful appearance, but "this animal has no venom." A few pages later Conrat has a surprising explanation for one particular dragon:

The classical hydra, as pictured in Gesner, but Gesner was careful to point out that the picture was just an artistic conception.

> Some say that Hydra is a dragon with many heads and that one of this kind lived in a swamp near Lerna in Arcadia. The storytellers say that it grew three heads for each head that was severed. But this is not true. . . . The area was rich with flowing water and the waters were so powerful and so wild that they ruined the city. If one spring was dammed

* The grass snake *Natrix* has two crescent-shaped bright yellow patches at the back of the head, still called its crown by many people. For the full story of the basilisk and a partial explanation see Chapter 2, "Fairytale Fauna," in my *Exotic Zoology* (New York: Viking, 1959).

up, three or four others came up elsewhere. This was seen by the hero Herakles who brought much soil and heavy stones and filled in the whole swamp, making it dry. A man of ill will acts just like the Hydra, if you punish him for having done some evil he will commit four new misdeeds for the one that was forbidden.

The remaining chapters of this section deal with other snakes, with the scorpion (probably considered a snake because it was venomous), with an animal called *tarantula,* but described as snakelike in appearance, with the lizard and the salamander (with reports on the fire-resistant "wool of the salamander," actually asbestos), and finally with another viper which hisses softly until a female viper comes to the male. "When the male sees the female approaching, the male ejects its poison, thereby honoring the female, so that their wedding will be without poison."

The final section consists of 31 chapters about "the worms." As with the fishes, both Thomas and Conrat could speak from personal experience, which makes the whole section far less fabulous than that about the snakes. The section begins with *apis,* the bee. After the nonsense which crept into the preceding section, the chapter on the bee seems surprisingly modern. Conrat knew that each hive contains three kinds of bees; his main mistake is referring to the queen as "king" (it was not then known that the queen is the only sexually functioning female in a hive). But aside from this mistake, and after eliminating the classical story that bees arise from the cadavers of dead cattle, the chapter could be in a current popular book on natural history. The chapters that follow deal with spiders, toads, silkworms and glowworms. A few superstitious stories are mixed in, but most of the time one can see that the author writes from more or less personal knowledge.

The chapter on the ant also bears this out, especially because of a mistake, strange to say. Conrat reported, among other things, that ants remove their dead from the nest and bury them and that they prevent grain from sprouting. "But if grain has been wetted, they carry the seeds out into the sunlight so that it will dry and not spoil"—but these "seeds" are the pupae of the ants, which are quite similar in size and shape to grains of barley or rye. The next chapter is about the "ant-lion," but by this time it has become the insect we still call by that name.

The remaining chapters deal with flies, grasshoppers, snails, fleas, and lice. In the chapter on frogs, the water frog (*Rana*) is clearly distinguished from the tree frog (*Hyla*). "If you put the tongue of a water frog under the head of a sleeping man he will begin to talk and reveal secrets, but the peasants say that he often makes mistakes." The tree frog "is green, climbs trees, and lives among the leaves. It is in the habit of calling before rain; at other times they rarely give voice. Some people believe that if you toss a tree frog into the mouth of a dog, the dog will no longer be able to bark."

Other "worms" described are the wasp, the cockroach, and a few real worms, including the leech and the earthworm.

> Now the third [actually the sixth] part of the book of many animals has reached its end.[15] From their diversity and nature one realizes the wonderful works of the Lord, and Holy Scripture mentions them in many places. But the stupid priests know little about them, though they could make many good sermons about them if they only knew the life of the animals.

chapter six

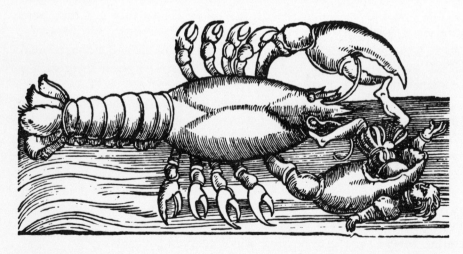

Lobster, from Ryff's translation of the book of Albertus Magnus, 1545. (A similar picture in Gesner.)

Man the Reformer

THE fact that Conrat von Megenberg's *Puoch der Natur* still exists in about a hundred handwritten copies and was printed six times in a quarter-century poses an interesting problem which has not been solved; in fact it apparently hasn't even been studied thoroughly.

The problem is this. During the fourteenth century virtually all education was provided by the church, either in cloister schools or, for children of the rich and the nobles, by private tutors. These tutors, if they were not clerics themselves, had come out of clerical schools. All schooling, then, began with Latin. To be able to read at all and to be able to read Latin were synonymous. But if this was the case why was there such a demand for a book in German?

Some gears fail to mesh properly when it is asserted that the clergy was the only literate class. To begin with, not every member of the clergy could be considered literate, as the biting remarks of Conrat von Megenberg (and some less biting remarks by Albertus) clearly prove. On the other hand the French troubadours and the German minnesingers were usually literate, though not of the clergy. Finally, as has been pointed out by historians with a sociological bend, there must have been a kind of anonymous reservoir of literacy among baronial bookkeepers and secretaries. Maybe they were the first avid readers of Megenberg.

Independent merchants must also have added their quota of literate people. It is almost impossible to imagine dealing in products of distant lands without being able to read. The demands of trade must have spread literacy to still another group of people, the sea captains who had to write reports of their experiences and adventures. Of course they could dictate to a scribe, but obviously a sea captain who could read and write had a great advantage over another who couldn't. Another class of people among whom literacy was not only useful but an indispensable prerequisite was the steadily growing number of medical practitioners.

By the middle of the fifteenth century the total number of people outside the clergy who could write and read (either their own language or Latin) must have been about equal to the number of literate clerics. At about that time printing was invented and after a somewhat reluctant start spread to all European countries as fast as firearms had spread a century earlier. The first books to be printed were of a religious nature, with the Greek and Latin classics following hard on their heels. The result of printing was an early "information explosion." A scholar no longer had to make a trip to Verona or Cologne to read a classical work in manuscript. All that was required was the expenditure of a few silver coins, and that expenditure also eliminated the need for making endless excerpts because now the scholar *owned* the book.

It must not be thought that every book printed during the second half of the fifteenth century was of value, though of course by now every one of them is valuable in terms of money as a collector's item. Among the worthless early printed works there was one that might be considered an item in the history of zoology. It had the title *Lucidarius* or *Elucidarius*. In spite of the title, it was in German and its contents consisted of all the zoological myths anybody ever invented. The first edition of 1479 was followed by innumerable reprints and translations into other European languages.* The author was never mentioned and later literary critics usually rejected the suggested authorship of St. Anselm, archbishop of Canterbury (1033–1109), and hunted around for another and later author. We now know that the book is at least a century older than Anselm's actual writings. The true author is still unknown.

The predictable result of the spread of printed books, plus new information that had become available because of voyages of exploration, was a new wave of all-embracing zoological works, comparable to the

* Rewrites of the *Lucidarius*—with the "wonder-people" moved from Asia to the interior of Africa and to "isolated South Sea islands"—were still being sold around the turn of the twentieth century at county fairs and similar events in Germany and Switzerland. The title had been changed to "Wonders of the Hot Countries," and companion volumes to these "Wonders" were "The Secrets of Albertus Magnus" and "The Suppressed Sixth, Seventh, and Eighth Books of Moses."

encyclopedias of the thirteenth century, but restricted to zoology only, or in some cases to zoology and botany. While all the thirteenth-century authors had been clerics, all the sixteenth-century authors were physicians. They were:

Edward Wotton	(1492–1555), a physician in London
Adam Lonicer	(1528–1586), City Physician of Frankfurt-am-Main
Conrad Gesner	(1516–1565), City Physician of Zurich, Switzerland
Ulisse Aldrovandi	(1522–1605), professor of medicine in Bologna

Edward Wotton, a native of Oxford, said that he had worked for many years on his book *De differentiis animalium* (On the Differences among Animals), which is probably explained by the fact that he was a busy physician. Apparently he also felt that he had not really done justice to the theme, for exhortations from his friends were required to make him send it to a printer. The work, in ten sections, appeared in Paris in 1552. Wotton tried to be systematic in his arrangements, and while he followed Aristotle in the general outline he was quite independent when it came to detail.

The first two sections deal with the bodies of animals in general and their different organizations; Wotton dealt with the existence or absence of limbs (for example, the tail), the kinds of motion, the difference in food, the various modes of propagation, and so forth. While the first two sections were quite general, the third is devoted specifically to the "differences" among animals having blood. The next section is along more "practical" lines, telling how the various parts of various animals are used for food or for medication. The last two chapters are a kind of appendix to this section, one dealing with milk, the other with excretions other than milk. The fourth section is about Man. The fifth is about the four-legged animals that give birth to live young, but one cannot say that it deals with mammals in our sense since all that do not happen to be four-legged are omitted. In this section the animals are subdivided into three groups: those with clearly separated toes (say rats or cats), those that are "cloven-hoofed" (for example, goats), and those with a "solid hoof," like horses. Such a scheme would naturally bring related forms together; on the other hand, it did not prevent the hare from following the fox, or the bat from following the mole.

The sixth section deals with the *Pholidota*—the word is derived from the Greek word *pholas,* meaning "lurking in a hole," and the *Pholidota* of Wotton are lizards and snakes. His term does not mean what we call reptiles, because it leaves out those reptiles that fail to lurk in holes, such as the marine turtles. The seventh section is about birds, the eighth about marine animals with blood—fishes and whales. That Wotton made a clear distinction between the two is indicated not only by the title of the section but also by the fact that he has a chapter on fishes that are so large that some think they are whales. The ninth section is devoted to the insects—spiders and scorpions are included—and the tenth is about "bloodless" and mostly water-dwelling animals—octopi, crabs, snails, clams, sea stars, and so forth.

Wotton was certainly closer to the present system of classifying animals than Aristotle had been, but he still did not know just which characteristics are important. This was partly due to a lack of knowledge of what the various organs do. The lack of legs, say in a porpoise, looked important to Wotton, and he failed to realize that the significant points were air-breathing lungs and a heart of specific construction.

Wotton's book was printed only once and was not translated into any modern language. It is hard to tell why it was so unsuccessful, because for its time it was a good book. It has been suggested that its readers were disappointed because it paid no attention at all to discoveries, mainly in America, made in the three decades before its publication. This may have been one cause, but no doubt a more important one was that only a few years after its publication the much more comprehensive volumes of Conrad Gesner began to appear.

Our second physician, Adam Lonicer, was born in Marburg in 1528, received his degree of Magister at the age of about twenty, and only five years later was made City Physician of Frankfurt. He married the daughter of the printer and publisher Christian Egenolph, the man who had published the last edition of Conrat von Megenberg in modernized German. Naturally Egenolph published his son-in-law's book. The publication date was 1551, and the title *Naturalis historiae opus novum*. A German translation, which was soon made, had the title *Kräuterbuch* (Book of Herbs), actually a better title, for of the 618 pages only 82 are devoted to animals, the others to plants. The medicinal value of a plant or of a part of an animal was the thing that was important to Lonicer.

The zoological section began with a discussion of the "parts" and products of mammals, in the following order: meat, blood, milk, butter, cheese, fat, marrow, urine, and excrements. Then the domestic animals are listed, beginning with the sheep and ending with the cat. After that a number of wild animals are described (all European, with the exception of the camel, elephant, and lion); all descriptions are quite short unless a medicinal use can be reported. The mammals are followed by frogs, toads, crocodile, lizard, several snakes, spider, ant, earthworm, snail, and caterpillar.

There was not even the faintest attempt to bring related forms together. It did not matter to Lonicer what belonged together, but only what was useful. It is almost logical, from this point of view, that the next section, the one on flying animals, begins with a long discussion of birds' eggs. After that he listed the better-known birds, following up with bees, wasps, and a few common beetles. A section on fishes, whales (*not* clearly distinguished), crabs, octopi, and clams, with a final chapter on the remora, concludes the book. Lonicer did not doubt at all that a single remora was able to hold even a large ship in one place. He could not think of a medicinal value for the remora—apparently the story had captivated him so much that he forgot the main theme of his book.

Lonicer's work, especially the German version, was reprinted repeatedly. Apparently the book was considered a kind of medical adviser for the household, as many of the remedies suggested were fairly easily available to homesteaders and even to city dwellers. Lonicer's medical approach is evident; quoted authors are few in number, but every one was a physician. The zoological value of the book is minor, though German zoologists working along historical lines were benefited by Lonicer's collection of local names of animals and plants.

The Swiss physician Conrad Gesner, who is known as the "Father of Zoology," became the greatest zoologist of his time and exerted enormous influence for centuries afterward.[1]

During the first decade of the sixteenth century two brothers, Andreas and Urs Gesner, moved from Solothurn in Switzerland to Zurich. Urs Gesner, a furrier by profession, was Conrad's father; the name of his mother was Agathe. Little Conrad [2] was born in Zurich on March 26, 1516.

Because Urs Gesner was poor and had several other children, Conrad did not grow up in his father's house. A close relative of his mother, Chaplain Johannes Frick, took him into his home. Chaplain Frick, Gesner wrote many years later:

> taught me to take care of his single and small garden which was full with plants of all kinds. There he spent his leisure hours with me and taught me the names of all the plants so that I, if he wanted some, could get them for him, either from the garden or from the open fields. He used plants and herbs for his own health as well as that of his friends and his

Conrad Gesner of Zurich. The somewhat idealized portrait shows him as he looked during the last years of his life.

> simple life and the use of the herbs had the result that he lived to over 80 years of age, without ever having been sick. ... He rarely moved beyond the limits of his small garden and house, unless he had to go somewhere to preach a sermon. ...

Chaplain Frick also sent Conrad to school, the "school near the Fraumünster" (church), which had just been built. Of the curriculum we know only that, after elementary instruction, it was devoted exclusively to the study of the classical languages. In 1523 a new instructor, Oswald Myconius, came to the school from Lucerne. He was aghast at the ignorance of the pupils, seven-year-old Conrad among them. But he found them willing and stated with some self-satisfaction that "they were soon able to read Cicero, Virgilius, Livius, Plutarch, Homer, and Aristophanes"—in the original languages, of course.

Gesner finished the school curriculum in a few years and was accepted into the Upper School ("near the Grossmünster") where Johann Jakob Amman was his chief teacher. Gesner's brilliance as a student seems to have impressed all his teachers. Oswald Myconius became his friend for life, and Amman, upon learning that Frick could not support the boy any longer, took him into his own house for three years. But then something happened which eased the situation somewhat. The city council of Zurich decided to establish a Student Office for the purpose of supporting brilliant but poor students.

On October 27, 1530, the fourteen-year-old Conrad sent a petition to Huldreich Zwingli, the religious reformer, who was also a most influential man in Switzerland in every respect. Around Easter, 1531, Gesner was informed that his petition had been granted, but only half a year later a catastrophe took place. In October 1531 five Catholic cantons declared war on the Protestant cantons. On October 11 battle was joined at Kappel and Zurich lost. Huldreich Zwingli was killed in the battle and so was Urs Gesner, Conrad's father. Conrad's uncle Andreas was severely wounded and almost beheaded as an enemy, but the sentence was not carried out and he recovered from his wounds.

The recently founded Student Office collapsed and Gesner was once more without a livelihood. His former teacher Myconius wrote to a friend in Strasbourg, a preacher and theologian called Capito, and suggested that he take Gesner into his house. He praised Conrad's abilities to the skies and added, very much *non sequitur:* "Don't be alarmed by his tall build; he is only sixteen years of age." Capito did take Gesner in, and Gesner recalled later that Capito was learned in Latin and Greek and that "nobody could compete with his knowledge of Hebrew."

In Capito's house Gesner not only learned, he also began to teach. His first pupil was the bookseller Wendelin Richelius who found it necessary to learn Greek. But Gesner wanted to learn more himself. He now knew what were then called "the three languages" (Latin, Greek, and Hebrew) and therefore had the equipment to study. He wrote to his former teachers, Myconius and Amman, asking whether they could obtain a scholarship for him. Any kind of scholarship.

Amman and Myconius somehow succeeded, but Amman also changed Gesner's plans for him. The young man had had theology as his goal; Amman insisted that he should study medicine. Early in 1533 Gesner and a friend of his, Johannes Friess, set out from Basel for Bourges in France. It was a walk of about six weeks; they arrived near the end of March, 1533. Both were disappointed. "All branches of learning are neglected here except jurisprudence," Gesner wrote to Myconius. Friess left for Paris soon. Gesner tried to endure and to earn some money by giving lessons, and in his spare time read the works of the Greek physicians "and especially books about plants and their virtues." In 1534 he went to Paris—again on foot, as a wandering scholar—and began a period of omnivorous and planless reading. He did not realize that he could not have spent his time more usefully; fifteen years later he wrote that no young man should be sent to a university in another city without an older mentor to advise him.

In December 1534 he left Paris and went to Strasbourg where he hoped to find a position. Failing, he returned to Zurich, handing Heinrich Bullinger, Zwingli's successor as rector of the Upper School, an expense account. He had spent 65 crowns during the two years in France, 15 crowns more than the scholarship money for two years.

Soon afterward he married—"a young and very beautiful modest girl of perfect character, but not rich," to quote his own words. Apparently everybody was furious about the marriage of the young man—he was not quite twenty—who had yet to earn both a degree and a living. He was forced, as a punishment, to become a teacher in the beginning grades of the school, teaching elementary grammar to pupils far less willing than he had been himself. But the authorities noted that he spent all his spare time reading medical works. An apology to Bullinger, via Myconius, resulted first in an increase in salary and, somewhat later, in permission to quit the school (still receiving his salary) and go to Basel to finish his medical studies.

During his stay in Basel the bookseller Heinrich Petri commissioned him to write a Greek-Latin dictionary. Gesner undertook the work, but when he saw the printed book in the fall of 1537, he was disappointed. The printer had severely cut the Greek notes and quotations which he had collected with much effort. Gesner, a number of years later, remarked, "I don't know whether the printer considered himself sufficiently learned to edit my collection; or whether he kept them back for a second printing in order to call it an 'enlarged edition' is something I cannot decide." Nor could he ask Petri, who had died only a few months after the publication of the work.

Apparently without any preliminaries Gesner learned one day that the University of Lausanne was willing to give him a professorship. He immediately accepted and instead of becoming the *Doctor medicinae* Gesner, was now Professor of Greek Gesner. During a visit to Zurich in 1540 the City Physician of his native town talked to him seriously and at great length, with the result that Gesner resigned and went to Montpellier to study medicine. But again he was disappointed, and when a fellow citizen of Zurich asked him whether he should send his son to Montpellier he wrote back: "I wish I could recommend this medical school, but [your son] will only learn anatomy and the knowledge of medicinal plants better than anywhere else. Philosophy and Greek are completely neglected." Presumably Gesner learned what he could learn and then went back to Basel, where he arrived early in February 1541.

In those days the acquisition of a doctorate required a public disputation with a professor of the discipline in question, while the rest of the faculty sat in, looking dignified and sometimes grim. Gesner disputed the problem whether the heart or the brain was the seat of sensation and of motion. He defended the viewpoint that both are influenced by the nerves which came together in the brain, "even though Aristotle had said differently." Early in March Gesner became Doctor Gesner, with license to practice in his home town where he also was instructor in physics (Aristotelian physics) at the Collegium Carolinum. The city fathers considered this an unimportant job and the salary reflected this opinion. But it was not much work and though he was a recognized practitioner of medicine, there were not many patients.

Gesner was free to write! And write he did. First a few works in Greek, minor both in content and size. Then the *Bibliotheca universalis,* a work about which he had thought for some time and which probably had germinated during the "undisciplined" reading in Paris that he deplored so much. The first part was what we would call a "universal bibliography," which was published in Zurich in 1545. It listed, in alphabetical order, the names of all the authors who had written in Latin, Greek, or Hebrew; the titles of their works that had been printed up to that time, plus, in many cases, the titles of works that so far existed as handwritten copies only, plus summaries of the books, and so forth. Authors living at the time were also included, provided they wrote in one of the "three languages," and in many cases Gesner's *Bibliotheca universalis* is the only reliable source about them.

This work made Gesner famous, and since the highest praise his contemporaries could think of had a classical flavor, they began to refer to him as the *Plinius germanicus,* the German Pliny.

We know a few instances of the reaction of the literary world. Archbishop Hoper invited Gesner to come to England and settle there. Duke Otto Heinrich ordered his librarian to obtain a copy of Gesner's book and to arrange the ducal library accordingly. The city council of Augsburg, through its City Physician, inquired whether Gesner would accept a position in that city. And the famous Fugger family, at the moment the richest in Europe, offered him a place in their own house. Gesner yielded to curiosity and in July 1545 traveled to Augsburg, accompanied by his Zurich publisher, Christoph Froschauer. But apparently the Fuggers, though generous in every respect, made the condition that Gesner become a Catholic. Gesner refused and soon returned to Zurich. While he had not gained anything materially, a new plan had been the result of the trip.

More specifically it had been the result of reading a manuscript copy of Aelianus in the private library of the Fuggers. Somebody should do in the sixteenth century what Aelianus had done in the third. Somebody should write a complete Natural History, containing all available information, both old and new. It was a job for somebody who had read everything worth reading—for the author of the *Bibliotheca universalis*.

But the *Bibliotheca universalis* was still unfinished. At the moment, Gesner immersed himself in work. The second part of the *Bibliotheca* was to be encyclopedic, a survey of the knowledge of the time in 21 "books"—sections, we would call them. The first 19 appeared in Zurich in 1548, the 21st as a separate book in 1549. This *liber ultimus,* as Gesner called it, was about theology. The 20th book, about medicine, was never published because Gesner always felt that whatever he wrote he was not up to date. The fact that "Book 20" remained unpublished and largely unwritten is regrettable, for it would have given us an insight into the medical thought of the sixteenth century. There are medical books from the period, but none that gives an overall and tolerant view of the contemporary medical thought.

One reason that "Book 20" was not completed was that Gesner had begun his big work on animals. His plan was vaguely Aristotelian. First one book about the life-bearing quadrupeds, the mammals, as we would now say. Then a book about animals with four legs which lay eggs. Then one about the birds. Then one about the animals living in water. After that one on serpents (dragons were considered a species of serpents), and finally one on insects. After that a book on plants, but that had to wait; other people were writing books on plants and it would be wise to find out what they said.

The first volume of the *Historia animalium,* an enormous folio tome of more than 1,100 pages, appeared in 1551. Soon after its publication Gesner fell sick, possibly with tuberculosis. At any event he was sick for a long time. Since he was overworked, undernourished, and generally exhausted, his recovery was slow. But, being Gesner, he used the time to think about the next volumes. I have used the plural advisedly. Since the fairly small second volume appeared in 1554 and the very large third volume, the one on the birds, in 1555, he must have worked on both simultaneously.

In fact, he had even done something more. There was much interest in his book on animals, but the large size made it so expensive that it did not sell fast. Moreover, the very large group of readers that may be labeled the lovers of curiosities were not especially interested in classical Greek poems just because these happened to deal with the animal under discussion. Hence a "popular edition" was made, consisting of the pictures, the names in Latin, Italian, French, and German, and short notices —for example about the area where the animal can be found. Simultaneously Gesner's colleague and compatriot Dr. Conrad Forer translated volume I into German with Gesner's consent and occasional assistance. The same cycle of publication—shortened Latin version, called *icones,* and German translation—was repeated with all the other volumes. The English translation by Edward Topsell was made after Gesner's death.[3]

THE
HISTORIE OF FOVRE
FOOTED BEASTES

THE ANTALOPE.

Title page of Topsell's translation of Gesner.

Whether because of his renewed fame from the first two volumes of his main work or just as a coincidence, in 1554 Gesner was made City Physician of Zurich. This meant a steady, albeit small, income.

In 1558 volume IV appeared. It was about the animals living in the waters, "in the seas as well as in the sweet waters" and was even bigger than volume I. But by that time Gesner was not only physically exhausted—visitors said that he looked far older than his forty years, being very tall and very thin, with chalk-white skin in strong contrast to his black hair and beard—he was also in such a desperate financial situation that he had even been forced to sell his herb garden. He wrote a long letter in Latin to the city council, telling in detail how bad things were and asking for an increase in his pay as City Physician, but before sending it off he showed it to his friend Bullinger who consoled him and advised him to write his petition in German. The petition was successful; the city council conferred on him the title and income of Canon.

Gesner could now relax, but he had another, smaller project, a book he evidently wrote because the subject matter fascinated him. Obviously a man who had mastered the "three languages"; spoke German, French, Italian, and some Dutch, and had started to learn Arabic would think about the relationship of languages and that is what the book was about. It was titled *Mithridates,* published in 1555, and only 156 pages in folio. Of course, in relation to modern linguistics, Gesner's approach was amateurish, though interesting.[4]

Not feeling well physically, Gesner did something that may strike one as strange, but which was completely in character for him. He began to work on his plant book, putting the unfinished volumes of the animal book aside for the moment. Since he did not expect to live long he wanted to do as much work on the plant book as possible.

Work progressed slowly, partly because Gesner himself was feeling weak, partly because of his duties as City Physician—during the following years there were repeated epidemics in Switzerland. And Gesner was a conscientious physician who even went so far as to test new medications by trying them cautiously himself. He was also one of the first men in Switzerland to try smoking.

The plague hit Zurich in 1563 and returned in 1564. Gesner's description of the disease makes it easy for a modern physician to identify it with the pulmonary form of the bubonic plague.

In 1564 he received a confidential letter from the court physicians of Ferdinand I, Holy Roman Emperor. The emperor had decided to ennoble Gesner—whom he called "honesty personified"—and Gesner was to suggest a coat of arms for himself. He suggested a shield divided into four fields, with a crowned dolphin top left, lion rampant bottom left, eagle with spread wings top right, and a snake holding an emerald bottom right. On top of the shield he wanted a swan with spread wings, with three stars on each wing and three stars on its chest. The meaning was easy to see— the four animals represented the main volumes of his animal book, the emerald a book on gems still to be written, and the nine stars on the eagle stand for nine classical authors whose books he had prepared for printing. In his reply Gesner asked for something else. Since he was child- less, he wanted the title of nobility to apply to his uncle Andreas Gesner and all of Andreas' children.

The emperor agreed and the patent of nobility was signed by Ferdi- nand on the third day of April, 1564. Dr. Conrad Gesner now was Con- rad von Gesner.

In 1565 the plague returned to Zurich. The City Physician worked as hard as he could, but early in December he was himself stricken. On the fifth day of his sickness he began to feel better and sent home his friends, most of them physicians too, because he did not think their presence necessary. But later in the evening he knew that he was going to die; a servant woke his wife who helped him from the bedroom to his study. There he died shortly before midnight. The date was December 13, 1565. He was buried in the Great Münster, next to the grave of his friend Johannes Friess.

Gesner had fully carried out his intention of producing a work on animals containing literally everything ever written about them. Any reader who had paid the rather high price for each volume as it appeared also felt that he had received his money's worth. The entry *Canis* (dog) comprised a full hundred folio pages in fairly small print; the entry *Equus* (horse) ran from page 404 to page 490; the entry *Bos* (cattle) from page 25 to page 146. The original Latin edition was incredibly compre- hensive, and it is valuable even today when there is a question about what was known about a given animal in Gesner's time.

The arrangement of the animals in each volume is by the alphabetical order of their names, their Latin names in the original work.[5] The trans- lators maintained this principle, but the German translators arranged the books in the alphabetical order of the German names, and the English translator, Edward Topsell, in the alphabetical order of the English names. This changes the order in which the animals are described in the different editions: in the Latin version *Alces* (the moose) is the first chap- ter, in the German version *Affe* (monkey) comes first, and in the *His- torie of the Fovre-footed Beastes* the first chapter is the one about the "Antalope," with the Ape taking second place.

Of course such a scheme could not be carried out without making exceptions. Gesner realized that domesticated cattle and various wild oxen belonged together, and also domesticated and wild goats. Gesner also treated the various kinds of martens and weasels together, likewise most rodents, beginning with the mouse. But he did not realize that there was a cat family. The house cat is followed by the European wildcat, but lynx, lion, and tiger appear in their places in the alphabet. In the book on birds the various ducks, the pigeons and to some extent the finches are treated as groups. However, Gesner's attempt to systematize (in the sense of the later systematics of Carolus Linnaeus and the Baron de Cuvier) did not go beyond the recognition of a few obvious and literally visible relationships. The idea of relationships in general was still missing.

A few authors of the nineteenth century have wondered whether Gesner should be credited with the introduction of the two-part Latin names which Linnaeus later used systematically. This was a well-meant attempt to credit the Father of Zoology with the most important innovation made between his time and the discovery of evolution, but it happens to be incorrect. Gesner's rather frequent use of two-part names was simply a result of writing in Latin. If you call the hare *Lepus* and have read somewhere that there are hares with horns you will almost inevitably call the horned hare *Lepus cornutus*. Or if you call the raven *Corvus* and you then have another bird that also seems to be a raven but prefers the forests to the open fields, the second bird will be called "forest raven," or *Corvus sylvaticus*. And if there are three birds that seem to differ in size only you cannot help calling them *Ochropus magnus, Ochropus medius,* and *Ochropus minor*. It does sound "Linnaean" to our ears, but it is just Latin.

Gesner's work was not only far more comprehensive in detail than any other written before his time, it also contained descriptions of quite a number of animals that cannot be found in earlier books. This was partly due to the fact that the first zoological results of the age of discovery had reached Europe, and partly because information about animals of the northern parts of Europe had become available. A Swedish bishop, Olav Stor, better known as Olaus Magnus (1490–1558) had left his Scandinavian home in 1527 and gone to Rome, where he wrote a book on the peoples, and incidentally the animals, of the European Far North. It was published in 1555 and contained information about three "new" animals: the wolverine, the *kraken* or giant cuttlefish, and the "sea serpent," which is an unsolved zoological problem to this day.

Gesner also used the work *Moscovia* by the Baron Sigismund von Herberstein (1486–1556), who had gone to Moscow on a diplomatic mission and after his return had put his experiences on paper. It was not a very good book, but it discussed two animals that had disappeared from western Europe, the animals which the Poles called *Zubr* and *Tur*. The former is the European bison or wisent, while the latter is the urus. The urus did not look unlike domesticated cattle (of which it is the ancestral form) but the bulls, at least, were much larger in size. Gesner knew that both animals had lived in Switzerland and along the upper Rhine in the past, and Baron von Herberstein supplied the information that they still existed in eastern Europe and enabled Gesner to print their pictures.

Topsell's version of Gesner's description of the urus reads, in part, as follows:

> They far excell Buls, and other wild Oxen, comming neerer to the quantity or stature of Elephants. . . . It is said they could neuer be tamed by men, although they were taken when they were young, yet they loue other heardes of cattell, and will not forsake them easily after they have once ionyed themselues vnto them, whereby many times they are deceiued and killed. . . . *Caligula Caesar* brought of these aliue to Rome, and did shew them in publike spectacle to the people, and at the time they were taken for wilde Buls. Some affirme that there are of these in *Prussia,* and that they are so wild, cruel, and vntamable, as they feare and spare neither man nor beast; and when they are set vpon and wounded by the hunters in the woods among the trees, feeling their hurts and perceiuing their bloude issuing out of their body, they rage aboue measure, for hauing no meanes to take reuenge vpon the hunter, by reason that he standeth behind some great tree, for very wrath and fury they kill them-selues with their owne headlong force vpon the same tree. It is said that

Killing an urus with a spear, from Gesner.

their foreheades are so broad and large that two men may easily sit
betwixt their hornes. They are able to take vp an Armed man and his
horse and to tosse him into the aire like a Bull, and the heads of these
and suchlike beasts are to be seene publiquely fixed up in common places
at *Mentz* and *Wormes,* which are worth the obseruation, because in all
proportion they are twice so big as the vulgar Bull or Oxe.

While the domesticated donkey is followed by the wild ass onager and
other wild asses, it is listed under A (for *Asinus*), far away from its relative the horse, which appears under E (for *Equus*). But, strangely
enough, the hippopotamus is described among the horses, probably because of its name. Gesner gives the Greek name hippopotamus, translating it at once into *Equus fluviatilis,* "river horse." The German name of
the animal is *Nilpferd* (Nile horse), but Gesner did not list it, because
in his time the German name did not exist. In general, the hippopotamus
was very much an animal of classical literature to Gesner. He recounts
that it had been pictured on classical coins, that it was brought to Rome
on several occasions, and so forth. How little was known about the animal itself is evidenced by the fact that Gesner permitted his artist to picture the hippopotamus eating a crocodile! The fact that both could be
found in the Nile was enough to render such a performance credible.

The animals of the Nile: hippopotamus and crocodile (from Gesner).

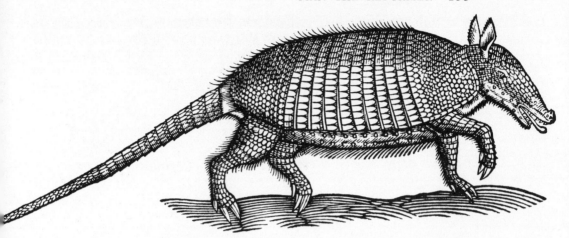

Armadillo as pictured in Gesner's work.

Of New World animals the armadillo appears under the name of *Tatus*—with a rather good picture—while one of the South American monkeys appears under the name *Galeopithecus,* which is rather misleading to present-day zoologists. It is not quite clear which South American monkey is meant; it might be a marmoset.* Another animal listed is the *Arctopithecus,* and neither the picture nor Topsell's translation of the name as bear-ape is of any help at first. Topsell's text begins:

> There is in America a very deformed beast which the inhabitants call *Haut* or *Hauti,* & the Frenchmen *Guenon,* as big as a great Affrican Monkey. His belly hangeth very low, his head and face like vnto a childes, as may be seen by this liuely picture, and being taken it will sigh like a young childe. His skin is of an ash-colour, and hairy like a Beare: he hath but three clawes on a foot, as longe as foure fingers, and like the thornes of Priuet, whereby he climbeth vp into the highest trees, and for the most part liueth of the leaues of a certain tree. . . .

The solution lies in the last sentence quoted—the "bear-ape" is the three-toed sloth. The artist seems to have had a mounted or dried specimen and depicted it walking on the ground, something a sloth cannot do at all.

* The name now designates a flying animal of southeast Asia; it might be described as an enormous flying squirrel, but it is not related to them in any way. In fact, neither living relatives nor fossil forms of this animal are known.

The animal "su," supposed to be large and elusive and living in Patagonia. The picture is probably based on stories about the opossum, from Gesner.

The animal "su" from Patagonia—left out by Topsell—is unexplained. The picture makes one think of an opossum but the description and the picture apparently have hardly anything to do with each other. The word "su" is explained as meaning "water," because the animal lives near water; then it is stated that it is caught in pits and shot with arrows. These statements indicate a fairly large animal but no known animal can be assigned to the description.

While Gesner fairly often repeated fabulous stories about animals, especially if he had a whole battery of classical writers to back up the story, the number of fabulous animals is quite small. He left out all the "wonder-people" but made passing mention that several kinds of monkeys at one time or another "were described and pictured as if they were strange people." But there was one fabulous animal which he did not dare leave out: the unicorn. The literary tradition was too large to be disregarded; moreover the unicorn was mentioned in the Bible.*

* Actually this was a mistranslation. The original called the animal in question Re'em and meant the urus, but the translators did not know which Greek word to use for it. They chose *monokeros* which, correctly, became *unicornus* in the Latin Vulgata, and thence *Licorne* in the French Bible and *Einhorn* in Dr. Martin Luther's German translation.

Gesner approached the case carefully and Topsell's English version mirrors his attitude:

> We are now come to the history of a beast, whereof diuers people in euery age of the worlde haue made great question, because of the rare Vertues thereof; therefore it behooueth vs to vse some dilligence in comparing togither the seuerall testimonies that are spoken of this beast, for the better satisfaction of such as are now aliue, and clearing of the point for them that shall be borne heereafter, whether there bee a Vnicorne; for that is the maine question to be resolued.

Gesner first quoted the classical descriptions of Pliny and of Aelianus, and then adds from Philostratos' "Life of Apollonius" that the horns of "wild asses" of India are used for making goblets: "and if a man drink from such a vessel he will not fall ill on that day; yes even if he were wounded it would not hurt; he can run through fire without being harmed; and if he were given poison in such a goblet it would do no harm." Gesner naturally quoted the story that the unicorn is attracted to maidens, but he also includes a later version on the authority of one Joannes Tzetzes. In this one—Gesner made it quite clear that he did not believe a word of it —a strong but slender young man is dressed as a maiden, with much jewelry and perfume to attract the unicorn, and the unicorn is not killed; the hunters merely wrench off its horn and then let it escape.

Gesner condensed his thoughts about the unicorn in two sentences:

> There is nobody who has ever seen this animal in Europe, and while Roman pomp knew how to bring all animals to their triumphal marches, one nowhere reads that a unicorn was ever shown to the Roman people. . . . But one has to trust the words of wanderers and far-going travelers, for the animal must be on earth, or else its horns would not exist; hence we'll accept that it roams in India, Arabia and the Land of the Moors.

The horns which convinced Gesner could be found in any well-appointed apothecary's shop and were worth their weight in gold. Since they were pictured carefully and many were preserved we know that they were in reality tusks of the narwhal.[6] Only a few decades after Gesner's death the story assumed a twist about as curious as the twist of the narwhal's tooth. All of a sudden the real nature of the "horn" became known and it was then promptly labeled *unicornum falsum* and declared to be worthless. But, said the apothecaries, *unicornum verum* still exists. It was found in the earth and was brown, not white. Actually this was the tusk of a mammoth which was thrown into the breach to comfort well-to-do patients and to keep the apothecaries' receipts at a reasonable level.

Before the true nature of *unicornum verum* became known, the belief in the medicinal value of the unicorn's horn, whether white or brown, had faded away.

The short second volume of Gesner's *Historia animalium* deals with four-footed land animals that are egg-laying—the reptiles and amphibians of modern classification, though not all of them. While the arrangement remains alphabetical in principle, certain groups which are obviously related, such as lizards or tortoises, are treated together. Snakes are not included, even though they live on land and lay eggs, because they don't have feet.

The subsection on lizards mentions all the common types of northern Europe and Italy; the large and beautiful bright-green emerald lizard appears under the name it still bears: *Lacerta viridis*. The common European newt is described next and then the shiny black salamander with sulfur-yellow spots that is now called "fire salamander." Its close relative the brown Alpine salamander is mentioned too, but they are not treated as two different species; the attitude is that they are the same animal and the color is different because they live in different places. Of non-European reptiles the Nile crocodile is described (still with the story that it moves its upper jaw) and the "land-crocodile" (*Crocodilus terrestris*), whose picture is obviously intended to show the Egyptian desert skink. But there is another "land-crocodile," one that "just became known from the country of Brezilla," meaning the iguana.

The book then moves on to various frogs and toads and to turtles and tortoises, including a marine turtle. Near the end of the section on the marine turtle Gesner mentioned that there are some islands in the ocean where turtles (or tortoises?) abound and that sailors have reported that their meat tastes like veal. This is one spot where one wishes that he had written a little more. Usually a complaint about his writing would run the other way.

The islands in the Indian Ocean that were later called "tortoise islands" do not form a single group; they are widely scattered and separated from one another and from the African continent by long stretches of blue water. They are the Seychelles group, quite isolated and just below the equator, the atoll of Aldabra to the north of Madagascar, and the Mascarene Islands (Mauritius, Réunion, and Rodrigues) to the east of Madagascar. We don't know which of these islands Gesner had in mind; to somebody living in Switzerland they were all islands in the endless blue of a warm ocean where winter never comes, reported on by sailors whose

Marine turtle from Gesner, vol. IV. The artist evidently had a specimen to draw, but that did not prevent him from putting teeth into the turtle's beak.

knowledge was uncertain even if one did not doubt their veracity. It is even possible that Gesner did not mean any of the islands of the big land tortoises but had been told about islands where the marine turtles come ashore to lay their eggs.

In volume III, the book on birds, the alphabetical order is still maintained in principle, but is interrupted far more often than in the first volume. All the falcons are treated as a unit, taking up considerable space, from page 3 to page 76. That the various geese belong together, as well as the various kinds of pigeons, was clear to Gesner; strangely enough, the various owls are not discussed in sequence but appear separately according to the alphabet. The first bird in the Latin version is the bird *Acanthidus,* the small European siskin. (Because of its German name *Zysele*—in modern high German *Zeisig*—the same bird is the last in the German version.)

There are three major stories that must be told in connection with Gesner's work on birds, but a few relatively minor items may be discussed first. In the Latin (but not in the German) version there is half a page on the *Canaria,* with no illustration. This is our well-known canary bird and Gesner reports that it is "brought around" by merchants which call it *Zuckervögele* in German or *aviculi sacchari* in Latin, both words meaning "sugar birds." The fact that the German translator left it out indicates that it was yet relatively unknown. The famous and long-established breederies of canaries in Central Germany were still to come.

The *nyktikorax* of the Physiologus is present, but all of a sudden it lives along the Rhine. The picture clearly indicates that it is one of the kingfishers; Gesner himself shook his head and remarked that this bird certainly did not look like a raven.

There are few fabulous birds; the Sirens are discussed briefly with much classical adumbration and ill-concealed doubts; the griffin is treated in a similar manner, and of the phoenix the by then customary story is told, with the statement: "it may live in India, it is certain that it comes to Egypt to die."

The spoonbill is well described, with a good picture, but the Latin name used for it is *Pelecanus;* Gesner, with every indication of being puzzled, said that there is an entirely different bird in other countries with the same name. Only the head of the latter is shown in another picture but it is evident that this is the bird *we* call pelican.

From somewhere Gesner acquired drawings of the heads of toucans which he printed without much comment as an example of birds from the New World.

Leafing through the book on birds, the modern reader will look with surprise at page 766 of the Latin version (or sheet LIII of the German version), where he comes face to face with the unmistakable picture of a bat. The explanation is given after only a few introductory sentences:

> The bat is the middle-animal between a bird and a mouse so that it may be called a flying mouse, although it cannot be counted among the birds or else among the mice because it is of both shapes. While the head is a mouse head it is also a dog's head; some bats are found to have four ears, although two ears are more common. The teeth in its cheeks are like dog's teeth, not like the teeth of a mouse which are long and in front. The voice is also closer to that of a dog than that of a mouse; the wings are made of skin and each finger bears a sharp claw so that it can cling to vertical rocks or stone walls. . . .

Gesner knew that the bats bear live young and correctly stated that their main diet consists of mosquitoes, along with flies and other flying insects. Albertus Magnus is quoted on two counts, first that the bats hibernate (correct) and second that they like fat meat to such an extent that they eat holes into the sides of live pigs—here Albertus had trusted one of his common people too much. Gesner also knew that there are much larger "bats" in the "warm countries," meaning southern Asia and Africa, and he had been told that the bats in America have poison fangs. But he quoted one man who said that, while in America, he had been bitten by a bat and that it had not been worse than being injured by any other small animal.

*Altera icon eiusdem auis ex Andrea Theueto &
Ambrosio Pareo.*

Two early toucan pictures, from Gesner after André Thevet.

Bird of paradise, from Gesner.

The three prize stories from the book on birds are the ones about the bird of paradise, about the tree-geese, and about the *Waldrapp* or forest raven.

Gesner's informant in the case of the bird of paradise was one Cunrat Peutinger, who sent Gesner the picture of the bird—which proves that the greater bird of paradise is meant—and wrote that he had seen such a bird, though dead, but that everything he reported had been told to him by reliable men. The name used by Peutinger is *Apus indica,* "the footless [bird of] India," while Gesner himself used the name *Paradisea.* The habitat are the "islands Moluchis,"which was then used as a rather general term for the area that two centuries later was referred to as the Dutch East Indies.

There a dead bird can be found on the ground or in the water, which (the natives) call Manucodiatam * in their own language. This bird can never be seen alive because it has no legs or feet, even though Aristotle did not permit the existence of birds without feet . . . but it has no feet because it always soars high in the air. His body and head is similar in size and shape to that of a swallow, but the wings and the tail, when stretched out, are larger than those of a falcon and resemble those of the eagle in size. . . . The male's back has a hollow and the female lays its eggs into this hollow and since the female's belly has a similar hollow the eggs will be hatched. The male's tail contains a long thread, black in color, which is not quite round and not quite square (in cross section)

* The Latinized word is the Malayan word *Manukdewata,* which is supposed to mean "bird of God."

and which resembles the wire used by shoemakers; with this thread the female is bound to the male while the eggs are hatching.

All the early stuffed specimens of this bird were without legs, for no known reason; this may have just been common practice among bird hunters. The beautiful story was probably made up in response to questions from white sea captains. By the time Gesner wrote about the bird the fact that it not only had legs and feet, but had unusually large feet for a bird of this size, was already known. Antonio Pigafetta (1491–1534), the Italian traveler who accompanied Magellan, had seen the bird in its native habitat and described it after his return. Emperor Charles V, to whom Pigafetta's report had been addressed, had it printed, but apparently Gesner did not see it.

If Gesner had bad luck in this case because information either did not reach him in time or else was not printed in time, he had bad luck with the tree-geese because somebody else was careless, to put it mildly. Gesner had read about the tree-geese in Conrat von Megenberg's book, and he must have known about the opinion of Albertus Magnus. His main source was the *Topographia Hibernica* of Sylvester Giraldus Cambrensis, originally written three hundred years before Gesner. Giraldus wrote:

> In this area there are many birds which Nature produces in a miraculous manner. They resemble marsh geese, but are somewhat smaller. They originate from pine wood which drifts upon the seas. The small

Unripe tree-geese from *The Herball or Generall Historie of Plantes* by John Gerard, 1597.

birds hang from the wood, protected by clam shells, by their beaks; after their plumage has grown they drop off and fly away. . . . I have seen with my own eyes more than a thousand of little birds of this kind hang from a piece of driftwood, still protected by sea shells but otherwise fully formed. . . .

Gesner had a friend in England, the clergyman, physician, and botanist William Turner (1510–1568). Turner had been disturbed by the story himself. Gesner's query amplified his doubts. As he wrote later:

Having uncomfortable misgivings, I asked a certain clergyman named Octavianus, by birth an Irishman, whom I knew to be worthy of credit, if he thought the account of Giraldus was to be believed. He, swearing by the Gospel, declared that which Giraldus had written about the bird was most true: that he had himself seen and handled the young unformed birds, and that if I would remain in London a month or two he would bring me some of the brood.

Turner passed the reply on to Gesner and it appeared in his book in grave Latin: *per ipsum iurans, quod profitebatur Euangelium, respondit verissimum esse.* No matter what Gesner had thought before, he was prepared to accept the statement of a clergyman, swearing by the Gospel *and* stating that he had personally handled the mysterious creatures.

Part of the mystery is easy to solve. What Giraldus and Octavianus thought to be the unformed birds was the very common marine creature named *Lepas anatifera* (one of the barnacles of the suborder *Cirripedia,* distantly related to marine crabs) that attaches itself to driftwood by a leathery "stem." It has two shells as described by Giraldus and its many legs might be taken for wet feathers. The second part of the mystery is more difficult. *Why* were the *Lepas* barnacles thought to be unformed birds? Once the idea has been put into your mind, the imagination will go to work and find similarities. But how did the idea originate? The linguist Professor Max Müller, who was active in London a century ago, blamed it on linguistic confusion, with the Latin name for Ireland, *Hibernia,* as the starting point. Irish geese would be called *Hibernicae* in Latin, or, since they were small geese, *Hiberniculae.* The barnacles were called *Bernaculae.* If somebody whose Latin was uncertain shortened *Hiberniculae* to *Berniculae* there remained a difference of only a single letter between the names of two entirely different creatures.

Because of Octavianus, who was obviously convinced that tradition was true, and because of Gesner who could not help accepting his word, the story of the tree-geese lasted about a century longer than it would have otherwise. It was finally discredited around the year 1700.

If Gesner had bad luck in these two instances, the case of the *Waldrapp,*
in which Gesner was thought to have been deceived by somebody, or, as
has also been suggested, to have mixed up his notes, resulted in his glori-
ous vindication a few centuries later.

After a sixteen-page chapter on the raven there follows the heading
De corvo sylvatico (On the Forest Raven) with a rather nice-looking
woodcut of a long-billed bird. The text reads matter-of-factly: "The bird
shown in this figure is called *ein Waldtrapp* by our common people and
in Bavaria and Styria *ein Claussrapp.*" Gesner, who on such occasions
always behaved as if his readers did not understand a syllable of German,
quickly explained, in Latin, what these words meant. *Waldt* means forest
and *Rapp* (*Rabe* in modern German) means raven, while *Clauss* refers
to the cell of a monk in a cloister, indicating solitary habits. Gesner then
ran through the names: the bird is also called *ein Steinrapp* (stone raven),
in Lorraine *corneille de mer,* and elsewhere in Germany *ein Scheller*
because of its voice (*Schelle* means a small bell).

In Italy, he continued, the name is *Corvo spilato,* "this means *Corvus
depilis* because he grows bald-headed in his old age, as I have seen." In
trying to determine what the classical authors had called the bird, Gesner
found himself in difficulties. His friend Turner in England thought that
the forest raven was the same as the *Corvus aquaticus* of Aristotle and
the *Phalacrocorax* of Pliny (the cormorant, especially the black cormorant), but this could not be correct because the forest raven does not
have webbed feet and is not even an aquatic bird.

Then Gesner went on to describe it:

> Our Forest Raven is of the size of a chicken, colored black all over
> if you see him from a distance; but if you are close and look at him
> against the sunlight, there seems to be an admixture of green; his feet
> are like those of a chicken with longer toes, the tail is not long and in
> the back of the head he has a tuft of feathers, pointing backward; I don't
> know whether this is seen on all birds and all year round. The beak is
> reddish and long and useful for digging in the soil and for thrusting into
> cracks of walls or of rocks so that he may pull out worms and beetles.
> The legs are long and dark red. . . . They eat grasshoppers and crickets,
> small fish and small frogs . . . when I cut the bird's stomach open I found
> many insects in it, mostly those that are harmful to the roots of plants,
> especially millet. They also eat larvae that will turn into May beetles.
> They fly very high. They roost on old and high walls like those of ruins
> of castles as can be found often in Switzerland. They lay two or three
> eggs. They are the first of all birds to fly away [migrate], unless I err,
> early in June.

The *Waldrapp* or "forest raven" from Gesner, vol. III.

It was a first-hand report all the way through. And, of course, it was accepted.

When, in 1758, Carolus Linnaeus tried his hand on a systematic classification of the birds, he had to decide where Gesner's forest raven belonged. Linnaeus did not know the bird himself, but that did not trouble him much, for he lived in Sweden and the birds of Sweden and of Switzerland are not necessarily the same. Gesner, for example, had not known about the great auk with which Linnaeus was familiar. The tuft of feathers on the head, Linnaeus reasoned, probably indicated that it was a hoopoe, a bird he knew. He named the hoopoe *Upupa epops* and coined the name *Upupa eremita* ("hermit hoopoe") for Gesner's forest raven.

Late in the eighteenth century the German forester and zoologist Johann Matthäus Bechstein wrote a book on birds. It was meant to be a practical book, containing only such birds as a man walking in German meadows and forests might see. Its strictly practical purpose was also expressed in the title, *Gemeinnützliche Naturgeschichte der Vögel Deutschlands* (General Useful Natural History of the Birds of Germany). The book appeared in 1791 and it contained the *Waldrapp*—it might be seen in the Alpine areas of the German-speaking countries. After the first edition had been published, Bechstein had second thoughts about the *Waldrapp* and did a great deal of literary research. His conclusion was incorporated in the second (1805) edition of his book and it read: Gesner made a mistake; there was no such bird as the *Waldrapp*.

Bechstein first pointed out that nobody had reported seeing one since about the year 1600. Secondly, he said, there is no evidence that anybody had *ever* seen a *Waldrapp* since all the literary sources went back to Gesner. The description of the bird by the Italian Ulisse Aldrovandi was probably based on Gesner, Bechstein said. (It can hardly be doubted that Aldrovandi's chapter is just a paraphrase of Gesner's Latin version.) Two English ornithologists, Francis Willughby and John Ray, had clearly taken their information from Gesner too; one of them uses the name "Gesner's Wood Crow" and the other the phrase the "Wood Crow from Switzerland." A chance mention by Gesner's contemporary and compatriot Johannes Stumpf—who called the *Waldrapp* a "common fowl"—was rejected by Bechstein as valueless because Stumpf had not given any description.

Since the *Waldrapp* was obviously a mistake by Gesner, which bird had he mistakenly described? Bechstein advanced the theory that Gesner had tried to describe the bird Linnaeus had named *Pyrrhocorax graculus,* otherwise known as the red-billed Alpine crow. The bird, Bechstein said, is not rare in general, but it happens to be rare in the Swiss section of the Alps so that Gesner could have thought he was dealing with a rarity. The Alpine crow is red-billed and the bill is curved. The legs also are red; the plumage is black with a greenish or bluish sheen. The diet is as described by Gesner, depending to some extent on the locality.

Bechstein's explanation actually rested on rather shaky grounds. The Alpine crow is considerably smaller than a chicken; its beak and its legs are far shorter than those of the bird pictured by Gesner; it does not have a feather tuft and does not grow bald. It usually lays four or five eggs. And it is not migratory. But all these rather major blemishes of comparison were overshadowed by the simple, and single, fact that the *Waldrapp* could not be found and had not been reported for centuries.

The rather unexpected solution to the *Waldrapp* puzzle grew out of a discussion held by three men in the library of the Rothschild Museum in Tring in Hertfordshire, not far from London. The year was 1897 and the three men were Lionel Walter, second Baron de Rothschild and a member of Parliament, a man who can be labeled an "amateur" zoologist only because he did not make his living as a zoologist; a professional zoologist, Ernst Johann Otto Hartert, co-editor of the zoological journal

Novitates zoologicae, and Pastor Otto Kleinschmidt, far better known in his own time as an ornithologist than as a clergyman.

The discussion had to do with the fact that a traveler named Wagler had discovered a new species of ibis in Egypt in 1832. It had not attracted much attention at the time and had remained generally unknown until the British ornithologist Henry Eeles Dresser made the mistake of including it in volume VI of his *History of the Birds of Europe* (1880). A bird discovered in Egypt and later found in Syria and Abyssinia hardly belonged in a work on European birds. Then one of the three grew suspicious. Wagler had named the bird *Geronticus,* from the Greek word *geron* which means an old man. The wrinkled skin of the head and its baldness explained the name. But baldness suggested Gesner's *Waldrapp!*

The three men started comparing illustrations. First the picture of the *Waldrapp* in Gesner, then that in the *Natural History of Birds* by Eleazar Albin (1740). Here the description had been written by John Ray who had simply followed Gesner, but the picture was different from the one Gesner used. And the picture of the *Waldrapp* in Bechstein's first edition was still another one, source unknown. All these three pictures agreed with the one in Dresser's book which showed the indubitably living *Geronticus.* An article announcing the "rediscovery" of the *Waldrapp,* and incidentally a vindication of Gesner, was published by Hartert.[7] The prefect Egnatius Calvinus, whose report of ibises in the Alps was doubted by Pliny, was also vindicated.

Later another zoologist with a bent toward history, Dr. Robert Lauterborn, tackled the problem of whether Gesner had been the only source on the *Waldrapp,* as Bechstein had claimed. Gesner proved to be the only *printed* source, but Lauterborn found many entries in chronicles dating from 1500 to about 1620. These entries made it clear that the bird had lived in northern Italy, Switzerland, Bavaria, Styria, and the northwestern sector of the Balkan peninsula. It had been, as Gesner had said, a migratory bird, but it stopped flying to Europe shortly after 1600. The reasons for this change in habit are unknown, but the identity of the *Waldrapp* with the living "crested ibis" of Asia minor, Arabia, Abyssinia, and Egypt is definitely established.

Volume IV of Gesner's work is about "fishes and other animals living in the waters," which accounts for its disorderly appearance as well as for its large size—it is the most voluminous of all of Gesner's works. The arrangement is still alphabetical and no distinction is made between freshwater and saltwater animals, with the result that eel, stingray, crayfish, lobster, monster whales, marine snails, and hermit crab follow each other in the sequence just given, by the accident of the first letter of their Latin names. The hermit crab is followed on page 220 by *Castor,* meaning, of course, the beaver. A little later the walrus makes its appearance and on page 366, near the end of the letter C, the crocodile, accompanied by the "land-crocodile." And soon after that we find the edible vineyard snail and the shell-less garden snail, which certainly do not belong in this volume at all.

Gesner undoubtedly realized that the various seashells (mixed up, as they are, with marine snails) actually belonged together. The various rays are also a group that can be recognized at a glance, and the same goes for the octopi. Gesner cannot have been satisfied with his arrangement but he was ill and overworked at the time and probably convinced himself that he should cling to the alphabetical scheme that had worked reasonably well for mammals and birds. For much of the book he relied heavily on two French scientists. One was the physician Guillaume Rondelet (1507–1566) who lived in Rome much of the time. The other was the naturalist Pierre Belon (1517–1564) who wrote in French [8] but whose name appears in the works of his contemporaries in the Latinized version of Petrus Bellonius.

A ray, from Gesner, vol. IV.

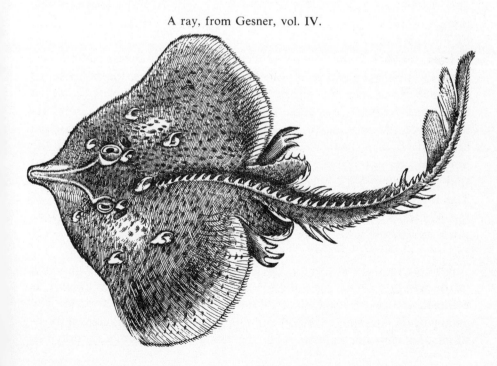

Petrus Bellonius (Pierre Belon), only known portrait.

In dealing with the strange life forms of the ocean Gesner was evidently less comfortable than he had been with mammals and birds when he could rely on personal knowledge much of the time. When he comes to a section where other literature existed, Greek, Latin, or recent, as for example in the case of the dolphin, Gesner is still the master compiler. But where he can only say what he had learned from Rondelet or Belon, the language becomes dry and almost formalized; the facts belong in the book, but they are new to him and he cannot pretend to be familiar with them.

The illustrations range from good woodcuts for familiar fishes that the artist could portray from nature to the wild monstrosities of whale hunts depicted by Olaus Magnus, though the first picture of the flensing of a whale is among these. Conrad Forer, the German translator for this volume, did not want to drop the pictures, but he left out all the meager commentary Gesner had written, saying merely, "These pictures were caused to be drawn by Olaus, how well and right is his sole responsibility."

Flensing of a whale, from Gesner after Olaus Magnus.

Still, the book is by no means without value; its standards just happen to be lower than those of Gesner's preceding books. Gesner tried to be critical; on page 433 there is a picture of the "fabulous sea horse," and on page 491 a picture of the fish now known as sea horse. There is an early and fairly good picture of the lamprey. The discussion of rays is followed by the earliest-known picture of the so-called Jenny Haniver, a dried ray that had, before drying, been cut to give it wings and a drag-onlike appearance. Gesner accompanies the picture with a description of just what had been done with the fish and a warning to credulous people that not only should they not pay a high price for such a monster, they should not buy it at all.

The last animal in this volume is the hammerhead shark.

Dr. Forer, the translator for this volume, was also not satisfied with the book as it stood. His translation is a wholesale revision in which he did just what Gesner should have done with the original.

Forer divided the whole book into three parts. The first deals with inhabitants of the sea exclusively. Of its sixteen chapters the first five are about saltwater fishes, sorted mainly by size. The sixth chapter deals with "fishes of a shape that might be compared to snakes" (conger eels, etc.), the seventh with flatfishes (for example, flounders), the eighth with large edible saltwater fishes (mackerel, tuna, swordfish), the ninth with rays, the tenth with sharks (called "sea-dogs"), the eleventh with fishes of a roundish shape (puffer fish, sunfish), the twelfth with whales, sea monsters, and marine turtles, the thirteenth with octopi (jellyfish appended, presumably because both have tentacles), the fourteenth with all kinds of crabs, the fifteenth with sea shells, marine snails, and sea stars, and the sixteenth with marine worms or creatures that looked like worms.

The second part is devoted to freshwater fishes. The fifth and last chapter of this section deals "with fishes that come up into the rivers from the sea." The third part, in five chapters, deals with lake fishes (as distinct from river fishes), freshwater crabs, freshwater snails, and worms (for example, leeches), and has a concluding chapter on animals that live both on the ground and in water, from the hippopotamus to snakes living near rivers and able to swim well.

Not much need be said about Gesner's fifth volume, the posthumous one that was to treat of the serpents. It begins with two long general sections, historical and literary in character, comprising a total of 45 folio pages without illustrations. Then follow a few chapters on specific snakes,

I N eadem tabula ad B. d. alius ferpens mar. ad centum aut ducentos pedes longus, ut deſcriptio habet, (uel etiã trecentos, ut numerus iconi adiunctus præ ſe fert,) circa Noruegiã interdum

apparet,

Sea serpents, from Gesner after Olaus Magnus.

again in alphabetical order. Among the snakes that have names beginning with the letter B the basilisk is given a good deal of space. In Gesner's work the basilisk does not have the fabulous shape, a mixture of serpent and rooster, which is pictured elsewhere; the illustration merely shows a snake wearing a crown. In connection with the story that the basilisk springs from the egg of a rooster that has been hatched by a toad, Gesner says that the rooster lays this egg during the last year of his life, "which is the seventh, ninth or fourteenth year, depending on his natural strength and on the question of how much work he did with hens." The rooster egg is laid during the hottest days of the year, "and it is not elongated like the hen's egg, but round like a sphere, pale yellow or bluish, sometimes speckled." He was really describing snakes' eggs, especially since he added, "Some say the eggs are without shells but only have a tough skin." But while he did not deny the existence of the eggs, he was adamant otherwise: "That such a harmful and poisonous animal is engendered in our lands by brooding toads is an old wives' tale."

Under the letter D we naturally find the dragon, essentially based on the pythons of tropical Africa and India but elaborated as a result of the finds of large fossil bones in Europe. If at all possible such bones were called giants' bones, but when their shape made such an "identification" impossible they were declared to be dragon bones. Gesner made a strict distinction between "dragons" and "flying snakes," and the picture of a flying snake which he gives in his chapter proves that a small tropical lizard from Java was known in Europe in his time, though not recognized. Gesner had a letter telling him of five specimens of flying snakes, dead and dried, that could be seen in Paris. They had two feet and their wings were so small that Gesner wondered how they could fly with them. Their heads had "been shaped like those of snakes, of pretty color, without hair or feathers, and the biggest of them was as large as a hedge-king (wren)." They were specimens of the tree-dwelling Javanese lizard *Draco volans.*

Apparently Gesner's manuscript was reasonably complete only as far as the letter H. What followed were a few short and scattered chapters, but the book concludes with a ten-page chapter on the viper which seems to have been written by Gesner himself. Of course it is anybody's guess how volume V would have looked if Gesner had lived another five or ten years and finished it himself. Much of the existing book may be labeled "printed notes"; Gesner probably would have done extensive rewriting.

But in spite of the imperfections of volumes IV and V Gesner's work deserves nothing but praise. It was *the* work of its time.

Gesner found a successor very soon; in fact his successor was born only six years later, so that the two were contemporaries. But this successor, the Italian Ulisse Aldrovandi, survived Gesner by two-score years. And Aldrovandi conceived his own great work long after Gesner was dead.

According to his biographer, Giovanni Fantuzzi,[9] Ulisse Aldrovandi was born in Bologna on September 11, 1522. Unlike Gesner, he came from a well-to-do family that had been quite important in its city. One branch of the family had even been ennobled and Aldrovandi was convinced, whether correctly or not, that his family and the noble family Aldobrandini had originally been identical. Aldrovandi's father died when the boy was only one year old, but the family saw to his upbringing and since his intelligence became apparent at an early age the family decided that he could make a brilliant career as a merchant. At barely 15 years of age he was apprenticed to a merchant in Brescia. For reasons we do not know he did not stay in Brescia but went to Rome, looking for

Ulisse Aldrovandi at the age of 78.　　Guillaume Rondelet at the age of 47

a similar position. Not finding anything he liked, he decided to go back to Bologna, on foot, as was then customary. On the road he met a pilgrim from Sicily and suggested to him that they make a pilgrimage to Jerusalem. The Sicilian declined, but the two young men walked to Genoa together. From there Aldrovandi, now 17, went to Bologna. He began the study of the liberal arts and of law, then went to Padua for a year and studied philosophy and medicine.

In 1549 somebody denounced Aldrovandi to the inquisition as a heretic. In Spain this might have been serious, but the Roman inquisition was different. It issued invitations first, requesting an accused man to defend himself, and in general one gets the impression that the inquisitors preferred animated argument (and thundering accusations leading to more argument) to drastic action, Spanish style. The 27-year-old Aldrovandi went to Rome to answer the charges. It is not quite clear whether he vindicated himself by feats of rhetoric or whether the death of Pope Paul III brought about a kind of amnesty for minor offenders. In any event he was let go free and was never troubled again. In fact, the trip to Rome became very important to Aldrovandi because he met the

French naturalist and physician Guillaume Rondelet who studied the fishes of the Mediterranean. Rondelet's example and advice started Aldrovandi on a collection of fishes as well as of plants.

At the age of 31 he received his degree from the University of Bologna, a doctorate in medicine. One year later he became professor, teaching logic and Aristotelian meteorology at first. He soon added a course about *simplicia*—that is to say, about medication, mainly the type derived from plants. Beginning in 1561 he taught *simplicia* exclusively and he felt strongly that he could do this better if he were able to show the plants to his students. But why build a house if one might build a *palazzo?* Why restrict a collection of living plants only to those of medicinal value? Why not have a collection of all the living plants that could grow in the climate of Bologna? Being a full professor as well as a member of an old and reputable family he had access to city councilmen and proposed the creation of what we would call a botanical garden. We don't know why the city fathers were reluctant; it is on record that they were. Still, in 1568 Aldrovandi won, and the city established a botanical garden with Cesare Odoni and Ulisse Aldrovandi as its directors.

By the time Aldrovandi's immediate goal, the botanical garden, had been achieved, Gesner's *Historia animalium* was complete, except for the posthumous volume on snakes and dragons. It was a spur to Aldrovandi to do something similar.

Aldrovandi was, in every respect, far better off than Gesner. Bologna was richer than Gesner's Zurich. He himself was financially secure, though he was not rich. He was in good health and he had had many more years than Gesner to collect both actual specimens and pictures. And, of course, he had Gesner's books as a general guide.

By the end of the sixteenth century he had several volumes of his own Natural History about ready for the printer. The first three volumes, dealing with birds, were given the collective title *Ornithologia*. Volume I appeared in 1599. By that time Aldrovandi had reached a decision. He was 77 years old and if he wanted to complete his zoological work he had to devote all his time and energy to the task, which meant that he would have to give up his chair at the university. He did, but he waited until December 6, 1600, because that date marked the fortieth anniversary of his becoming a professor. When he retired, volume II of the *Ornithologia* had already been printed; the third volume appeared in 1603.

But Aldrovandi had waited a bit too long.

He completed only five volumes of his work; volumes VI and VII were completed by his pupil and successor Iohannes Cornelius Uterverius—a Dutchman—and by Hieronymus Tambrinus. For the completion of the eighth volume, Uterverius had the help of a Scotsman who signed himself Thomas Dempsterus. Up to that point the volumes were still mainly by Aldrovandi; the editorial work consisted of arranging his notes and filling in missing parts. But the volumes that followed contained less and less genuine Aldrovandi. Aldrovandi seems to have planned ten volumes, but editing and the demands of booksellers resulted in a total of thirteen.[10]

Aldrovandi died on March 10, 1605—neither poor nor blind, as later sentimental descriptions would have it. His home town of Bologna acquired his large and valuable collections.

Without trying in the slightest to minimize the labors of Aldrovandi, one can best describe his work as an "improved Gesner." He follows Gesner's example in giving *all* the information about an animal—zoological, historical, cultural, and mythological—and he does it better. Since more than three decades had gone by since Gesner's death, he had more material. Too, he had learned from Gesner's mistakes and did not use an alphabetical order but a logical sorting into groups. The wordage of the *Ornithologia* is greater than that of Gesner's book on birds, but the volumes look somewhat smaller since the art of printing had advanced. The illustrations do not interrupt the text, as in Gesner, but are grouped together on separate pages. The first volume of this edition has 427 folio pages (not counting foreword, indexes, and similar matter); the second volume has 373 pages, and the third 209 pages.

Volume I begins with the eagle, in two sections comprising 122 pages. The illustrations no longer merely show the birds in a more or less artistic view; they go further. On Plate I, for example, the pictures of several kinds of eagles are augmented by a picture of an eagle's skeleton and a large detail drawing of an eagle's foot and claws. Sections 3 to 7 deal with vultures, falcons, and hawks; section 8 with "nocturnal birds," mainly the owls but with bats as an afterthought. Then follows a section chiefly devoted to the ostrich, also showing the skeleton of the bird. The tenth section is about birds of fable (harpy, siren, griffin); the eleventh section deals with parrots, mentioning New World forms (and showing, in one illustration, "the Queen of the Island of Florida"), while the twelfth and final section of the first book deals with the ravens, but woodpeckers, toucans (named "pepper eaters"), the bird manucodiata, and some smaller insectivorous birds are thrown in.

The second volume of the *Ornithologia* begins with section 13 "on forest birds," including pheasants, peacocks, and the turkey. Section 14,

Guinea hen

White-crested chicken

Persian rooster

Persian hen
Four pictures from the so-called chicken page of Aldrovandi's work.

on chickens, is extraordinarily comprehensive and Charles Darwin called it the "oldest document we can rely on for determining the age of our domestic breeds of fowl." Section 15 deals with pigeons, section 16 with berry-eating birds, section 17 with worm-eating birds, and section 18 with songbirds.

The third volume consists of only two sections. Number 19 deals with birds with webbed feet, like swans and geese (including the tree-geese, about the existence of which the oath of Octavianus still prevents doubts), and number 20 with birds that live near the water but are not swimming birds, as for example storks and cranes.

The next book in the series was on insects. Insects intrigued and enchanted Aldrovandi; he never got over his astonishment that something so small could be alive. "They should be called *atoma* [atoms] rather than *entoma* [insects]," he said on one occasion, and in a letter to Cardinal Barberini, the later Pope Urban VII, he wrote:

> What my labours have been, and to what lengths I went, I could wish you to judge; and when I reflect on the many days I have given to this study, and what expenses I have incurred, I cannot but wonder how I have been able to obtain possession of, and to examine, and to describe such a number of minute creatures. For the attainment of my object, I was in the habit of going into the country for months during the summer and autumn, not for relaxation, like others; for at these times I employed all my influence, as well as money, to induce the country-people to bring me such insects, whether winged or creeping, as they could procure, in the fields or under ground, and in the rivers and ponds. When any were brought me, I made inquiries about its name, habit, locality, &c. I often, too, wandered over the marshes and mountains, accompanied by my draughtsman and amanuenses, he carrying his pencil, and they their notebooks. The former took a drawing if expedient, the latter noted down to my dictation what occurred to me, and in this way we collected a vast variety of specimens.

The insect book has precisely 300 pages and consists of seven sections. The first section begins with the bees and insects similar to the bee, like wasps and hornets. It comprises 95 pages, almost a third of the whole book. The second section is entitled *"De papilionibus"* but it describes not only butterflies and moths but dragonflies and similar insects as well. The third section deals with two-winged insects, like flies and mosquitoes; the fourth with insects that have more than two wings: grasshoppers, crickets, beetles, the praying mantis, and so forth. The fifth section is devoted to "insects without wings" like the true bugs and the ants; it is

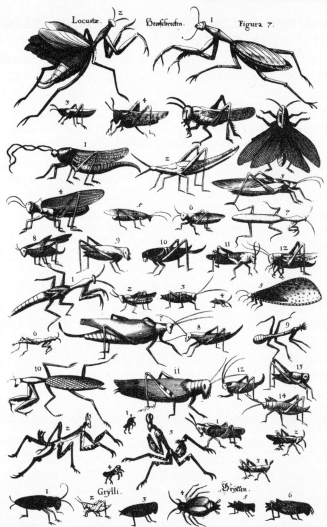

Part of the "grasshopper page" in Aldrovandi's book on insects.

an understandable mistake that the arachnids—spiders and scorpions and centipedes and millipedes—were taken to be insects. The sixth section is called *"De vermibus"* but in addition to true worms, like the earthworm, it also describes shell-less snails. The seventh section speaks of "insects" of the water, like marine worms and the sea stars.

The last book that Aldrovandi himself nearly finished was the one on the "bloodless animals." Its 192 folio pages consist of four sections on what would now be called "marine invertebrates"—octopi, crabs, marine snails, sea urchins, and jellyfish.

Of the posthumous publications, only the three volumes on fishes and quadrupeds deserve mention. The book on fishes has a total length of 280 folio pages and is in six sections, of which the sixth is devoted to the whales; most of the sea monsters introduced by Olaus Magnus have been dropped, although the sea serpent appears in section 3. The first section deals with fishes living among rocks, the second with fishes near the shore, the third with pelagic fishes, the fourth with fishes occurring both in fresh and in salt water, while the fifth is about river fishes.

Volume VII, which first appeared in Bologna in 1616, is called *De quadrupedibus solidipedibus* ("On Quadrupeds with Solid Feet"), a title that sounds as if Aldrovandi already had the concept of single-hoofed mammals like the horse. But apparently he used the term *solidipedibus* in contrast to "flexible feet." Quite predictably the book begins with the horse; 294 of its 495 pages are occupied by this one animal. I don't know just where the editors added or rewrote in this book, but it is unlikely that they had to do any work on the horse chapter. That chapter is Aldrovandi with all his comprehensiveness: first the horse as an animal, its food, habits, sex life, diseases, cures therefor, different races, its voice, the habits and characteristics of castrated horses; then the names of horses in different languages, the names of especially famous horses, the use of horses for agriculture, warfare, parades, and oracles; the medicinal values of horsemeat and horse milk; fables about horses, proverbs about horses, and poems about horses; famous statues of horses and coins on which horses or horses' heads can be seen!

A chapter on the donkey follows, then one on the Indian onager and a separate chapter on mules. Then there is a long chapter—30 pages— on the unicorn, with pictures of unicorns' horns, which are the *unicornum falsum*, narwhal tusks. On page 416 there is a picture of a zebra,

The Wisent of northern Europe, called *Bison lubatus* by Aldrovandi. From Aldrovandi's work, redrawn from Gesner whose picture is based on an illustration in Baron von Herberstein's *Moscovia*.

the earliest I know of in books from that period. The concluding chapter, running for 70 pages, is about the elephant. The differences between the African and the Indian elephant are explained, but only the African elephant is pictured.

The eighth volume bears the title "History of all Cloven-footed Quadrupeds" and is 425 folio pages in length. This volume begins with cattle, which take up the first 145 pages, being given the same treatment as the horse in the preceding volume. Among the pictures there is an interesting one of a cow with short legs, a mutation that has also occurred in dogs (dachshund) and sheep. The urus is given a few pages after the chapter on cattle, but Aldrovandi did not provide any new material. The rest of the book is taken up by goats, stags, deer, antelopes, gazelles, the moose, the Indian rhinoceros (with a note that it is *not* identical with the unicorn), camels (both types pictured), the giraffe, and finally the pig.

After the *Ornithologia* was printed, Aldrovandi sent a copy of it to his friend, Cardinal Barberini, who replied with a poem, part of which, in translation, reads as follows:

> The various forms that swim the watery plains,
> Whate'er the earth's capacious womb contains,
> The trees and herbs that on her face appear,
> And all the winged inhabitants of air,
> In thy stupendous work collected lie,
> To feast the soul, and strike the astonished eye.
> Her own productions industry no more
> Dares own, but wonders at the fruit she bore,
> And faithful nature at thy deeds amazed,
> Wishes her own those works thy art has raised.

But in spite of this praise from a high place, and in spite of the high quality of his work, the name Aldrovandi did not prove quite as durable as that of Gesner. Was it only because Gesner had come a few decades earlier and his works had therefore been circulated first? Or was it because Gesner's work was immediately translated into modern languages, while Aldrovandi remained untranslated?

The latter would seem to be the main reason. Scientists had gradually begun writing in the everyday tongues—Galileo Galilei's chief work, which caused all the furor and was condemned by the same Cardinal Barberini after he became Pope, was written in Italian—and books in Latin began to look as if they were for scholars only and could not be read for enjoyment by ordinary people.

chapter seven

Reindeer, from Gesner, vol. I.

Man the Systematizer

GESNER and Aldrovandi had collected in their books what could be collected then. But even these superbly erudite and thorough men did not succeed in tapping all the sources. Some sources were inaccessible to them, either because of language or because they existed only in a few manuscript copies. When Gesner copied what Olaus Magnus said about whales, he certainly would have added some information from the Norse "Mirror of Kings" if he had known of the book's existence. It had been written around the middle of the thirteenth century and while it was mainly concerned with noble families it contained a great deal of information on hunting, fishing, and even trading. It lists no less than 23 Nordic names of whales.

Both Gesner and Aldrovandi failed to mention Arabic works which we know to have existed in their time, though the loss here was small. The Arabs made important contributions to geography and less important contributions to astronomy but hardly any to zoology. Later scholars were disappointed (though not too surprised) to find that Arabic zoological information consisted of paraphrases of excerpts from Aristotle and Pliny. The Koran contains far fewer zoological references than the Talmud, but neither Gesner nor Aldrovandi—nor Belon nor Rondelet, for that matter—had ever seen the Talmud or any part of it.

No major zoological work was to be written during the greater part of the seventeenth century. The Italians had their Aldrovandi, the Germans their German Gesner, and the English their English Gesner in Edward Topsell's translation. Learned men with zoological interests had turned, even in the sixteenth century, to more specialized pursuits, beginning with a series of books on the zoology of the Bible that was started in Germany.

The two most "zoological" sections of the Bible are the Book of Job and Leviticus, the latter because of all the instructions on which animals are "clean" and which are not. But references to animals can be found throughout the Bible, a little more often in the Old Testament than in the New. The difficulties facing writers on Biblical zoology were enormous. The authors of the books of the Bible almost never gave descriptions, since they were talking to the people around them about the animals around them. And, of course, the animals of Biblical Palestine were not the same as the animals north of the Alps in Europe in A.D. 1600. There had to be a large amount of guesswork on what the Hebrew words meant. As long as the references were to domesticated animals like horses and donkeys, camels and cattle, the commentator's life was easy. Even dogs (only semidomesticated then; nobody in the Bible owns a personal dog) and the larger forms of wild life, say lions, posed no problem.* But small animals often do not have definite names. (The word translated as "mice" really means "corn-eaters" and certainly included rats.) In some cases even the original author used a word loosely, with the result that the same Hebrew word, appearing in more than one place, had to be translated differently according to the context. The "howlers" of the original became "dragons" in translation; they were, zoologically speaking, jackals. The "tortoises" of one translation became "sand heaps" in another and *altars* (?) in a third.

Though aware of these difficulties, Pastor Hermann Heinrich Frey wrote his *Biblisch Thierbuch* and had it printed in Leipzig in 1595. His intent was "to show that animals have not been created just for the sake of the belly." In spite of this noble thought, Frey follows the Jewish system of sorting the animals into "clean" (edible) and "unclean" (not edible). Among the "clean" there are again two different groups, those that could be eaten and also used for sacrifices—namely cattle, goats, and sheep—and those that could be eaten but not sacrificed. Among the animals good to eat, Frey, in a show of Christian independence, included the hare as very good and clean to Christians. Then he treats of domesticated "unclean" animals, not to be eaten but needed for work, such as horses, donkeys, and camels. Then come the wild and dangerous animals

---

* It will surprise many readers that the cat is not mentioned in the Bible.

such as lions and panthers, and finally there is a catch-all section for all other animals mentioned in the Bible.

Frey's *Biblisch Thierbuch* was for the layman, as indicated by the fact that it was in German. The Latin *Historia animalium sacra* (Wittenberg, 1612) by the professor of theology Wolfgang Franz was for "students of theology and servants of the Word" to provide them with zoological examples for their sermons. Franz also divided all animals into several groups, but without regard to the "classification" of Leviticus. Animals are "imperfect" (sponges, clams, and in general everything that does not move) or "perfect." The latter are sapient (Man), or they are not.

Not written by a professional theologian but showing strong theological leanings was the *Zoologia physica* by Johann Sperling (1603–1658). Sperling started out with the statement that zoology is a very difficult science because there are so many different animals—especially insects. Sperling made just one division: an *animal* could think to some extent—lions, dogs, and people—while the other kind, called *brutum,* could not think.

The most erudite of the books on Biblical zoology was the *Hierozoicon* of Samuel Bochart (1599–1667), which appeared in 1663. The arrangement of the animals was about the same as that in Frey's book, but the learned apparatus is overwhelming. Bochart quoted Syriac and Arabic authors whose works had not been printed then and have not been since, examined the meaning of Hebrew words not only etymologically but in the context of the cultural conditions of time and place, gave parallels from Syriac authors, and so forth. His book is not really about animals, but as a work on a rather restricted cultural area it is a great undertaking that has been unjustly forgotten.

Meanwhile, news about more and more animals from the newly discovered continents kept trickling into Europe. One should expect that it would have been a broad stream, but that was prevented by such commonplace circumstances as delays in printing, for one. The French physician and botanist Charles Lécluse (1526–1609), who called himself Carolus Clusius and who is credited with having introduced the potato into Europe, was probably the first to describe a penguin, under the name "Magellanic goose." His writings also contain the first mention in Europe of the manatee, the dodo, and the horseshoe crab. But his *Exotica* pays more attention to botany than to zoology; like some of his predecessors, he was chiefly interested in medicinal properties.

Since the Spaniards had been the first to acquire a foothold in the New World it is only natural that the early reports from America should be of Spanish origin, though the Dutch soon entered into the competition. The first work was the *Historia general y natural de las Indias* by Gonzalo Fernandez d'Oviedo y Valdy. Parts of it were printed in Salamanca in 1535, but a complete edition did not appear until 1835! Another book, by José d'Acosta, S.J. (1539–1600), appeared soon after d'Acosta's return to Spain in 1588, but it was quite short and mainly devoted to the discussion of such problems as how the animals that had been in the Ark had been brought to America. Father d'Acosta also thought that he had discovered the remains of giants in the New World.

The King of Spain, Philip II, probably read d'Acosta's book. In any event he was curious to learn more about his new domain and sent his physician, Francesco Hernandez, to Mexico in 1593 to collect animals, plants, and minerals. Hernandez spent seven years on this errand and it is reported that he had not less than 1,200 pictures drawn for the book he was writing. The book, written in Latin, was finally printed, incomplete, in Rome in 1628.[1] The printed version again put all the emphasis on the medicinal aspects. A more complete version was printed in 1651, with commentaries by others and pictures of doubtful origin. In all, 40 four-footed animals, 229 birds, 58 reptiles, 30 insects and worms, and 56 "water animals" are mentioned, but because the book went through so many hands before it reached the printer it is impossible to say what the value of Hernandez's original might have been.[2]

The Dutch also had established colonies in the New World and in 1637 Prince Johann Maurits of Nassau-Siegen sent two men to South America with specific orders to devote themselves to an investigation of its natural history. Both men were physicians. One was Dutch, Willem Piso of Leyden, who worked mainly along medical and mineralogical lines. The other was German, Georg Marcgrav from Liebstadt near Meissen in Saxony, who was well prepared for the job. Though he was only 27 years old at the time of his departure, he had read Gesner, Belon, and Rondelet and made references to their writings in his descriptions of the South American animals. He also was a skillful amateur astronomer; unfortunately his observations of the southern sky were never published. Marcgrav himself could draw, but he also was accompanied by an artist whom he mentioned repeatedly, never by name. Whether this artist came with Marcgrav from Europe or was already a member of the Dutch colony when the small research team arrived is not known either.

Marcgrav, in 1644, went from South America to West Africa, fell sick immediately after his arrival, and died. His manuscripts were brought back to the Netherlands by Willem Piso. He handed everything over to

Jan de Laet, one of the directors of the Dutch West India Company, who had already written a book about South America based on the numerous reports and letters by company officials and ship's captains. Jan de Laet acted as editor of the Piso-Marcgrav manuscripts. The book, as printed in 1648, consisted of four sections by Piso on medical problems in what is now northern Brazil and eight sections by Marcgrav on the natural history of the same area. A year or so after the book had been published, Prince Johann Maurits bought all the original drawings from the West India Company and later gave them as a present to Friedrich Wilhelm of Brandenburg, known as the Great Elector. They were still preserved in Berlin in 1900.

Marcgrav described many New World animals for the first time, and gave much more detailed descriptions of certain known animals, such as the llama, the opossum, and hummingbirds. More important than his descriptions, though this was not realized until much later, was Marcgrav's statement that the animals of South America do not show a single form identical with European animals. Some look similar, but not one of them occurs elsewhere.

It may have been the Piso-Marcgrav expedition to South America under the auspices of the Dutch West India Company that caused the Dutch East India Company to assist another such project later during the same century. The center of the East India Company's activities was the island of Amboina. In 1653 a young man 26 years old arrived there, unnoticed by anybody except the commander of the garrison to whom he reported.

His name was Georg Eberhard Rumpf, easily Latinized into Georgius Everardus Rumphius when the time came for this step. He was born in 1627 (date unknown), presumably in Hanau in western Germany. It is likely that his parents were Dutch Protestants who had fled to Germany, but it is not certain, though both Dutch and German historians have tried hard to establish his ancestry. After one year on Amboina, Rumpf could speak Malay and was writing a Malay-Dutch dictionary. At the same time he was transferred at his own request to the civilian branch of the company and became an *Onderkoopman,* or Junior Merchant. He must have done his job well because in 1662 he was promoted to *Koopman*—Merchant without the qualification. And he began writing about the strange plants and animals around him. But he wanted to know what was already known. He needed books.

That meant that he had to inform the company about his plan because somebody had to buy the books for him in Europe. The company at first

George Everard Rumphius a few years before his death, from the *Herbarium amboinense*.

just gave permission, then became interested, and when Rumphius became almost blind in 1670 it actively assisted him. Rumphius was promoted to *Oud Koopman* (Senior Merchant) and simultaneously relieved of all company duties. His son *Koopman* Paulus Augustus Rumphius was assigned to helping his father, a secretary for Rumphius Senior was selected from among the clerks on Amboina, and the artist Philips van Eijck was brought all the way from Amsterdam to do the necessary illustrations for his work. The result of all this—after some vicissitudes like the destruction of the nearly complete manuscript by fire in 1687—was two books. One was a fairly small volume on the unusual animals on and near Amboina. Written in Dutch, it had the title *D'Amboinsche Rariteitkamer* (The Amboina Cabinet of Rarities) and was also translated into German.* The other, a very large work, was called the *Herbarium am-*

* I have been unable to find a French edition that is mentioned by a few authors.

boinense; it is written in Dutch and in Latin, with the two versions printed in parallel columns. The final part of the manuscript was shipped to Amsterdam in 1701. On June 15, 1702 Rumphius died. The manuscript was printed in Amsterdam, in six volumes in largest folio, over a period of several years, beginning in 1708.

Since Rumphius' larger work was botanical, we are more concerned here with the *Rariteitkamer.* There we find the first picture of the horse-shoe crab of the Molucca Islands, quite similar to the larger North Amer-

Horseshoe crab from the Molucca Islands, from Rumphius' *Amboinsche Rariteit-kamer.*

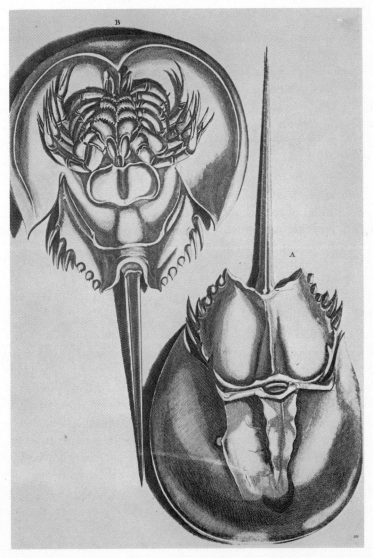

ican version, unfamiliar to Rumphius, that occurs along the Atlantic shore from Nova Scotia to northern Florida. Rumphius wrote that travelers had told of tropical bushes with leaves that turned into butterflies. Not so, he said, the butterflies are butterflies that hatch in the normal manner, but the undersides of their wings are marked in such a manner that they look like leaves when they sit with the wings folded up. He reported on a large crab, looking like a lobster but more massive in build, that can often be found on dry land near the shore. This is the coconut eating crab now called *Birgus latro*. Rumphius called it *Cancer crumenatus*. If natives had told him about the crab's feeding habits he evidently had not believed them, for that fact does not appear in his writings.

All through his work Rumphius has a habit of naming which, like Gesner's, looks, in retrospect, as if he had anticipated Linnaeus. The crab *Cancer crumenatus* was just mentioned; in the *Herbarium amboinense* the arrow poison tree of Java appears as *Arbor toxicaria*. But, as with Gesner, Rumphius' two-part names were simply the result of writing in Latin. If you have a species of wild cattle living on Java and you want to say "Javanese cattle" in Latin the name will come out as *Bos javanicus*. It is possible, however, that Linnaeus was influenced by reading the *Herbarium amboinense;* we know that he was much impressed by Rumphius, whose work he called *solidissimus,* the strongest form of "solid" that the Latin language will provide.

Rumphius' botanical work has been compared to Gesner's zoology, but except for great size and devotion to accuracy the two works have nothing in common. Rumphius, like virtually everybody else at the time, wrote in Latin, but he was not a classicist like Gesner. Moreover, in most cases he was dealing with material that nobody had written about before him. He worked in a restricted, though large area and the only sections that are not based on his own observations are those in which he relates native tales, sometimes accompanied by strong remarks impugning their veracity.

If Rumphius' work is to be compared with another book, it must be with a book by a professional fisherman who lived from 1612 to 1694 in Strasbourg. This was Leonard Baldner, who neither had literary ambitions nor expected to become a kind of toll collector for his city. But in 1646 he saw "several strange and beautiful waterfowl" that he had never seen before. "Moved" as he put it, "by curiosity and strange thoughts," he paid an artist to paint the birds and kept on collecting pictures and information, producing in the course of time a workmanlike book. He

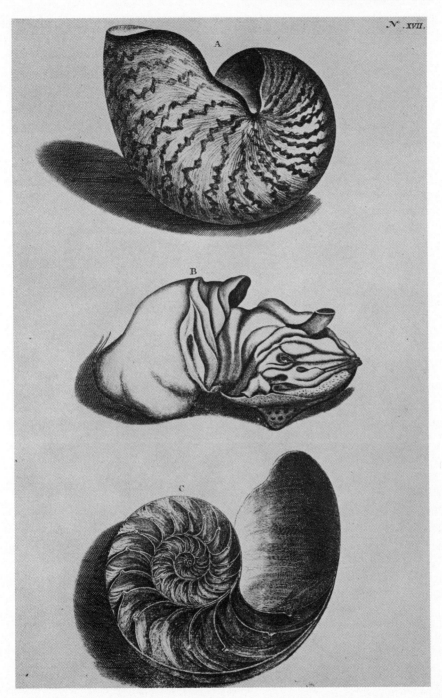

Chambered nautilus from the *Amboinsche Rariteitkamer* by Rumphius.

did not rely on statements by other people, and the only two sources he mentioned are the Bible and Gesner.

Baldner's book is a description of the local fauna. The chief reaction of the reader of our time is surprise at the number of animals in the vicinity of Strasbourg only three centuries ago. The beaver was common, as was the now very rare Rhine salmon. Nobody around Strasbourg now knows the "night-raven" (a heron) but Baldner knew it well; he reported that "it flies out of the islands about one hour after the night bell and screams just once." Baldner also made one genuine zoological discovery about two hundred years before this was made "officially." There were lampreys in the local waters and Baldner and his contemporaries, who considered pickled lamprey a delicacy, were not as unhappy about this as are modern fishermen when their domains are invaded by lampreys. There also was a wormlike creature that went under the name of Querder. Baldner discovered that the Querder was the juvenile form of the lamprey.

Baldner had his book copied by hand several times. When, in his old age, he wrote his last will he did not enjoin his children to have it printed but said that the original should stay with successive generations of his family, instructing them never to turn the pages with their fingers but to use a bone knife for this purpose. In 1783, after the death of the last of the Baldners, the original manuscript was deposited in the library of the City of Strasbourg. Unfortunately it was destroyed during a fire in 1870. A number of years later one of the contemporary manuscript copies was used as the basis of a French translation, which appeared in 1887 as *L'Histoire naturelle des eaux Strasbourgeois de Léonard Baldner*. Another twenty years later Dr. Robert Lauterborn had the German original printed, but only the text. There was not enough money to reproduce the illustrations.

All this sounds as if Baldner only received posthumous glory and failed to influence zoological thought. This would have been the case except for a visitor from England who, in 1663, purchased from Baldner one of the manuscript copies of his book, "with beautiful illustrations," as is specifically stated. At the time the English visitor acquired a copy of his book from Baldner, he signed his name John Wray. A few years later, in 1670, he changed the spelling to Ray, for Ray can be latinized as Rajus, while the case is hopeless for the spelling of Wray.

John Wray/Ray was born on November 19, 1627, in the smithy of Black Notley in Essex. Young Ray was supposed to become a cleric and was ordained as one later. He was admitted to Trinity College, Cambridge, and acquired his B.A. degree in 1648 and his M.A. in 1651 and

John Ray at the age of about 60.

during the same year was appointed Greek Lecturer. It looked as if he was embarked on a solid academic career and his name might now be forgotten or mentioned only in a list of Deans of Cambridge (which he became) if it had not been for an illness in 1650 and a political event in 1662. During an illness he began the study of botany, which was still regarded mainly as a handmaiden of medicine. That study, in time, made Ray into one of the great botanists of the century. The political event of 1662 was an Act of Parliament forcing all academic men to take an oath of conformity. Ray and thirteen others declared that the oath was incompatible with their consciences and they lost their fellowships as "nonconformists." A consequence of this loss made Ray an outstanding zoologist and a direct precursor of Linnaeus.

While at Trinity College, Ray had met a somewhat younger man, Francis Willughby (1635–1672), who became his best friend. Walking in the countryside near Cambridge, often with Willughby, Ray decided to study plants in the open and not from books, and after having made (alone) a trip to Derbyshire and North Wales, where he saw different plants, he made a listing of all the plants that grew in the vicinity of Cambridge and published it under the title *Catalogus Cantabrigiam.* In the foreword he announced that he hoped to follow it with such a catalogue for all of England. More trips followed, one with Willughby to the north of England and the Isle of Man, one to York, Edinburgh, and Glasgow with his pupil Philip Skippon, one through Wales with Skippon and Willughby. The trips resulted in a book of the plants of England (the *Catalogus Angliae* in 1670) and two books on another subject. People did not talk alike in the different areas and Ray took notes, from which came the *Collection of English Proverbs* and the *Collection of English Words,* in 1670 and 1673, respectively.[3]

In April of 1663, after he had forfeited his fellowship, Ray, with Willughby, went on a long trip, via Calais through the Netherlands, then up the Rhine—where he sought out Baldner—to Vienna and on to Venice. He spent all of 1664 in Italy and Sicily—Willughby went on a side trip to Spain—and traveled to Switzerland during the spring of 1665. In the spring of 1666 he returned to England. The purpose of the long trip had been to study the plant life of as many areas as possible. There had been an agreement between Ray and Willughby—Ray would devote all his time to botany; zoology was to be left to Willughby.

In November 1667 Ray became a Fellow of the Royal Society. At that time he was working on his *Catalogus Angliae,* with a bigger work on all the plants he had studied—16,000 of them—on the horizon.

Only five years later Willughby, though only 37 years old, suddenly died in July 1672. Willughby, a well-to-do country squire, had left Ray an annual stipend on the condition that Ray would educate Willughby's children. Consequently Ray, who had already lived at Willughby's manor house Middleton Hall from time to time, moved in there, Willughby's widow agreed to pay for the publication of her late husband's zoological works, even though during his lifetime he had rejected the idea of publication. Ray had to arrange and polish the numerous painstaking descriptions that Willughby had made. This was no problem because he was well acquainted with all the detail and had no doubt rendered assistance and given advice all along.

For three years Ray was busy with two main projects, Willughby's zoological work and his own work on plants. As a sideline he composed a Greek-Latin-English dictionary which was to sell at a modest price. Because it was short, Ray did not want to call it a "dictionary," so he coined the diminutive *Dictionariolum.* It appeared for the first time in 1675 and turned out to be Ray's most popular work; three more editions (under the changed title *Nomenclator Classicus*) appeared during his lifetime, and it continued to be reprinted after his death. In 1676 the first volume of Willughby's work, the volume on birds, appeared in Latin. Two years later Ray published an English translation. There was apparently a demand for a book on birds in English, perhaps because Topsell had not translated Gesner's volume on birds.

Then the second of Willughby's volumes, the one on fishes, appeared, and also the first volume on Ray's big work on plants (the second volume followed in 1688). In 1690 Ray, after having survived an attack of pneumonia, began collecting insects; it was his plan to continue Willughby's work for all the other types of animals. He very nearly succeeded, but two of the books had to be published posthumously. Ray died on January 17, 1705, in the house called Dewlands at Black Notley, into which he had moved in 1679.[4]

As we have seen, animal books were arranged alphabetically by names, with some exceptions (for example, all types of oxen in Gesner and the hawks in Aldrovandi) being made where similarities were overwhelming. Ray followed the saying of Caesalpinus that science consists in bringing together what is similar and in sorting apart what is dissimilar. Fine, but what were the *true* similarities? Evidently the fact that they lived in water did not make animals similar. Nor did the fact that they could fly, which had placed the bat among the birds. That, one might say, was judging by the costume. Looking for something more fundamental, Ray went back to Aristotle and to the observation that there are red-blooded animals and others that are not red-blooded.

Ray seems to have leaped instinctively to the concept that it was the structure of the animal's body which mattered. The red-blooded animals breathed either by means of lungs, or through gills. That was the first major division. Those that had lungs had a heart with one ventricle (reptiles) or a heart with two ventricles. The latter either had hair and bore live young (mammals), or else they had feathers and laid eggs (birds). Ray, who was very careful about his language whether he wrote in Latin or in English, had an unfortunate linguistic situation on his hands. What we call mammals, he had to call quadrupeds. This brought the hippopotamus, the seal, and the beaver safely into the fold in spite of their aquatic habits. And while bats did not have, strictly speaking, four legs, they had at least four limbs, so that they, too, could be listed among the quadrupeds.

But the whales, the porpoises, and the manatees would not fit into Ray's scheme. They had red blood, a heart with two ventricles, and lungs, but they did not have four legs. Ray put them in a special group but left them with the fishes. His discussion contains two interesting remarks. One was that it would be useful if the term quadrupeds could be dropped. The other was that Englishmen often use the word "fish" for anything that lives in the sea, including "starfish" and "jellyfish," both of which were most decidedly not fishes.

Ray went into much detail with the "quadrupeds," establishing subdivisions based on the number of toes, the type of teeth, and other structural characteristics. The birds he divided first into waterfowl and land birds and went on from there, putting emphasis on the shape of the beak. The insects he divided into two main groups: those that go through a metamorphosis like a butterfly and those that do not. The further subdivisions were based on the number of legs and wings. (Scorpions, spiders, and centipedes were still considered insects at the time.)

Ray went a very long way on the road of establishing a system of the animals based on their structure. That he did not complete the task is chiefly because even a long-lived man has a limited number of years at his disposal. Carolus Linnaeus could succeed because he started where Ray left off.

During the early decades of the eighteenth century much progress was made in establishing the "structure"—the anatomy—of specific animals. One study deserves special mention. In 1699 Edward Tyson published a book entitled *Orang-outang, sive homo sylvestris,* which George

Tyson's "Pygmie," actually a chimpanzee.

PHOCÆNA,

OR THE

ANATOMY

OF A

PORPESS,

DISSECTED AT

Greſham Colledge:

WITH A

Præliminary Diſcourſe concerning Anatomy, and a Natural Hiſtory of ANIMALS.

The World was made to be inhabited by Beaſts, but ſtudied and contomplated by Man: 'tis the Debt of our Reaſon we owe unto God, and the Homage we pay him for not being Beaſts.
Religio Medici.

LONDON,
Printed for *Benj. Tooke* at the Ship in St. *Paul's* Church-
yard. 1680.

Title page of Tyson's treatise on the porpoise.

Sarton called "an epochal contribution to science and philosophy." The book dealt in fine detail with the anatomy of the chimpanzee—not the orangutan *—and Tyson put great emphasis on how similar the chimpanzee is to Man. Later Tyson published equally careful anatomies of a marsupial and of the dolphin.

* The Malay term *orang utan* does mean "forest man," or, in Latin, *homo sylvestris;* Tyson complicated things a little further by using the subtitle "is the history of a pygmie." Apparently he thought that the rumors about pygmies referred to the chimpanzee, which is much smaller than a man.

Karl Linnaeus was born May 13, 1707, in Råshult in Småland, Sweden, and baptized by his own father who was the pastor of the nearby church of Stenbrohult. Local legend has it that the name is derived from a very large and old linden tree near the neighboring village of Linnhult. All the men of a large family of Swedish peasants who acquired academic rank (a pastor was considered to have such rank because he had to know the classical languages) took names from that tree. One called himself Lindelius, another Tiliander, and the father of the future scientist, born Nils Ingemarsson in 1674, named himself Linnaeus. Karl Linnaeus was to change his name to Karl von Linné when the Swedish parliament, late in 1762, approved his ennoblement. But in the English-speaking world he remained Carolus Linnaeus.

Young Karl was very much interested in plants and herbs, but his father naturally wanted him to be a pastor. He was sent to the High School in Wexiö but soon the teachers began sending very discouraging reports to his father. As these reports, in spite of parental private sermons, kept coming, the father threatened that he would apprentice his son to a shoemaker. But the local doctor liked the boy and realized that his poor performance in school was not due to lack of intellect but to lack of interest. He persuaded the father to let Karl study medicine. The father, still disgruntled, handed his son a sum of money, announcing that this was the last money he would ever get out of his pocket, and sent him off to the university at Uppsala. His teacher was the naturalist and historian Olaf Rudbeck. Financial help came from Olaf Celsius, a professor of theology who was trying to write a book on the plants of the Bible and needed help in botany.

By 1730 Linnaeus had progressed far enough to substitute for Rudbeck in the classroom when the professor was busy with other things.* At the same time he formed a friendship with a young man his own age, Peter Arctaedius, who later simplified his name to Artedi. The two friends decided to reform two branches of science—Linnaeus had botany in mind and Artedi, ichthyology. They had just about formulated the outlines of their reforms when Linnaeus had to leave on a journey that lasted six months. The Literary-Scientific Society of Uppsala had decided to send somebody to Lapland, Sweden's northernmost province, which was virtually unknown as far as its natural history was concerned. Linnaeus was chosen as the explorer. He left Uppsala in May 1732 and re-

* Nowadays Rudbeck is chiefly remembered for a book in which he tried to prove that Atlantis had been in Sweden, in fact, in the vicinity of Uppsala. This is in a way an injustice; Rudbeck was otherwise a sound scientist.

Carolus Linnaeus as a young man.

turned in October, saying later that this had been the most strenuous but also the most rewarding of all his journeys. Other trips inside Sweden followed, and in 1735 he went to the Netherlands to obtain his medical degree. His first botanical works were written in Holland. His friend Artedi, who had gone to England, joined him, and one dark night fell into a canal in Amsterdam and drowned. An English friend recovered Artedi's manuscripts from his landlord and gave them to Linnaeus as a present. Artedi's work on fishes, completed and edited by Linnaeus, appeared in 1738. The same year Linnaeus went to Paris, where he was made a Corresponding Member of the Academy of Sciences. Then he returned to Sweden, settling in Stockholm.

At first he was received coolly in academic circles and had to practice medicine in order to live. But then he was introduced at court and made some influential friends. In 1741 he was appointed professor of medicine at Uppsala where a Professor Rosen had the chair of botany and natural history; by the end of the year the two changed places. Linnaeus immediately rearranged the botanical garden of the university and started a natural history museum. He sent advanced students to as many different countries as possible to collect for the museum, and each addition to the knowledge of nature resulted in additions to his main work, the *Systema naturae.* The book was reissued again and again and each edition was reworked so much by Linnaeus that it was actually a new book. Linnaeus himself wrote twelve editions, the last one in 1768, printed in Stockholm. The final, thirteenth edition was not completed by Linnaeus but by Johann Friedrich Gmelin. It was printed in Leipzig ten years after Linnaeus had died of a stroke on January 10, 1778.

The lifework of Linnaeus was to find and construct a system into which every living thing could be fitted. Looking at his book, one is tempted to give some credit to his father, the stern pastor. Linnaeus was stern with nature, with himself, and with his fellow naturalists, even telling them the maximum number of words that could be used for the formal description of a new plant or animal. His father had probably never quoted a line from the Bible without giving the book, the chapter, and the verse. The son did just that to nature, the "verse" being the species, labeled with a so-called binomial name.

Thus the house cat became *Felis domesticus,* the second part of the name indicating the species. The first word (the Latin word for "cat") denoted the genus. The lion belonged to the same genus and became *Felis leo,* the tiger became *Felis tigris,* and so forth. Similarly the dogs formed the genus *Canis* with *Canis domesticus* the most familiar species. They had it in common with the cats and others that they were meat eaters, so all the genera of meat eaters formed the class called *carnivora*. The class of the *carnivora*, along with other classes, formed the order *mammalia*. Unlike Ray, who had considered Man as something separate, Linnaeus incorporated Man into the system, since all his physical characteristics said "mammal." So Man became genus *Homo* and species *sapiens;* this comprised all living races. But in his system Linnaeus had several species of the genus *Homo,* based on reports from distant parts of the world. One was *Homo troglodytes,* a "cave-dwelling" man. The orangutan was meant and the mistake was a double one: in the first place the orangutan is an ape and in the second place it is a tree dweller, not a cave dweller. There also was a *Homo nocturnus,* a nocturnal man— it is not certain just which kind of monkey was meant.

Linnaeus thought it necessary to assume the "fixity of the species," for how could a system work if species were capable of crawling from one cubbyhole into another? Using language his father might have used, he wrote: "There are as many species as the Creator produced diverse forms in the beginning." Later in life, however, he became more lenient. Of course he had always known about varieties, which, in the case of plants, he ascribed to the influence of environment. A flower normally growing in moist heavy soil might turn out to be different if its seeds sprouted in sandy and rather dry soil. But if the seeds of that variety were planted in moist heavy soil, the "original" would appear again; therefore varieties need not worry a classifier. But later he received samples for which this explanation would not hold; after some hesitation he considered them hybrids and was even willing to admit that new species might be produced in that manner.

Any occupation can become a preoccupation and the latter can grow into a mania. The "system" had been invented to produce order out of the multitudes of living things; but after it had been established and had proved useful, newly discovered animals or plants seemed to exist for the sole purpose of being filed in the proper slots. Jules Verne, in his *Twenty Thousand Leagues Under the Sea,* has such a classifier: the assistant of Professor Arronax spends his time at the main window of the *Nautilus* classifying everything that swims into view.

At a later date some evolutionists, annoyed by the sharply proclaimed "fixity of species," were especially gleeful when a newly discovered animal, such as the Australian platypus, failed to fit into a Linnaean slot.

The platypus has fur, a heart with two ventricles, and lungs enclosed in *pleurae,* all strictly mammalian characteristics. But it had a beak like a bird, seemed to lack milk glands (actually only the teats are lacking), and laid eggs. But the evolutionists who condemned Linnaeus and his system should have been grateful because the "misfit," being somewhere between designations when compared to modern animals, would not have been spotted so clearly without the system. You can't find an exception to a rule unless you have the rule first.

While Linnaeus spent his life stating as clearly as possible what exists, the Frenchman Buffon spent his looking for causes and reasons. Georges Louis Leclerc, Comte * de Buffon (1707–1788) was born in the same year as Linnaeus.

The Comte de Buffon at the age of about 50.

Buffon was a highly original thinker and his originality caused some mild trouble with the ecclesiastical authorities, who demanded retractions or at least emendations in his writings. Buffon complied by writing appendixes that say, in effect, "This is what one might think if one did not

* Not a count by birth, Buffon was elevated to that rank by Louis XV.

know what Genesis says." One of the things one might think was that the sun had been without planets originally but that, at one time, a massive body coming from somewhere in space struck it a glancing blow, scattering into nearby space solar material which then condensed into planets.

Such an origin might enable philosophers to calculate the age of the earth. Buffon went about this experimentally. He had a number of solid spheres made, all of them of the same size but of different materials—iron, copper, brass, granite, sandstone, limestone, and so forth. He had the spheres heated to the same red-hot temperature in a blacksmith's furnace and then placed on wire holders. Watch in hand, Buffon would carefully touch the spheres with a gloved hand and note down the time that had elapsed before he could touch them with his bare hand without feeling a sensation of heat. This moment, in the case of real planets, would be the moment life originated. After having gathered his information, Buffon, who was an excellent mathematician, sat down and made some calculations. Considering the actual size and composition of the earth, he figured that the number of years which had elapsed from the red-hot state to the origin of life had been 74,832 and life had appeared 40,000 years ago.

It was obvious, Buffon went on to state, that there had been several geological periods in the past—maybe six, which could be compared to the six days of creation, a thought repeated by very many writers during the nineteenth century. It seems to have been so common that many authors did not know that it had originated with Buffon.

Buffon's main work, entitled simply *Histoire naturelle,* consisted of a large number of volumes, 44 in all, but of unequal size, of which the first appeared in 1749. For all the volumes except the first three, he had collaborators who helped with the large amount of material or else added their specialties to his general knowledge. When Buffon died, the volumes on whales and dolphins, on reptiles, amphibians, fishes, and other groups were not finished, and their completion had to be accomplished by Bernard Germain Etienne Delaville, Comte de Lacépède. Later editions contain additions (which are sometimes corrections) by still other French naturalists.

That Buffon did not add much to the science of zoology is generally admitted. That his work, because of the enthusiastic manner in which it was written, greatly charmed and influenced all readers of the period is equally certain. But the question of whether Buffon should be counted among the early prophets of evolution is a different story; here we have almost as many opinions as there are writers who have gone into this question. Later evolutionists have counted Buffon as one of their fore-runners mainly because he disliked the system of Linnaeus. But one cannot draw convincing conclusions from a mere dislike: a man who dislikes the administration is not necessarily a member of the opposition party.

Isidore Geoffroy Saint-Hilaire, who was an evolutionist, thought that he could detect three periods in Buffon's thinking. From 1749 to 1756 or 1758 he shared the views of Linnaeus, from 1761 to 1766 he strongly championed variability, and from 1766 to the end of his life he believed in "limited mutability." No doubt one can find passages in Buffon's work that would support Saint-Hilaire's case. But the fact is that there are internal contradictions in the *Histoire naturelle,* not at all surprising in a work of this size, written over a period of nearly four decades. In spite of many lapses Buffon tried to be careful and he realized how many things had not been established. In 1755 he write: "We do not know whether or not the zebra can breed with the horse or ass; whether the large-tailed Barbary sheep would be fertile if crossed with our own; whether the

Zebra from Aldrovandi. This is probably the earliest published picture of a zebra.

chamois is not a wild goat . . . whether the differences between apes are really specific or whether the apes are like dogs, one species with many different breeds. . . ." *

Though Buffon may have occasionally had thoughts that vaguely foreshadowed later evolutionary ideas, he should not be considered an early French evolutionist. That honor belongs to two other Frenchmen, both somewhat in disrepute otherwise. They were Pierre Louis Moreau de Maupertuis (1698–1759) and the Chevalier de Lamarck (1744–1829), whose full name was Jean Baptiste Pierre Antoine de Monet, Chevalier de Lamarck.

Maupertuis was primarily a mathematician and was one of the first Frenchmen to realize the importance of the theories of Sir Isaac Newton. Maupertuis went to London in 1728, the year after Newton's death, and was elected to the Royal Society. Eight years later he headed a French expedition to Lapland, not for collecting purposes but for the purpose of measuring one degree of latitude precisely in order to calculate the curvature of the earth. Mainly for this work he was elected to the French Academy in 1743. A result of that election was a letter from Frederick the Great of Prussia, inviting him to head the Prussian Academy of Science. Maupertuis did go to Berlin and by that time he already had ideas that were unusual for his time. He amused the King of Prussia during the evening discussions in the castle with the speculation that the inhabitants of the Great Unknown Southland might turn out to have tails. He was of the opinion that the gigantic inhabitants of Patagonia, rumored to exist at that time, the dwarfs thought to live in the Far North, and the Negroes of Africa had been originally the offspring of "normal" people and that they had been expelled to form self-perpetuating colonies elsewhere. So, if there had been tailed offspring, they must have gone to the still undiscovered Southland because they had not been found elsewhere.

* Buffon and his contemporaries considered the ability or inability to crossbreed with fertile offspring the touchstone for distinguishing a variation, or a race, or an artificial breed, from a species. To Linnaeus all living human races were *Homo sapiens* because they could crossbreed with fertile offspring. For the same reason the many different domesticated dogs were all taken to be the same species. Horses and asses could crossbreed, but the offspring were not fertile; hence horse and ass had to be different species. But tame dogs can crossbreed with wolves, lions and tigers can be crossed, zebras do breed with domestic horses, and the various kinds of wild oxen can usually crossbreed among themselves and with domestic cattle. All these animals are now accepted as different species, and in almost all the cases just mentioned the offspring is fertile. The ability to crossbreed is not the important criterium it was thought to be.

In Berlin Maupertuis found something that interested him very much, a couple named Ruhe with six children. Jakob Ruhe, the father, was a so-called hexadactyl, with six fingers on each hand and six toes on each foot. His wife was a normal pentadactyl, but two of the six children were hexadactyls. Jakob Ruhe had been one of eight children of whom four had been hexadactyls. His mother had been the hexadactyl and she had inherited the characteristic from her mother. From these facts Maupertuis evolved a theory of inheritance. Reading it one has the feeling that Maupertuis would now be considered the discoverer of the laws of inheritance if he had had a few more instances to examine and had spent a few years digesting them. He had a vision of what we now call genes (he called them "elementary particles") and a general concept of mutation— "fortuitous productions in which the elementary particles failed to retain the order they possessed in the father and mother animals; each degree of error would have produced a new species and by reason of repeated deviations would have arrived at the infinite diversity of animals that we see today."

With such a degree of insight, how is it possible that Maupertuis usually gets only a footnote in books on the history of science? To his contemporaries Maupertuis was mainly the man who had helped to measure the earth. Indeed Voltaire had praised him highly for this accomplishment. But later Voltaire, for reasons known only to himself, reversed his attitude and wrote some of his nastiest pieces against the unfortunate Maupertuis. Voltaire's witticisms were read, Maupertuis' answers were not. And then Maupertuis made another mistake. Sir Isaac Newton and Baron Gottfried Wilhelm von Leibniz had invented calculus independently and at about the same time. Two parties formed, each claiming full and sole priority for its respective hero. Maupertuis, remembering that he was a mathematician, joined battle in favor of Newton, but he did so while living in Switzerland and on the continent almost everyone was in favor of the versatile and charming gentleman-diplomat Leibniz and opposed to the retiring, humorless, and insular Newton.

As a result not Maupertuis but Lamarck was acclaimed for one and a half centuries as the first French evolutionist or even as the first evolutionist in general.

When the Chevalier de Lamarck was a boy his father issued the same decree the father of Linnaeus had issued—the boy was to enter the clergy. Linnaeus had had to rebel openly. Lamarck did not need to take this step because his father died and the son joined the army (he was even commissioned for bravery). After the war—it was the Seven Years War—was over, Lamarck was without an occupation. But he had always been fascinated by plants and he wrote a book on the flora of France, followed by a book on medicine. By that time the system of Linnaeus had reached its final form—the book on French flora appeared in 1778, the year Linnaeus died—and Lamarck studied his system with great care. He was appalled by one aspect of it. The vertebrates had been classified with the greatest of care; the invertebrates were just lumped together. Linnaeus appeared to have taken to heart the criticism made against Thomas Mouffet.* It is more likely that Linnaeus was simply tired and left the classification of the invertebrates to somebody else.

Lamarck, at the age of 49, was appointed professor of invertebrate zoology in Paris and then he went to work to remedy the shortcomings of Linnaeus. He did not pay much attention to Ray's major criterion—whether the "insect" went through a complete metamorphosis or not—but, literally, counted legs. Insects, he said, were all those with six legs—beetles, butterflies, cockroaches, dragonflies, earwigs. Spiders had eight legs and were something else, as were ticks, mites, and scorpions; these formed a separate group. The water-dwelling "insects" were still another group, not because they lived in water but because they had characteristics in common—namely a hard shell that was shed at regular, usually yearly, intervals. They were the crustaceans—crayfish, lobsters, langoustes, crabs. Other water-dwelling "worms," such as sea stars, sea urchins, and the fossil sea lilies (the living forms were not then known so that only fossils could be considered), also had characteristics in common. They did not have six or eight legs, but five or ten or twenty arms and they have a prickly skin. *Echinatus* is Latin for prickly, and *derma* is Greek for skin; hence this group was called the echinoderms.

It was sound work and in retrospect it is amusing to see how much the Chevalier de Lamarck and the Baron de Cuvier, sworn enemies in every respect, influenced each other in this field. They also joined hands—unwillingly, to be sure—in asking for a longer past than the six days of creation and the six thousand years since then permitted. Cuvier looked for a diplomatic way out of this dilemma; Lamarck was openly disdainful, declaring that the antiquity of the terrestrial globe is great and the ideas of those who will grant it only six thousand years are small.

* Mouffet's friends, when learning that he devoted all his spare time—he was a physician in London—to a book on insects, said that the study of insects "lacked dignity, decency, and value."

The next step in his reasoning was still sound. Since the earth must be very old it is logical to think that the animals that inhabit it had sprung from a comparatively small number of forms. It was the step after that that miscarried—namely Lamarck's answer to the question of what causes changes in an animal's body.

This was, Lamarck said with utmost seriousness in his *Philosophie zoologique* (1809), the animal's desire for a change. Fishing birds, wading in shallow water, do not wish to get their rumps wet; hence they strive for longer legs. The young then inherit the longer legs that the parents have acquired and in that way the wading birds of our time have acquired their long legs. Or, Lamarck said, consider the giraffe, the longest-necked animal alive. Its long neck, long legs, and long tongue are due to the fact that the ancestors of the present-day giraffe preferred the leaves of trees to grass, or else they happened to get into an area where grass and undergrowth were scarce and trees abundant. In an effort to get at the leaves they stretched legs, neck, and tongue and their offspring inherited the somewhat longer members. Then the offspring stretched its legs, neck, and tongue still further through a lifetime of striving for the leaves on the higher branches and again these characteristics were passed on.

His contemporaries were aghast at a reasoning which denied the fixity of species and implied that the wading birds and giraffes had not been created in their present forms. The scientists did not know what to think. Could a tree frog "desire" to turn green? Could a tree frog even see color?

About a century after the publication of the *Philosophie zoologique* the fundamental assumption of "desire" was subjected to experimental tests. Of course there are people who desire a deep tan and expose themselves to the sun to get it. Of course one might call hunger a desire for food and a browsing animal would naturally stretch its neck if that was the way to get at leaves. But even whether the neck would grow noticeably longer was questionable. Certainly the man who had spent twenty summers on acquiring a tan did not pass that tan on to his son. The son had to go through the same procedure. Would a slightly longer neck, provided it had actually grown longer, be passed on to the offspring?

The fundamental assumption was that something which had been acquired by a living organism could be inherited. Folklore tends to accept this assumption. If the father had suffered a saber cut resulting in a big scar on his face, his son showed a reddish streak in the skin in the same place. Or so folklore said. Logic said otherwise. Your ancestors and my ancestors have been speaking the same language for generations, but baby still has to learn even its "own" language. The Jews have been practicing circumcision for thousands of years, yet there is no record of even a single boy baby born without a foreskin.

Professor August Weismann, around the year 1890, had his assistants run a simple experiment. They bred white mice and, as soon as feasible after birth, cut off their tails. Then they bred the tailless mice to each other and when offspring arrived they snipped off the tails again. They kept this up for more than twenty generations of mice. Never was a mouse born without a tail. Weismann concluded that acquired characteristics are *not* inherited, folktales notwithstanding. After Weismann there came a few scientists who wanted to prove that acquired characteristics can be inherited, but they failed to produce a single convincing case.

The overall result is that to this day there is no proven case of an inheritance of acquired characteristics. Lamarck's fundamental assumption was wrong.

chapter eight

Georgius Agricola as he looked in 1550.

Man the Digger

RECALL the tale of Herodotus about the gorge in the mountains where he saw the backbones (*akanthai,* he called them) of the winged serpents that had been killed by the sacred ibises.

What Herodotus saw were fossils, but neither the word nor the concept existed in his time, so he had to accept the fanciful tale handed to him. But when, elsewhere in Egypt, he saw petrified clamshells in the hills, he immediately drew the conclusion that this area must once have been covered by water.

It is a historical fact that Xenophanes of Kolophon made the same observation and drew the same conclusion about one and a half centuries earlier. It is, therefore, possible that Herodotus was reminded of the older statement when he saw the fossil shells. Fossil clamshells are not only common, but also easily recognized. Hence they constantly posed the same question to anybody who saw them: How did clamshells get into the hills and to the tops of mountains? Did they indicate a former flooding by the sea, or only that a river had shifted its course?

Unfortunately the first book devoted to what we now call fossils has not survived. It was the work of Theophrastos of Eresos (on Lesbos, 368–284 B.C.) who succeeded Aristotle as leader of the Lyceum. We know only that such a book once existed. We don't know how large or how small it was and we can only guess what Theophrastos thought about fossils. These guesses are based on another work of his that has been pre-

191

served. It bears the title *Peri lithōn* (On Stones) and mentions not only shells but also fossil fishes.[1] He called them *ichthyes oriktoi* or "dug-up fishes," although he was uncertain whether they really indicated a former flooding by the sea. Maybe they had come from nearby rivers, or possibly fish eggs that had been carried to higher ground by a river flood had grown in moist sand until they died because the sand became thoroughly dry. Aristotle generally agreed with this latter point of view.

Herodotus was the first to mention a larger fossil, again without having any knowledge of what it was he was describing. A blacksmith at Tegea, he reported, dug a well and found the bones of a giant that must have stood seven ells (say about 20 feet) tall. This probably was the skeleton of a large mammal of the Tertiary Period, but the Spartans thought that it was the skeleton of Orestes, the son of Agamemnon, and since an oracle had told them that they would be victorious if they had the bones of Orestes in their possession they arranged to steal them during a moonless night. Unfortunately the bones have not been preserved.

Another classical mention of large and presumably fossil bones can be found in the *Lives of the Twelve Caesars* by Gaius Suetonius Tranquillus. He was a friend of Pliny the Younger and *magister epistolarum* (confidential secretary) to Emperor Hadrian during A.D. 119–121, presumably with access to state archives that were sealed to less important writers. But what he has to say about fossils has nothing to do with state secrets and is tantalizingly short. He merely stated that Emperor Augustus' collection of large bones could still be seen in this Emperor's villa on Capri.

So far fossils had been interpreted correctly in one respect: they were accepted as the remains of something that had once been alive. But then one important man made an important mistake. Abu 'Ali al-Husayn ibn Abdallah ibn Sīnā, best known by the Latin version of his name, Avicenna, lived from 980–1037, spending the latter part of his life in Hamadhān (Iran) where he died. He was the most famous physician of his time and was (and among Arabs still is) known as the "Prince of Learning"—more or less a Mohammedan equivalent of Conrad Gesner, except that he came five hundred years earlier and that he had the means of living well. (In fact, he seems to have died of overeating.) Among the topics of discussion in his circles was the transmutation of metals—the early Arabic version of alchemy. Ibn Sīnā did not believe a word of all these discussions; he thought metals differed from one another in more fundamental aspects than just color and hardness. But since he considered it impossible that lead might be changed into gold, or iron into silver, he also could not believe that a bone could turn into stone. They were two different things. But bone-shaped stones and stone fishes did exist. Hence there had to be another explanation.

Now a piece of bronze could assume all kinds of shapes, even though it always remained bronze. Stone also evidently could assume a number of shapes—one only had to assume a "shaping force" of some kind. Latin versions of Avicenna's manuscript used the term *vis plastica,* which is probably not a good translation of the original term. However, *vis plastica* it became and *vis plastica* it remained. If somebody asked for the origin of the *vis plastica* he was told that it was probably a manifestation of the influences of the stars. But while the idea of Avicenna that fossils had never been alive exerted a great deal of influence it never reigned supreme. One might say that Avicenna's *vis plastica* was called in only if every other attempt at explanation failed.

It was much easier to believe in a former race of giants. For example Giovanni Boccaccio—he of the Decameron—in his work *De genealogiis deorum* (On the Genealogies of the Gods), which he finished in 1371 after thirty years, reported the finding of the dead body of a giant. In his sixth book he told that a cave near Trapani in western Sicily had yielded the body. When it was touched it crumbled into dust but the bones were left. And *tres dentes monstruosae grandiciei,* three monstrously large teeth, as well as parts of the skull, had been salvaged and brought to the Santuario dell' Annunziata. In this case the idea that these bones and teeth might be due to the action of *vis plastica* was not even considered, and soon somebody said that *vis plastica* did not account for anything at all.

The man who said this was Leonardo da Vinci (1452–1519), artist, experimenter, inventor, and practicing engineer. This particular statement was the result of his activities as a builder of canals. Leonardo had noticed that a river cuts its way into the landscape so that certain layers are visible in both banks at the same, or nearly the same, elevation. While investigating river beds for practical purposes—such as navigation, fortification, and water supply for cities—and while supervising the digging of canals and the leveling of land, he had seen many fossils. He was convinced that they were not *lusi naturae* ("sports of nature") but simply animals that had lived there when the area was covered by seawater. After the sea had changed its place, presumably because the land had been lifted by some force, the bottom mud had slowly turned into stone and the clam shells which had been filled with mud (because the clam itself had died) showed an internal stone—a stone core, we would call it.

But couldn't this be the result of astrological influences? Of course not.

If astrological influences could produce such things, then all the animals of an area would be alike—that is, they would be of the same size—"but we find old clams side by side with younger ones and we find clams of a different kind sitting on their shells." Of course in Leonardo's time the finds of clamshells and of fishes far from the sea could also be explained by the Flood of the Bible. Leonardo did not like this explanation either. In fact, he doubted the story itself. Where could the waters have gone, after they were so high that they covered the peaks of the highest mountains?

Since Leonardo never published anything, his ideas did not exert any influence. Many of the inventions he sketched had to be made again independently by others and until less than a century ago he was known only as a great artist. His ideas about fossils had to be rediscovered much later, like almost everything else about his work.

Then there is a man known as Georgius Agricola, who is famous for a book that had nothing at all to do with his real profession. His *De re metallica* has been called "the greatest treatise on technological chemistry, mining, geology, and engineering of modern times." Its fame in the English-speaking world is entirely due to the translation from the original Latin edition of 1556 by Herbert Clark Hoover (later President of the United States) with the assistance of his wife Lou Henry Hoover.[2] The author was born at Glauchau, Saxony, on March 24, 1494, and christened Georg Bauer. But the German word *Bauer* means "peasant" and is rarely, if ever, used as a complimentary term. Hence Georg Bauer, after entering Leipzig University in 1514, inevitably became Georgius Agricola. He graduated in either 1517 or 1518 with the degree of Bachelor of Arts in classical languages and literature and his first publication was a Latin grammar. His first professional activity was teaching Latin and Greek in Zwickau. In 1522 he began to study medicine at Leipzig. He continued his medical studies at Padua and Bologna and in 1526 the Ferrara University of Bologna granted him the degree of Doctor of Medicine.

After that he returned to Zwickau, this time for the purpose of practicing medicine. Only one year later, in 1527, he was appointed City Physician of the city of Joachimsthal, where extensive silver mines had been opened up only ten years earlier and where the large silver coins known as the *Joachimsthaler* (later shortened to *Thaler,* and dollar) were first minted. He stayed there for six years, then moved to the bigger city of Chemnitz, the city council of which had appointed him City Physician. Agricola stayed in Chemnitz until his death, November 21, 1555.

But Agricola's fame resulted not from his activities as a physician, but from his surroundings. His very birthplace was at the edge of a mining district, and his later medical practice was in the heart of active and flourishing mining districts. Many of his patients were miners and Agricola became very much interested in their activities. He said himself that he was always eager to watch miners and their machinery at work and that he enjoyed talking to the more learned of them. Probably the miners talked far more freely to their doctor than they might have talked to city officials or to miners from other areas. While the miners had the practical knowledge, Agricola's classical training had provided him with the ability to organize knowledge. And so the most important early works on mining were written by a man who was not a miner himself.

While putting down the information Agricola ran into a curious difficulty. Of course he was writing in Latin, and Latin was a fine language for medical books and almost everything else. But it faltered when it came to hoists, treadmills, vertical and inclined shafts, ventilation holes, and stone-crushing equipment. And, of course, there was a host of minerals that had not been known in classical times. Agricola had to make up names and terms and one of the words he coined was the word "fossil" itself. Since mining means digging, and "to dig" is *fodere* in Latin, Agricola referred to miners as *fossores* and to the things they dug out as *fossilia*. As used by Agricola the term "fossil" meant anything that had been brought to the surface: minerals, ores, coal, as well as fossils in our sense. For this reason his earlier book *De natura fossilium* does not contain what a modern reader would expect from the title.* The original use of the word also led to the strange term *flumen fossilis* for a canal. One has to make a kind of mental stop to remember that *flumen* means a "river"; *flumen fossilis,* then, was a "dug river."

One might say that Agricola lived in a period when fossils were impressing their existence upon the minds of people. They were found on all sides. In Italy the citadel of San Felice at Verona needed repairs and huge blocks of stone had to be quarried for the purpose. The stones carted up for the repair of the citadel in 1517 showed a great many fossils, and a native of Verona, Girolamo Fracastoro (1483–1553), physician,† astronomer, and poet, set out to explain them. He concluded that they were actually organic remains and went on to say that the Biblical

* The translators prudently put "Textbook of Mineralogy" as an explanatory subtitle on the title page of their translation.

† His poem *Syphilis sive Morbus Gallicus* gave the disease the name that is still used.

deluge might be the explanation for some fossils, but could not explain all of them. In the first place, he reasoned, the deluge had in all probability been a local event which only looked universal to the victims, and in the second place the deluge had only lasted for a total of 150 days, while fossils were found in many places *and at many different levels!*

And in Germany a very special geological formation began to produce more and more fossils. This formation is known as the Mansfeld copper slate, adjacent to the mining area where Agricola lived. The blackish and heavy slate had been known for a long time; it was mentioned in a local document as early as A.D. 1216. We know now that the copper slate covers an area about thirty miles in length in a natural depression that runs roughly between the two cities Halle and Giessen. The average thickness of the copper-slate formation is 20 inches; in places it is a yard thick. The name is not fanciful at all. The slate has a copper content of 2.9 percent and a total metallic content of an incredible 9 percent. And it is rich in fossils,* most of them showing a metallic luster. We now know that this copper slate was formed 220 million years ago and that it is a marine deposit formed quite close to the shore of an ancient sea. Agricola could not know any of this, but he was shown fossils from the copper slate and he was asked for an opinion. Agricola had seen plant fossils before and had felt sure that they were former plants, and naturally he was plagued by the question of how the change from a soft and pliant leaf to hard stone could possibly take place.

Agricola had knowledge of natural events that seemed to furnish analogies. Strong acids would destroy some stones; wet mortar would become hard, harder than wet soil that merely dried out. Maybe under certain circumstances a moisture formed in the ground which made soft things hard. He named this hypothetical moisture *succus lapidescens* or "petrifying juice." It was not the correct explanation, but it was a step in the right direction. At least one could imagine now how the dead body of a fish or of a crab *might* be turned into stone. Agricola then proceeded to describe a number of fossils of marine organisms, which he, living far inland, had never seen and did not know about, without realizing that they were fossils.

There was, for example, the *lapis judaicus,* mistranslated as "Jewish stone" by practically everybody (the designation really meant "stone from Judaea"; it reached Europe for the first time during the Crusades). In shape it resembled an olive with a pitted surface and a short stem, and

* From this formation are known not less than 38 species of vertebrates of all kinds, 32 species of marine invertebrates, and 17 species of plants.

since it came from Palestine and was unusual, it was thought to have medicinal value, being especially efficacious for bladder stones and other urinary complaints. Even a well-educated man of our own time would have trouble figuring out what the *lapis judaicus* really was. During the Cretaceous Period there occurred in the area of the eastern Mediterranean a type of sea urchin which had such clublike excrescences instead of spines. The fossil sea urchin that produced the *lapides judaici* now bears the zoological name of *Cidaris glandaria*. A related form (*C. globiceps*) that flourished in what is now western Germany produced similar fossils; we can't tell whether Agricola saw the Palestinian or the German version.

Lapis judaicus from Palestine. Actually an appendage of the outer skin of a fossil sea urchin from the Upper Cretaceous.

In describing the marine organisms found in the copper slate, he said:

> *Trochites* is related to *lapis judaicus* and takes its name from a wheel. Since nature has given it the form of a drum the round part of it is smooth and each side has a certain degree of smoothness. Radii, so prominent they form striations, extend in all directions from the center to the outer rim like spokes in a wheel. It varies much in size . . . the largest is the width of a finger in diameter and a third as thick.

What Agricola described were segments of the long stems of fossil sea lilies, animals distantly related to sea stars and sea urchins. The still living forms are much smaller than the fossil ones. Agricola then gave an excellent description of a fossil sea urchin, handicapped only by the fact that he had never seen a living one. Fossil oyster shells go under the name "ostracites." His description of belemnites is good, and he also made it clear that he did not think that they were the petrified urine of a lynx, but naturally he could not tell what a belemnite really is, namely a part of the body of octopuslike animals that are now completely extinct. He also knew the *glossopetrae* (tongue stones) and said that they resembled the tongue of a woodpecker in shape. Actually they are the fossil teeth of various kinds of extinct sharks.

All in all, one begins to feel that Agricola should not have rushed home to Saxony after receiving his medical doctorate in Italy. He should have spent a year among Greek or Italian fishermen in some Mediterranean village. If he had done that he would have become acquainted with the marine life forms of our own geological time and would have been far better equipped to recognize and to understand what his miners brought him.

Some of the earliest pictures of fossils were published by Johannes Bauhin of Basel in 1548 and by Conrad Gesner in 1565. The fossil pictures were in Gesner's last work; in its title (*De natura fossilium*) he used Agricola's term in Agricola's sense.

Gesner's last book was a poor book. He sorted the *fossilia* into fifteen groups and the organization as well as the writing is careless. There are some true fossils in practically every one of his groups, and while Agricola had the excuse that he was unacquainted with current marine animals, Gesner knew about as much about them as anybody in his time. Yet he failed to see even the most obvious similarities. Of course we know that he was sick and overworked and harassed in various ways and that he died only a few months after the book was completed. But if we did not know this and if, by some unlikely mischance, only his last book had survived, his name would not be mentioned except in the most scrupulous and voluminous histories of science.[3]

Another man who recognized at an early date that fossils were the remains of animals that once lived was the Frenchman Bernard Palissy (1510–1590). Palissy's birthdate is not known because he was born a peasant, and there is some doubt about his birthplace, which was either in the diocese of Agen or that of Saintes. The two places are close together near the Atlantic coast of France. Palissy decided to become a *vitrier*. The word now means a glazier, but then it was mainly used to mean a man who made colored glass for church windows. Palissy traveled all over France as a journeyman. He must have read a great deal, but he never learned Latin. Like Agricola (who did know Latin, but for another reason), he amassed a wealth of practical experience, even more directly than Agricola because he actually worked with the minerals. Being a French Protestant, Palissy did not have an easy life but in spite of the combined handicaps of peasant origin, lack of formal education, and the wrong religion he rose to an important position and in 1575 gave public lectures in Paris on natural history. He may have been the world's first public lecturer; certainly he was the first in Paris, and also the first to bring fossils and other natural history objects with him to show his listeners. They were not pupils in the strict sense of the word, for, as Sarton said, "he appealed to physicians, dilettanti and *gens du monde.*" The substance of his lectures has been preserved in a book entitled *Discours admirables . . .* which was printed in Paris in 1580.

Recognition that a fossil was once alive was the first hurdle of the science of paleontology, which was very slowly being born during the seventeenth century. Nobody yet dared to think of extinct life forms; considering fossils former organisms was intellectual adventure enough. Leonardo da Vinci and Girolamo Fracastoro had embraced this intellectual adventure. So had Georgius Agricola and Bernard Palissy, followed by Geronimo Cardano (1501–1576) and Andrea Cesalpino (1519–1603), an Italian physician and botanist. The ones who emphatically denied that fossils had once been alive included Gabriel Fallopio (1523–1562; the Fallopian tubes are named after him), Michele Mercati, who had examined a collection of fossils that had been acquired by the Vatican (1574), and Giovanni Battista Olivi, who had examined a similar collection at Cremona (1584). Conrad Gesner does not qualify for either side, while Aldrovandi should be counted with Fracastoro and Cesalpino, for he pictured fossil fish and living fishes of similar appearance side by side in his book. Aldrovandi was also the first to use the word geology in its present sense, even though it was not then a scientific discipline.

Fossil fishes from Aldrovandi.

The man who might be called the Father of Geology had not even been born at the time. And while he lived and worked in Italy, he was not an Italian. He was a native of Denmark, born in Copenhagen in 1638. His original name was Niels Pedersen. Since his father's first name was Sten he became known as Niels Pedersen Stensen. Later, when he studied medicine, he Latinized his name into Stenonis and still later shortened it again so that he appears as Nicolaus Steno in the annals of science. In 1665, just a hundred years after Gesner's death, he went to Italy, having been appointed personal physician to the Grand Duke of Tuscany. In Florence he was converted to Roman Catholicism, ordained a priest in 1675, and even made a bishop in 1680. He died six years later and it was then discovered that the well-paid physician to the Grand Duke was penniless—he had lived up to his vows and given everything to the poor of Florence.

Steno's interest in geology began with *glossopetrae*. In 1667 he published a study of the head of a shark, proving that these much-discussed "tongue stones" were actually sharks' teeth. Being convinced that all readily recognizable fossils were of organic origin, he began to explore and think and finally, in 1669, published a small book with a fulsome scholarly title, which, translated, is "Prodromus of a dissertation on solid bodies which are naturally contained inside of other solid bodies." At no time did it produce much of a stir, but some people always realized its value so that it was reprinted fairly often (though the printings of the twentieth century were no longer prompted by a desire for information, but were belated honors for the author).[4]

The book was nothing less than the first attempt to write a regional geology, the region being Tuscany. After laying down a few rules which now are elementary, such as that a sediment can only form on an already existing solid layer and that all sediments are originally horizontal, Stenone, as the Italians called him, proceeded to fossils. Apparently there was much talk about "giants' bones" in Italy at the time because Steno discussed them first, with a reasonableness that should have been a model for his contemporaries. Occasionally one meets with an unusually big man, he wrote, and unusually large men must have existed in the past too. But very often the bones of large animals were mistaken for the bones of former giants. He had a good idea of how fossils come into existence. The number of *glossopetrae* is so large, he wrote, because dead sharks are transported by currents of the sea to quiet spots where they are buried in the bottom mud.

It is unfortunate that Steno's book is so short and that he wrote it so

Nicolaus Steno

late in life. If he had been twenty years younger, he would probably have written a book that might now be considered the beginning of paleontology.

Steno's contemporary, Father Athanasius Kircher, S.J., was an immensely erudite but strangely careless man, whose books were often ridiculed only a few years after their publication. Still, in almost every one of them something new can be found. He was born in 1602 at Geisa near Eisenach, lived in Würzburg for some time, then went to Rome and taught mathematics and Hebrew at the College of Rome, until he gave up teaching in 1643. He gave up his post because he wanted to study, specifically archaeology and hieroglyphics. At some time after his retirement he invented the magic lantern. Then conditions on other planets, animals, and volcanoes successively captured his interest, with three books as the result. The interest in other planets produced the strange *Ecstatic Voyage* (*Iter ecstaticum coeleste*, 1656) in which the author is taken on a trip to the known planets by the angel "Cosmiel." The conditions on the planets are described according to astrological concepts. Kircher's interest in zoology produced his *Noah's Ark* (Amsterdam, 1675), in which he lists all the animals that were admitted to the Ark "and therefore did not perish in the Flood." He even pictured the cages built by Noah for the various kinds of animals. His interest in volcanoes resulted in the two folio volumes of *De mundus subterraneus* (The Subterranean World, Amsterdam, 1678) in which he tried to explain the existence of volcanoes by assuming very numerous and very large subterranean caves. These caves were usually filled with water, but some were filled with fire. A few other caves were filled with air only, and these caves were inhabited by dragons—which explained why dragons were so rare. The dragons that had been encountered and slain by heroes were single specimens that had blundered onto the surface of the earth and could not return to the interior for some reason—for example, because the exit had been collapsed by an earthquake.

But, as I have said, one can usually find new facts in Kircher. For one, the fact, ascertained by having many priests question many miners, that the temperature rises as one penetrates down into the earth's crust. And, as regards fossils, Father Kircher was of two minds. Fossil wood, fossil leaves (more accurately leaf prints), and fossil fish were of organic origin. But fossil bones and fossil teeth were not; they had been formed in the ground by an agency Father Kircher called *spiritus plasticus*. The new thought in his book about the Ark was that there were some animals which Noah did not admit and which had then perished in the Flood.

This was the first—or if not the first in any event a very early—mention of the thought of extinct species. Kircher spoke generally; he did not state which animals had not been admitted and, if questioned, probably would have answered that that cannot be known.

But others must have specified a particular animal as being left out of the Ark. Professor Johann Sperling of Wittenberg left the manuscript of a book on animals which seems to have been meant as a textbook in zoology. His friend Professor Kirchmair saw to it that the manuscript was printed (1661). This book contains the sentence: "Some people believe that the unicorn perished in the Flood so that only its horns are left now/ But the care of the Creator is such that no species will disappear." I feel absolutely certain that Thomas Jefferson—who became one of the earliest fossil collectors in the United States—had never heard of Professor Sperling and his hardly important book. Yet he, too, contradicted the idea of extinction of species and even used more or less the same words: "Such is the economy of nature, that no instance can be produced, of her having permitted any one race of her animals to become extinct; of her having formed any link in her great work so weak as to be broken." [5] Jefferson's belief was, very simply, that if a fossil of a strange animal, found, say, in Virginia, was brought to him and if nobody had ever seen it in Virginia or elsewhere, it must now live in one of the unexplored areas of the Americas. Of course in Jefferson's day the unexplored areas were still very large and it was prudent to be cautious, but we now know that the case for extinct species was already well established in his time.

One of the geniuses of the second half of the seventeenth century, Robert Hooke, had the bad luck to be a contemporary of Sir Isaac Newton, Sir Christopher Wren, and Dr. Edmond Halley, all of whom overshadowed him. Hooke was brilliant and had many original ideas, yet he scattered his talents and wasted time on polemics. Some of his writings were not even printed during his lifetime. An essay written in 1688 and published posthumously dealt with fossils. Were they of organic origin? Hooke had absolutely no doubt of that and said that "fossils are more important documents than chronicles and coins and have the advantage that they cannot be counterfeited." He admitted that basing a chronology on fossils would be difficult but he pointed out that at some time in the past England must have had a warmer climate than in his time since the fossil turtles and the larger ammonites found on English soil could not have survived under the current climate. That seashells and other fossils are often found at a great height has nothing to do with the Flood. Hooke thought they had been lifted up to such heights by earthquakes.

Interest in fossils must have run high in Great Britain during the second half of the seventeenth century. Martin Lister (1638–1711), physician to Queen Anne, was interested both in zoology and in the emerging science of geology. In fact, he was the first man to suggest what we now call a geological survey. He had the brilliant and correct idea that certain stones—sediments, we'd say—can be distinguished by the fossils one can find in them. But after having realized this he took a long step backward: different stones can be distinguished by different fossils because different stones *make* different fossils; "to me ironstone clamshells are ironstone and sandstone shells sandstone."

Lister's contemporary Edward Lhwyd (who wrote under the name of Luidius) published a very good description of the fossils of Great Britain. But he assumed an *aura seminalis,* a fructifying force, probably coming from the ocean, which made stone shape itself into leaves and fishes and forms resembling large snails.

The idea of the *aura seminalis* was picked up by a physician in Lucerne, Dr. Karl Nikolaus Lang, who published a History of All Figure-Stones of Switzerland (*Historia lapidum figuratorum Helvetiae*) in Venice in 1708. The book sorted the "figure-stones" by their shapes, which, of course, brought many related forms together. Some of the 163 plates of unusually good pictures compare figure-stones shaped like seashells to actual seashells of today. Lang admitted the similarity, of course, but emphasized the differences which he explained by saying that the living seashells are found near the shore, while the seashell-like figure-stones were caused by an *aura* from the high seas!

While "Luidius" and his followers were defending ibn-Sīnā's *vis plastica* under a different name and with a semiplausible explanation, John Woodward (1665–1722) defended Biblical tradition. His *Essay towards a Natural History of the Earth and Terrestrial Bodies,* published in 1695, assumed organic origin for all fossils and explained both their death and their location by the action of the Flood.

Needless to say he found followers, but he only expressed what many of his contemporaries seem to have assumed, since the Flood had been held responsible for the distribution of fossils before Woodward. Among those who shared this view was Gottfried Wilhelm, Baron von Leibniz,* diplomat, philosopher, politician, and mathematician. Born in Leipzig on July 1, 1646, he traveled a great deal, was adviser to both Louis XIV

---

* The spelling Leibnitz, though often encountered, is incorrect. But the pronunciation of the name is Lyep-nitz.

Gottfried Wilhelm von Leibniz

of France and Peter the Great of Russia, convinced Friedrich I of Prussia that Prussia should have an academy of sciences like that of Paris, was present when the Akademie der Wissenschaften zu Berlin was decreed in 1700, and became its first president. In between he tried to reconcile the Papacy and the Protestants, unsuccessfully, and to invent a new method of calculation, successfully. This method was what is now known as calculus, also invented by Sir Isaac Newton at about the same time. In spite of the painful argument about the priority of the invention of calculus, Leibniz was elected to the Royal Society and when, some time later, the Academy of Sciences in Paris decided that it might be proper to have a few sufficiently famous foreigners among their members, Leibniz was elected. But one cannot say that he was the first foreign member, for two were elected at the same time, the other one being Newton.

Around 1690 Leibniz became interested in the past of the earth. Some strange fossils which somebody sent to the famous man seem to have triggered his thoughts. He called his manuscript *Protagaea* ("Proto-Earth") and sent excerpts to Professor Otto Mecke, founder (1682) and editor of the first German scientific journal, *Acta Eruditorum*. The excerpts appeared in the volume for the year 1693. The whole work was not published until some time after Leibniz' death.[6]

The book began with general speculation. The earth, Leibniz said, probably was hot and liquid originally, then cooled off; a hard crust was formed and because the cooling earth contracted, enormous blisters [hollows] were formed, some filled with air and some with water. (This sounds as if Leibniz had read Kircher, a reasonable assumption.) Collapse of such blisters as were filled with water caused numerous floods which changed the surface of the earth many times over. But these floods were not the Flood of the Bible, which was a later event, though it also probably was caused by the collapse of enormous water-filled blisters. "I do not dare to assume an event like the close passage of a comet or of our moon as the cause," he remarked at that point.

The book is not very orderly and Leibniz may have postponed its publication because he planned to go over it thoroughly at a later time. After the general speculation about the origin of the earth, the book suddenly goes into a description of the Brocken, the highest of the Harz mountains, and of mining in these mountains. Then fossils are mentioned.

> Some are surprised that there are to be seen everywhere in rocks such objects as one might seek for in vain elsewhere in the known world. . . . Such are the horns of Ammon [ammonites] which are reckoned a kind

of Nautilus, although they are said to differ always both in form and size—sometimes indeed being found a foot in diameter—from all those animal natures which the sea exhibits. Yet who has thoroughly searched those hidden recesses or subterranean depths? (Translated by Thomas Huxley.)

Leibniz was much impressed with the fossil fishes of the copper slate occurring in the Harz mountains; they looked to him "most artistic, as if an artist had skillfully inserted an engraved piece of metal into the black stone." The fishes looked "as if they had been caught alive and turned into stone by the power of the gorgon." Ideas like the *aura seminalis* are mere "empty words of philosophers," he declared. In his opinion, a large lake filled up with soil, perhaps as a result of an earthquake, and the soil then slowly turned into stone, preserving the dead creatures. After their soft flesh had rotted away, the resulting hollows were filled with metal. Quite modern thoughts, and rather daring for their time. But when he discussed seashells found high up in the Alps, Leibniz grew cautious again. Of course they had once been alive, but he could not believe that mountains as high as the Alps could erupt from an earth that was already solid. The shells were probably carried there by the Flood.

Figura Sceleti prope Qvedlinburgum effossi

The "reconstructed" unicorn from the *Protagaea* of Leibniz.

After some remarks about caves in the Harz mountains, about amber, about wood buried in the soil, and about peat, Leibniz ended his work with a description of a deep well near Amsterdam where several layers of soil, sand, and marl can be clearly seen, the bottom layer of gravel containing seashells. He concluded that this place had originally been sea bottom and had been flooded repeatedly after it became dry land. The copper plates of the first Latin edition show fossil fish, ammonites, a collection of *glossopetrae* and a shark's head, a number of minor fossils such as belemnites and crinoid stems, and finally a few bones of a large mammal.

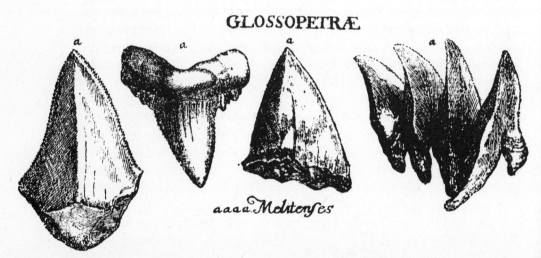

So-called *glossopetrae* or "petrified tongues," correctly explained as fossil shark's teeth; from the *Protagaea* by Leibniz.

At some places in the *Protagaea* there is evidence that Leibniz conceived of changes of living beings: "It is possible that during all the big events the species of living beings underwent great changes." In another book, the *Nouveaux essais,* he developed his idea about a "law of continuity" and wrote: "It is possible that somewhere and somewhen—present, past or future—the species of animals were far more subjected to changes than we observe now. Again and again I am compelled to say that our classifications are only provisional and in accordance with our current knowledge." It is not quite clear just what he meant. Did he mean that his "law of continuity" saw to it that there were always intermediate forms (in the sense in which this term was used by Albertus Magnus) or did he mean that species were maintained by the law of continuity in spite of the changes he considered possible? The former is more likely because in the *Protagaea* he wrote: "Some * go as far in their willful speculations as to say that at the time the ocean covered everything the animals that now live on land were living in the waters, that they then became amphibians and that their offspring, finally, was unable to live in the original home. But such thoughts contradict the Holy writers and it would be sinful to deviate from them."

By the year 1700, one would think, the problem of whether fossils were of organic origin or not must have been decided in favor of organic origin. But such a conclusion would be the result of hindsight, and even hindsight is less infallible than is generally supposed. In reality the question was still wide open to discussion and disagreement. Steno's work was not well known north of the Alps. Of the *Protagaea* only excerpts had been published and even if the whole work had been in print not everybody would necessarily have agreed with Leibniz.

The "mammoth of Tonna" is a fine example.

Tonna is a small place in the vicinity of Gotha in Germany and in 1696 a fairly complete skeleton of a mammoth was found there on the occasion of digging a foundation for a building. One of the teachers at the High School of Gotha, Wilhelm Ernst Tentzel, described it carefully and stated that these were the remains of a formerly living animal.†
But the *Collegium medicum* of Gotha re-examined the find and declared officially that Tentzel had been mistaken and that the so-called bones were just a "play of Nature."

Then there is the famous case of "Beringer's Lying Stones." The man who gave his name to the case was Professor Johann Bartholomaeus

---

* The "some" probably refers to Anaximander (611–545 B.C.) who in his work *Peri physeōs* (Concerning Nature) wrote that men, first living in the waters, progressed to the point where their hard shells burst so that they could live on land.

† Tentzel's statement represented progress, as most of the earlier similar finds had been taken to be giants. A leg bone of a mammoth found in Vienna in 1444 was attached for some time to one of the three doors of the Cathedral of St. Stephan. The door came to be named "Giant's door," to the puzzlement of later generations after the bones had been removed, for it happens to be the smallest of the three doors. Remains of a mammoth found in 1577 near Cloister Reyden in Switzerland were labeled the Giant of Lucerne by Felix Platter and the remains of two mammoths found near Krems in Austria by Swedish soldiers engaged in building fortifications (1645) also were declared to be giants—the justification, in all cases, being the line in Genesis 6:4: "There were giants in the earth in those days."

Adam Beringer, M.D. and Ph.D., Court Councilor and personal physician to the Prince Bishop of Würzburg.

This learned man loved his evening walk in the countryside outside the town and often went on longer excursions. If he found fossils—not too rare an event in that area—he carried them home with him and in the course of time accumulated a small collection. One day he was given a slab of stone with a strange figure in bas-relief. The young man who brought it was one of three brothers, sons of a poor widow. Doctor Beringer was interested and asked some questions. The young man told him that he as well as his brothers worked in a quarry to support their mother and that one of them had come across the fossil by accident. Beringer asked for more in case more were found. New finds were forthcoming, with the result that Beringer gave the three brothers "plenty of money" (his own words) so that they could quit their jobs and dig for his collection only.

The brothers were quite lucky. Beringer's collection of strange bas-reliefs grew; they showed spiders, crayfish, birdlike creatures, pictures of the sun and of stars and comets, and a few Hebrew letters. Just to be certain that he did not misinterpret these letters, Beringer showed that slab to a rabbi who confirmed his thought that the letters spelled the Hebrew name of God. By the year 1725 the collection was quite large. Beringer had pictures of his fossils engraved on copper plates and wrote a book entitled *Lithographia Wirceburgensis,* which was published in May 1726.

Most readers of the book, not having been gradually indoctrinated as Beringer had been, said immediately that these fossils were the product of art and not of nature. And then, according to books written more than a century after the event, "Beringer realized that he had been hoaxed, spent his fairly large fortune trying to buy back every copy of his book in order to destroy it and died soon after of a broken heart."

Having accepted this version, including the medically difficult death of a broken heart, historians still wanted to know who had perpetrated the hoax and for what reason. One fairly late version was that it had been a students' prank that got out of hand. Another was that the librarian of the college, Georg von Eckhart, and his friend J. Ignaz Roderique, professor of geography and algebra, had been the real culprits. It is not quite clear what basis there was for these accusations. That the three young men had been subjected to questioning by church officials was mentioned in the documents of the local church, but nothing was known

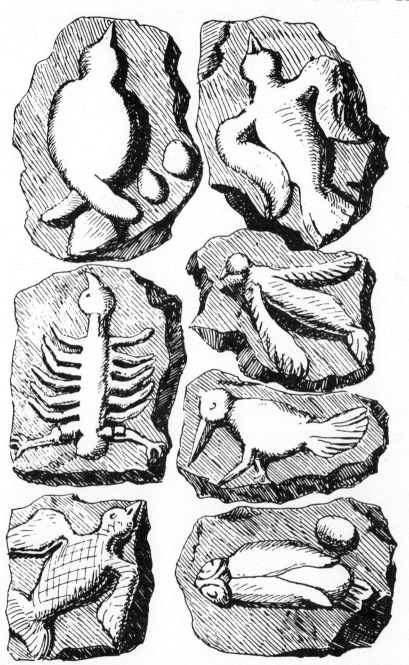

Birds, beetles, and centipedes on a page of "lying stones" of Beringer's *Lithographia Wirceburgensis*.

about the results of the questioning. It was not until January 1934 that Dr. Heinrich Kirchner, while going through the archives, found the long-wanted protocol of the questioning; one suspects that it had been filed under a heading which made earlier researchers disregard it.

The truth about the case of the Lying Stones, as now known, is as follows: Only two of the three young men were actually brothers; their names were Valentin and Nikolaus Hehn. The name of the third was Christian Zänger. The Hehn brothers were innocent, if singularly naive. They dug in the places suggested by Zänger and carried their "finds" to Beringer. The stones had been made by Professor Roderique in his own home, with Zänger's help (apparently Zänger was accomplished in polishing stones). The polishing was often done in the home of Georg von Eckhart, the librarian. Zänger admitted that one day, after making a delivery to Beringer, he had reported how happy Beringer had been with the latest discoveries, and Mrs. von Eckhart had been so pleased that she had handed him (Zänger) some extra money.

But there must have been some suspicions, because Von Eckhart wrote to one Dr. Hugo (a physician in Hanover) that Roderique had made a few stones that were obvious fakes—for example, a marine horse—to make Beringer realize that somebody was trying to deceive him. But *all* the stones, including the admitted fakes, show the same style and the same workmanship.

There is no indication that Beringer used up his fortune to buy back all the copies of his book, nor did he die soon afterward. He lived for another fourteen years, in comfortable circumstances, and was active as a physician. He died in 1740 at the age of seventy. And he never destroyed any of the Lying Stones—thirty of them can still be seen in the Geological Institute of Würzburg.

The main question is, of course, what Beringer thought himself. He does not seem to have written anything about the stones after his book was printed, so one has to look for the answers in the book itself. Beringer strictly distinguished between these stones and the ordinary fossils of which he had a collection. In fact he pictured in his book only one fossil from his original collection and this one only because he thought he detected some resemblances to the others. He offered the pictures of his figure-stones to other learned men for their judgment. In twelve long chapters he told how the stones came into his possession and advanced arguments, rejecting *vis plastica* and *aura seminalis* and that Nature was likely to "play." Sometimes, he wrote, one finds "phantom fossils" which are

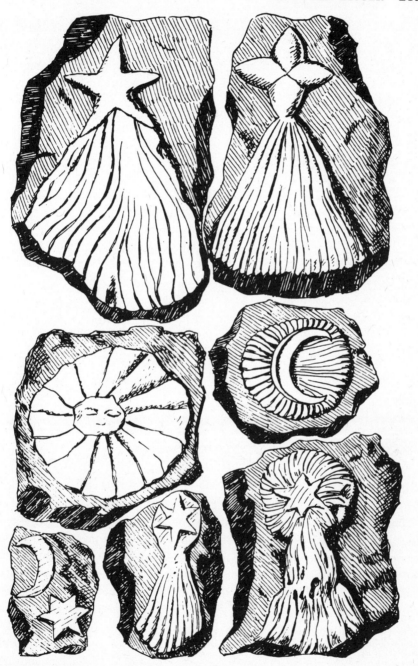

Sun, moon, and comets on another page of "lying stones" of Beringer's *Lithographia Wirceburgensis*.

not real fossils (whatever *they* may be) but which are the result of crys-
tallization in closed caves or in cracks in the rock, and he saw no reason
why such accidental formations might not resemble a spider or a toad
or a comet by accident. But he offered this idea only as a possibility, to
get away from astrological influences and similar thoughts. He expected
some of his readers to offer a better explanation.

Of course such things as Beringer's "phantom fossils" do exist: in fact
there are two kinds of them. One is the so-called concretions of sandstone
that are sometimes found in marl; they are lumpy things that may resemble an animal. One example which I have seen looked somewhat like
four tiny mice suckling, but then you had to assume that the head, the
tail, and the legs of the "mother mouse" had been broken off. The other
kind consists of crystallized salts from a drying solution in a rock crack.
These often assume a mosslike shape, and sometimes they look like a tuft
of grass. The technical name of this kind of pseudo fossils is "dendrites,"
from the Greek word *dendron,* meaning "tree."

The next event of interest was a book written earlier than Beringer's,
in 1715–16, but published later (in 1749) under the title *Telliamed,* an
inversion of the author's name: De Maillet. The full title is *Telliamed, ou
Entretiens d'un philosophe indien sur la diminution de la Mer avec un
missionaire français.* Benoît de Maillet (1656–1738) had a nice safe
device, as the title shows. Anything that anybody might consider hereti-
cal is said by the "Indian philosopher," while everything traditional is
said by the French missionary. In De Maillet's picture of the history of
the earth, the earth is first covered completely with water. The animals
of the water, or rather some of them, then change into flying animals and
the flying animals settle on land.

> Driven out of the water by the ardor of the chase or by pursuit, they
> [the flying fishes] might have fallen some distance from the shore among
> plants which, while supplying them with food, prevented them from
> returning to the water. Here, under the influence of the air, their anterior
> fins with their raised membranes transformed into wings . . . the ventral
> fins became limbs, the body was remodeled, the neck and the beak
> became elongated and the fish discovered itself a bird.

It was evolution of a sort, but the idea that birds were the offspring of
flying fish, lions the offspring of sea lions, and man the offspring of
l'homme marin, defined as "the husband of the mermaid" was too much
even for progressive thinkers. *Telliamed* was regarded by contemporaries

somewhat the way the not yet written adventures of the Baron von Münchhausen were to be, and Cuvier later said that it was "the most superficial and most fruitless idea I ever had to criticize."

The famous German paleontologist Karl Alfred von Zittel (1839–1904) said in his *History of Geology and Paleontology* (in German, Munich, 1899) that the books about fossils written from about 1650 to about 1750 fall into two classifications. The first class is popular and meant for contemplation of God and Nature, while the second class does not attempt to explain or to understand but consists of richly illustrated works describing the fossils of a specific region.

Belonging to the second class is the magnificent four-volume *Sammlung von Merkwürdigkeiten der Natur und Altertümern des Erdbodens* by Georg Wolfgang Knorr (1705–1761) and Johann Ernst Immanuel Walch (1725–1778). The title is difficult to translate because some of the words have changed their meanings to some extent since. The best that can be done is: "Collection of memorable things of Nature and of ancient things in the ground." The first volume appeared in 1755, under the editorship of Knorr, who was a collector and an artist. The title page is a picture of the famous quarry of Solnhofen in Franconia where the stones needed for lithography were quarried and where in the process of the work especially beautiful fossils were found. Naturally the plates in this volume picture fossils from Solnhofen. The remaining three volumes were edited by Walch, the son of a professor of philosophy and himself professor of eloquence and poetry. It is not too surprising, therefore, that the book has a certain poetic style. The fossils were treated with loving care and the text was written in a happy mood; Walch ended the last book by saying that "the hours devoted to this work were the happiest of my life."

The four volumes contain a total of 275 copper plates in folio, most of them hand-colored. The pictures in volume II are mainly of fossil seashells and marine snails. While Walch was firmly convinced that they were of organic origin, he was surprised by the conclusion he had to draw—namely that his area, the southern Germany of today, must at one time have been flooded by the sea. But he rejected the glib explanation of everything by the Flood, for there were land animals among the fossils. "It cannot be proved that all the fossils in the soil owe their existence to flooding; hence it can even less be said that their existence apodictically proves the Mosaic Flood without fail." Walch returned to the theme in volume III, which was devoted to remains of plants: "Plant fossils are not due to flooding, but owe their existence to the drying up of lakes and swamps." The fourth volume (it appeared in 1773) is a systematic survey of everything that had been learned. Walch concluded that all fossils are the remains of formerly living things, that the Flood may have taken place but that it did not explain the distribution of fossils, and that one has to assume that places that are now dry land must have been covered by water for a long time, not just temporarily.

The big work by Knorr and Walch was the culmination of a method of presentation that had become customary, all of the examples belonging to Zittel's second class. In 1708 Johann Jakob Baier (1677–1753) of Nürnberg, physician and professor of medicine, had published his *Oryctographia norica*. The title means "Description of dug-up [things] around Nürnberg" and the copper plates show many fossils which we now know belong to the Jurassic Period. Baier defended the Flood as either the cause or the distributor of fossils but stated sharply that the idea that fossils may be "plays of Nature" is merely "an expression of our ignorance of the true causes."

Baier corresponded a good deal with a Swiss scientist who happened to have the same first names, Johann Jakob Scheuchzer. Scheuchzer's father, like Conrad Gesner, had been City Physician of Zurich. The son became Second City Physician and professor of mathematics in one of the schools where Gesner had been a pupil.

Since Scheuchzer lived a generation or two earlier than Knorr and Walch—(1672–1733), he had a harder struggle with contemporary beliefs than the later researchers. Early in his life he was convinced that fossils were just "plays of Nature," but then he read the book by John Woodward and was so impressed with it that he translated it into Latin to make it accessible to the savants of continental Europe, very few of whom could read English. Scheuchzer began to collect fossils with enthusiasm. He had two goals in mind: to convince his contemporaries that fossils were of organic origin and to show that the fossils proved the reality of the Flood. In 1702 he published a pamphlet called "The Complaint of the Fishes," in which fossil fishes berate humans for continuous ill-treatment. People, by their sins, first caused the Flood and now they don't even wish to accept fishes as witnesses of this event but try to pretend that they are only mineral stone of marl birth.

Scheuchzer was learned, pious, and conscientious, but he is remembered chiefly for an instance of pious zeal which happened late in his life. He found a fossil over a yard in length which clearly showed a skull and

Johann Jacob Scheuchzer of Switzerland, one of the early scientists who realized the true nature of fossils.

218

TAB.VI

A dendrite as pictured in Scheuchzer's *Herbarium diluvianum*. Scheuchzer was quite certain that this was not a true fossil.

the column of the vertebrae as well as a number of ribs. The fossil, as we now know, was that of a giant salamander of the late Tertiary Period, but to Scheuchzer salamanders were creatures that could fit in one's hand. The thought of a giant salamander did not occur to him, and the fossil amphibian, under his hands, turned into "the sad remains of a sinner who drowned in the Flood." He did not date his publication with the year 1726, but "In the Year MMMM XXXII * after the Great Flood."

The truth did not become known until 1811.

* 4032.

HOMO DILUVII TESTIS.

Bein-Gerüst,

Eines in der

Sündfluc ertrunkenen

Menschen.

Wir haben / nebst dem ohnfehlbaren Zeugnuß des Göttlichen Worts / so viel andere Zeugen jener allgemeinen und erschröcklichen Wasser-Fiut; als viel Länder / Stätte / Dörffer / Berge / Thäler / Stein-Brüche / Leim-Gruben sind. Pflanzen / Fische, vierfüssige Thiere/Ungezifer, Muscheln / Schnecken / ohne Zahl, von Menschen aber / so dennahls zu Grund gegangen/hat man biß dahin sehr wenig Ueberbleibselen gefunden. Sie schwimmen tod auf der obern Wasser-Fläche / und verfaulen / und läst sich von denen hin und wider befindlichen Gebeinen nicht allezeit schliessen / das sie von Menschen seyen. Dieses Bildnuß / welches in sauberem Holz-Schnitt der gelehrten und curiosen Welt zum Nachdencken vorlege / ist eines von sichersten so ohnfehlbaren Ueberbleibselen der Sünd-Fiut; da finden sich nicht einige Lineament, auß welchen die reiche und fruchtbare Einbildung etwas / so dem Menschen gleichet / formieren kan / sondern eine gründliche Uebereinkunft mit denen Theilen eines Menschlichen Bein-Gerüts; ein vollkommenes Eben-Maß / ja selbs die in Stein (der auß dem Oningischen Stein-Bruch) eingesenkte Bein ; selbs auch welchere Theil sind in Natura übrig / und von übrigem Stein leicht zu unterscheiden. Dieser Mensch / dessen Grabmahl alle andere Römische und Griechische auch Egyptische / oder andere Orientalische Monument an Alter und Gewüßheit übertrifft/ præsentiert sich von vornen. A B C. ist der Umbfang des Stirn-Beins (alles in natürlicher Grösse) B. die Mitte der Stirn. A. das rechte Joch-Bein. C. das linde, D E G H, die Augenleser. K L die Dicke des Stirn-Beins, mit dessen beyden Tafelen, der ausseren und inneren, M das Loch der unteren Augenlese / welches die Senn-Ader des fünfften Nerven hindurchläßt. N. Sind Reliquien von dem Gehirn / oder des harten Hirn-Häutleins. O. Die Gebein / welche die Augenleien formiren, P. Die Siebförmigen und schwammichten Bein. P Q. Die Pflug-Schar / so durch die Mitte der Nasen hinunter gehet. U. Ein zimbliches Stuck vom vierten Baden-Bein. W. Scheinet seyn ein Stuck des Stirn-Muskuls. X. Uberbleibselen der Nasen. Y. Ein Stuck vom käuenden Muskul. B C. Ein Durchschnitt von dem untern Kiefel wie der von dem dickeren Fortsaz gehet zu dem untern Et oder Winkel. D. Stüker vom untern Kienbaken gegen dem Kien. 1. 2. 3. &c. biß 16. sind 16. Rukgrat-Wirbel / namlich 6. vom Hals / und 10. vom Ruken / da gemeinlich die Nebenfortsäze bloß ligen. E F. Ein Stuk vom Rabenförmigen Fortsaz des Schulter-Blatts. G H. Ein Stuk vom ersten Ripp / welches annoch mit Stein überzogen. i. Uberbleibselen von der Leber. Auß der ganzen Grösse läßt sich schliessen / in Gegenhalt der übrigen Theilen / daß die Höhe dieses Menschen steiget auf 58¾. Pariser Zoll / welche entsprechen 5. Zürcher Schuhe 9¾, Decimal-Zoll.

PES PARISINUS.

12 11 10 9 8 7 6 5 4 3 2

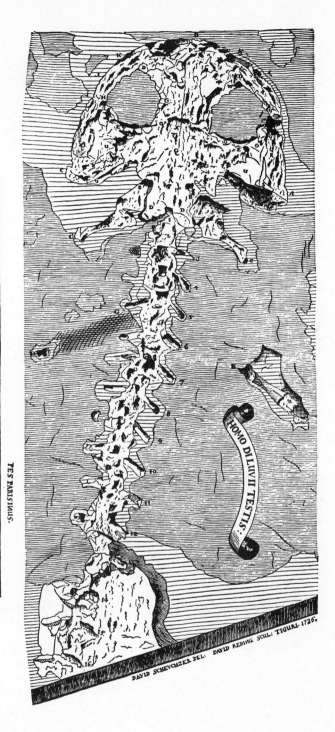

HOMO DILUVII TESTIS.

DAVID SCHEUCHZER DEL: DAVID REDING SCUL: TIGURI. 1726.

Scheuchzer's *Homo diluvii testis*. Scheuchzer thought it to be the skeleton of a man who had drowned in the Flood; actually it was the remains of a very large salamander.

The Baron de Cuvier at the height of his career.

The man who was to transform the scattered knowledge about fossils into a definite science, Georges de Cuvier, had looked at Scheuchzer's plate of the "sinner" and thought that it might depict a salamander. He then inquired what had happened to the original and learned that it had been sold to Tyler's Museum in Haarlem. In 1811 he traveled to Holland and began to lay open those bones that were still imbedded in stone. As a guide he had the skeleton of a small salamander next to the fossil. If he could find the forelimbs of the fossil and expose their bones the case would be proved. Cuvier did find and expose the forelimbs—and the fossil *was* of a giant salamander. A few decades later a salamander of similar size, though not closely related, was found to be still living in the mountainous areas of Japan. This living giant salamander bears the heavy-handed scientific name of *Megalobatrachus maximus* (the maximal giant batrachian); Cuvier named the fossil form in memory of Scheuchzer *Andrias scheuchzeri.*

chapter nine

The Chevalier de Lamarck, *ca.* 1800.

Man the Explainer

COMMUNICATIONS were slow in 1832, but by the end of the
month of March of that year all educated people knew that two
towering figures in the world of letters and knowledge were gone. On
March 13 the great Georges de Cuvier, who almost single-handed created the then new science of paleontology, had died in Paris. And less
than two weeks later, on March 22, Johann Wolfgang von Goethe died
in Weimar.

They had been contemporaries all through Cuvier's life (Goethe was,
within one week, older by precisely twenty years) and had read each
other's works. But that did not mean that they always agreed. In one
point of view especially they represented diametrically opposed sides.
This difference is explainable, perhaps, by the fact that one was a poet
and the other a practicing (and, in every sense of the word, practical)
scientist.

Cuvier, or, to give him his full name, Georges Léopold Chrétien
Frédéric Dagobert, Baron de Cuvier, while examining and describing his
fossils, had a sharp eye for similarities to life forms still running, crawling,
or flying around in the French countryside. But his eye was even sharper
when it came to differences. A fossil animal from the vicinity of Paris
resembled the tapir of India, but it was not a tapir. A column of vertebrae
from Bavaria might look as if it had come from a large fish, but its original owner had been more akin to lizards. And this fossil, also from

223

Bavaria, had been something that had no living counterpart anywhere on earth—for it had been a flying reptile.

Cuvier drew the obvious conclusion: there had been many life forms that were decidedly and completely extinct. He said so in so many words in his main work, the *Recherches sur les ossemens fossiles* (Researches on Fossil Bones, 1812). Looking for similarities and differences Cuvier realized that the external shape could be quite misleading, so he went by structure. He was probably goaded into thinking about structure by the fact that it is mainly bones that fossilize. He established four broad groups (called phyla) of living *and* extinct animals: vertebrata (everything with an internal skeleton), mollusca (no skeleton but often shells), articulata (external skeleton, like lobsters and beetles), and radiata (a category which, though it recognized the five-sided symmetry of life forms like sea stars, sea urchins, jellyfish, etc., was still largely a "miscellaneous file" for whatever failed to fit the first three phyla). Of course he saw, better than any other man alive then, that each geological period had fossils that were typical for this period, of animals now extinct. He felt obliged to explain this fact in the introduction to his *Recherches sur les ossemens fossiles* [1] and to do so advanced an idea that was not quite new.

He took this idea from Charles Bonnet (1720–1793), a Swiss naturalist who had conceived the notion that the animal of the next generation already exists, completely formed, in small, within the egg laid by the preceding generation. Of course this egg also had to contain the preformed individuals all of future generations to come. The French referred to this idea as *emboîtement* (boxes within boxes). Since everything was preformed, changes would naturally have been impossible. But Bonnet was already convinced that some life forms were extinct. Such extinction could have been caused only by worldwide catastrophes that destroyed all life on the globe. However, Bonnet added, the Creator will not permit complete extinction, hence some *germes* survived the catastrophes but were subtly changed by the catastrophe itself, so that the new creation brought different forms. Bonnet's idea of worldwide catastrophes would not have lasted long if Cuvier had not adopted it.

Just how complete Cuvier thought his catastrophes were is a matter of argument. After his death it was usually said, both by people who followed him and by people who thought the whole idea ridiculous, that he considered them worldwide and complete, so that after the end of each geologic period creation had to be performed again. But, according to Charles Depéret, Cuvier never considered a truly worldwide catastrophe, and in Cuvier's own writings there is an example of what might be called a restricted catastrophe. Supposing, he said, that a gigantic flood covered Australia with a deep layer of sand. Then all the animals that are so specifically Australian and that cannot be found anywhere else—like the platypus, echidna, the diverse kinds of kangaroos—would be extinct. But the same cataclysm might turn into dry land the straits that separate Australia from the Indonesian islands and these islands from the Asian mainland, and then Australia would be repopulated by "rhinoceroses, buffaloes, horses, camels, tigers, and all the other Asiatic animals."

But Cuvier's successors talked of complete catastrophes. Thus we have the strange situation that Cuvier's fame rests solidly on the *Recherches* while his biggest mistake was the introduction to the same book.

Goethe's opinion about the Bonnet-Cuvier catastrophes is not a matter for conjecture; he stated it in one forceful sentence. He called it *die vermaledeite Polterkammer der Weltgeschichte,* "the accursed pelting chamber of world history" and would have none of it. When in Italy Goethe, walking through botanical gardens which Aldrovandi had started by his example, looked for what he called the *Urpflanze,* the archetype of plants. As early as 1790 Goethe had published his *Versuch, die Metamorphosen der Pflanzen zu erklären* (Essay toward an Explanation of the Metamorphoses of Plants), and later admirers said that it had the one drawback of having been published half a century too early.

Wherever he went, Goethe looked for the archetypes of everything. He was convinced that the enormous variety of life around him must have started with comparatively few forms which changed and proliferated later. "The conviction that everything must be in existence in a finished state . . . had completely befogged the century," he wrote.

Thus, when the bones of a giant sloth from South America arrived in Paris (where Cuvier supervised their assembly) Goethe felt moved to write a short essay about this "miraculous animal." Because it was so large, its ancestor could only have been something still larger, the whales of the open ocean. When he saw the sun-baked and broken skull of a cow in the Roman campagna, he concluded that the bones of a vertebrate skull were just changed vertebrae, adapted in shape to meet special requirements.

Goethe, while usually wrong in detail, was forever the evolutionist who rejected natural discontinuities of any kind, and who considered steady change normal. He never read Lamarck; he seems to have been completely unaware of Lamarck's existence.

Goethe and Lamarck actually were "early evolutionists," but that term has to be handled with some care, especially since different people used certain words in a meaning different from the present meaning of these words. When Bonnet used the word "evolution" he meant the growth of the individual from the preformed "germ." What *we* call evolution was often referred to as "development" or "the developmental idea." The possibility (usually hotly denied) that one species may rise from another was called "heterogenesis," or "transmutation," a word that makes us think of alchemy and the Philosopher's Stone.

Erasmus Darwin (1731–1802), the grandfather of Charles Darwin, must also be counted among the early evolutionists. Erasmus Darwin was a physician of fierce countenance who was given to writing endlessly cascading poems about natural history, beginning with plants. One of these poems contains the lines:

> Hence, without parents, by spontaneous birth
> Rise the first specks of animated earth. . . .
> Organic life beneath the shoreless waves
> Was born, and nurs'd in ocean's pearly caves;
> First, forms minute, unseen by spheric glass,
> Move on the mud, or pierce the watery mass;
> These, as successive generations bloom,
> New powers acquire and larger limbs assume;
> Whence countless groups of vegetation spring,
> And breathing realms of fin and foot and wing.

They not only express his opinion but are also a typical example of his style.

Charles Darwin's strangest forerunner [2] mentioned by Darwin himself, was probably Patrick Matthew, who had written a book entitled *Naval Timber and Arboriculture* in which he said that living organisms have a "circumstance-suiting power" of "transmutation" and which even included the struggle for survival as an auxiliary cause.

But the most important evolutionist in Great Britain before Darwin was the author of a book called *Vestiges of the Natural History of Creation,* which appeared in 1844 and by 1860 had reached ten editions in England, had been translated into Dutch and twice into German, and had been pirated in America at least three times. Darwin did not like the book because of its mistakes and his dislike may have been heightened by the fact that its author remained strictly anonymous for the rest of his life (he died in 1871). For that reason he had to be referred to as "Mr.

Robert Chambers, some years after the publication of *Vestiges*.

Vestiges." He was Robert Chambers, co-founder (with his slightly older brother William) of the still existing Edinburgh publishing house of that name.

Chambers' book, considered by many "the greatest scandal of the nineteenth century," * because of its wide circulation, exerted such influence that the history of evolutionary thought during the nineteenth century has to be divided into three periods: the period from 1800 to *Vestiges* in 1844; the period from 1844 to 1859, the date of the publication of Darwin's *Origin of Species,* and the period from 1859 to the end of the century.

* The Reverend Samuel R. Bosanquet said in a review, "We readily attribute to it all the graces of the accomplished harlot."

Chambers began work on *Vestiges* some time in 1842,[3] at a time when geology had become both intellectual amusement and a kind of outdoor sport for Englishmen and especially Scotsmen. James Hutton (1726–1797), who is generally considered the founder of modern geology, was also a Scotsman, one of the rather numerous nonpracticing physicians who made their voices heard in science during the seventeenth and eighteenth centuries. His ideas, though novel then, were essentially simple and reasonable. There were two kinds of rocks, those that were brought to the surface by volcanic action and those that had formed by sedimentation, by the compacting of rock dust from older rocks of both kinds, formed by erosion first and then carried out to sea by rivers.

Hutton's book, called *Theory of the Earth,* was published in 1785. To conservative Scotsmen and Englishmen it was vaguely disturbing because it was hard to see how all this could have taken place during the mere six thousand years of time that the Bible seemed to allow as the age of the earth.

Aside from these scruples there was also a scientific attack, originating with Abraham Gottlob Werner (1750–1817) in Saxony. Holding a professorship at the famous Freiburg School of Mines Werner taught that Hutton's idea that sedimentary rocks must have formed in a specific sequence was correct. But what he could see in Saxony indicated clearly that volcanism had never played a role worth mentioning, and "evidently" what was true for Saxony must hold true for the earth as a whole. Werner's teachings were referred to as "neptunism," since water was the important agent. In order to give the other side a name, Hutton's school was dubbed "vulcanism" and some of Werner's adherents made it appear to those who had not read Hutton's book as if Hutton had said that the earth had been formed by volcanic action only.

The almost unnecessary debate between "vulcanists" and "neptunists" was ended by still another Scotsman, Sir Charles Lyell (1797–1875), with his *Principles of Geology,* which appeared in three volumes during the years 1830–1833. Lyell agreed with Hutton, but he was not writing so much *for* Hutton as *against* Bonnet and Cuvier, the "catastrophists." He pointed out that there was no need for catastrophes of any kind. The surface of the earth had been shaped by the action of the same forces that we see in action now: wind, rivers, tides, storm and rain. Since he stressed that catastrophes had been absent and the action of natural forces had always been uniform, Lyell's teachings became known as "uniformitarianism" in England; in continental Europe they were called "actual-

Sir Charles Lyell.

ism" because the same forces were acting now as had acted in the past.

Lyell himself realized that such slow uniform shaping of the earth's surface features was very favorable to Lamarck's ideas of gradual evolution but he would have none of that. His work contains four long chapters contradicting Lamarck at every point. It is one of the ironical twists in history that the first volume of *Principles of Geology* had just appeared when H.M.S. *Beagle* was ready to start on a trip around the world, with young Charles Darwin aboard as the expedition's naturalist. Darwin took Lyell's book with him, and his *Origin of Species,* 28 years later, converted Lyell to the evolutionary point of view.

Before *Vestiges,* no matter who wrote about geology—Hutton, Werner, Cuvier, or Lyell—the implication always existed that the earth had to be older than had been computed by Archbishop James Ussher who had dated creation 4004 B.C. On the continent that was not an important question. If an Anglican theologian had confronted a Lutheran theologian with this date the Lutheran would have replied that it was not in the Bible but just derived from it by fallible Man and that furthermore the same calculation had been made about a century before Ussher by the Rabbi Shemayah Hillel. And in the unlikely event that a Lutheran pastor had accused a "natural philosopher" of impiety, that philosopher would have shrugged his shoulders (if that) and gone right on with his particular philosophical system.

In England and Scotland at the time the situation was different. There a literal belief in Genesis was still solidly entrenched, and a prudent man avoided the accusation of impiety. But by a curious coincidence many of the English and Scottish amateur geologists of the time were clergymen, so it is only natural that they tried for a "reconciliation." As a result a whole specialized literature came into being. One of these books, by George Bugg, was an especially poor example of the genre but it had an especially good title—*Scriptural Geology*—and the whole class of these books is now designated by that name. There were various ways out of the dilemma. One was to say that Moses, though divinely inspired, had to use the language of an early semibarbarous culture to be understood and therefore used the word "day" where he should have said "era." This—shades of Buffon—converted the six days of creation into six eras of any desired length.

Another theologian asked himself just how Moses had been inspired and concluded that Moses had had six visions in six consecutive nights and assumed the duration of his visions to be equal to the duration of the actual events. Anybody who did not want to go along with this had still another compromise at his disposal—namely "the interval." The first verse of the first chapter of Genesis is, "In the beginning God created the heaven and the earth," the second verse states that "the earth was without form and void," while the third contains the statement that light was created. Nothing was said about the time that had gone by from "the beginning" to the creation of light—this was "the interval" which, again, could be made as long as desired. Many a theologian must have secretly wished that Archbishop Ussher had been too busy to sit down and add up the generations of the Old Testament.

It was against this background that Robert Chambers, specialist in Scottish history and folklore, began to write his *Vestiges*. His book began on an astronomical note, partly for general background, partly in order to show that Nature is governed by law. Following, as was then customary, the so-called Kant-Laplace hypothesis, Chambers explained how nebulae had condensed into suns and suns had thrown off planets. Bodies had been formed in space in the past and they were still being formed. In the next chapter he pointed out that Nature anywhere must consist of the same chemical elements and that the multitudes of worlds must be of about the same chemical composition. While asserting that there must be many inhabited worlds, he was especially interested in the question of whether our moon was inhabited. He denied it, but said that it would only need water and an atmosphere to blossom forth as an inhabited body. Then he went into geological evidence. The fossils indicated a progression: "There was a time when the cephalopoda were the highest forms of life . . . fishes next took the lead, then reptiles. Mammals were added next, until Nature became what she is now, by the addition of Man."

Chambers then proceeded to explain that life could originate from inorganic substances that are subjected to the action of electricity. He thought that he could cite recent experiments as a proof for this assertion. A well-to-do amateur experimenter, Andrew Crosse, claimed that tiny creatures, *acari* (mites), had been produced in a poisonous solution after a weak electric current had acted on this solution for weeks.[4]

Citing Crosse's *acari* was one unfortunate slip by Chambers; another was discarding Cuvier's system of classification in favor of the weird "five-sided" system of Chambers' contemporary, W. S. Mcleay. And finally, for the purpose of proving that Man is a member of the animal kingdom, Chambers very nearly advocated phrenology, though his actual point was that even Man's mind needs a material organ, namely the brain. Chambers concluded his book with a sentence conveying his overall attitude: "The inorganic has one final comprehensive law, *gravitation*. The organic, the other great department of mundane things, rests in like manner on one law, and that is—*development*. Nor may even these be after all twain, but only branches of one still more comprehensive law, the expression of that unity which man's wit can scarcely separate from Deity itself."

Chambers probably expected to be attacked, hence the anonymity which was not officially dropped until after his death. He probably also expected some philosophical debates in restricted circles. But neither he nor his publisher (who was also kept unaware of the author's identity) expected that his book would be the big publishing success that it turned out to be. Among its readers were Ralph Waldo Emerson (who was converted to evolutionary thought by it), Benjamin Disraeli (who made fun, not of the book, but of its readers), Sir John Herschel (who was not convinced), and Abraham Lincoln (whose opinion about it we don't know), Alfred, Lord Tennyson (who slowly became convinced), Thomas Henry Huxley (who had a very low opinion of the book), Alfred Russel Wallace (who had a better opinion of it and later wrote that it had always been undervalued), and Arthur Schopenhauer. The attitude of the lay public was best expressed by the actress and writer Fanny Kemble, who wrote: "Its conclusions are utterly revolting to me—nevertheless they may be true."

Of course the journals asked the well-known scientists of the time for opinions—that is, for reviews. The scientists obliged and the reaction of most of them was fairly uniform. They concentrated on mistakes and slips, mostly minor in nature but numerous in quantity, and then said that they could not follow a reasoning based on faulty and insufficient information. It is quite likely that the anonymity of the book annoyed them. After all, *they* were expected to sign their names to their reviews. A zoologist, for example, might have been more lenient with zoological slips if he could have said, "The author, being a physician (or whatever) cannot be expected to know that, etc., etc."

One of the German translations of the work was by a man then very well known, the zoologist Karl Vogt, who had taken an active part in politics and, since his side had lost, had been forced to live in exile in

Switzerland—not precisely a sad fate. Naturally Karl Vogt's introduction has political overtones:

> To the Constitutional Party of Germany, whose influence should soon be limited to the innocent reading of innocent books, I recommend this book in all good will. It will find here a constitutional Englishman * who constructed a constitutional God, who at first made laws as an autocrat but then of His own accord gave up autocracy and, without direct influence on the governed, allowed law to rule in His stead. A splendid example for princes!

Arthur Schopenhauer's main works had been written by the time *Vestiges* appeared. Though a German translation of *Vestiges* was then available, Schopenhauer obtained a copy of the English original. It probably was his experience that translators can be trusted much of the time, but not all of the time.

Schopenhauer, though he had criticized Lamarck severely, had always been inclined toward evolution, saying that the common anatomical features of many animals can be explained by assuming that "the original forms of the various animals have arisen one out of another." After having read *Vestiges* Schopenhauer considerably sharpened both his opinions and his arguments, which are expressed in the essay *Zur Philosophie und Wissenschaft der Natur* (On Philosophy and Knowledge of Nature).

Life must have originated by *generatio aequivoca* (Schopenhauer's term for what others called "spontaneous generation") but this "cannot be conceived to occur in the higher grades of the animal kingdom as it does in the lowest. The form of the lion, the wolf, the elephant, the ape, or that of man, cannot have originated as do the infusoria. . . ." For the higher forms of life, Schopenhauer continued, one has to assume a *generatio in utero heterogeneo,* a "generation in the uterus of another species"; what is now called a mutation. He explained what he had in mind immediately: "from the womb, or rather from the egg, of some especially favored pair of animals . . . there arose, exceptionally, a being no longer of the same kind as its parents." Furthermore:

> The batrachians visibly go through an existence as fishes before they assume their characteristic final form, and, according to a now fairly generally accepted observation, all embryos pass successively through

---

* Another drawback of anonymity—the very Scottish Mr. Chambers was everywhere criticized or praised as an Englishman.

the forms of lower species before attaining to that of their own. Why, then, should not every new and higher species have originated through the development of some embryo into a form just one degree higher than the form of the mother that conceived it? This is the only reasonable, i.e. the only rationally thinkable, mode of origination of species that can be imagined.

Having stated his beliefs, Schopenhauer stated that he had been started on this trend of thought by another book.

The conception of a *generatio in utero heterogeneo* which has here been expounded was first put forward by the anonymous author of the *Vestiges of the Natural History of Creation* (6th ed., 1847), though by no means with adequate clearness and definitiveness. For he has entangled it with untenable assumptions and gross errors, which are due in the last analysis to the fact that to him, as an Englishman, every assumption which rises above the merely physical—everything metaphysical, in short—is forthwith confused with the Hebraic theism.

Robert Chambers, who could read French but not German, never saw this appraisal of his work, for it was not translated into English during his lifetime. If he had, somebody would have had to explain to him that Schopenhauer's judgment was one that Schopenhauer himself would have considered lenient, since Chambers was given full credit for having had the idea first, while his faults were explained as being due to environment and upbringing.

Today's reader, who has grown up with evolutionary concepts both as environment and background, is apt to wonder why there was, on the one hand, such a frantic scramble for theories during the nineteenth century and, on the other hand, such frantic resistance to them. Nobody can fully grasp the motives of the anti-evolutionist any more because they involve a willful disregard of logic. The English parson who insisted that items that were difficult to explain could be "explained" by way of a miracle would have been horrified if a defense lawyer had told the court that the murder weapon had not been purchased or stolen by the defendant but had appeared on the scene miraculously at just the proper moment.

The reason for the search for a theory is found much more easily in the desire for law and order, as stated by Chambers in the last sentence of his book. Long before Chambers, the naturalist Gottfried Reinhold

Treviranus (1776–1837), who introduced the term biology * as the name of the study of living things, both animals and plants, voiced the desire for law and order eloquently:

> An author can have no sadder and more spirit-killing duty than the reading and writing of compilations. The teachings of Natural Science have long been standing isolated like the pyramids in the deserts of Egypt, as if the value of Natural History were not rather the application than the mere possession of facts. What have Botany and Zoology been hitherto but a dry register of names, and what man who has not lost his sense for higher work can find time for these gymnastics of memory? But once regard systematic work as a part of Biology, and nomenclature as a means rather than as an end, and both take their place in science, contributing to the whole in which the intellect of man perceives the unity and harmony of Natural Law.

Needless to say, Treviranus tried to find such a unity but the time was not ripe; another half century had to pass before Darwin could actually do it.

Charles Darwin was born in Shrewsbury, Shropshire, England, on February 12, 1809—the same day as Abraham Lincoln. His father was a physician. Neither of his famous grandfathers was still alive at the time. His father's father, Erasmus Darwin, had died in 1802 and his mother's father, Josiah Wedgwood the porcelain maker, in 1795. Since Charles was the son and the grandson of physicians, it was taken for granted that he would become a physician, too. But medicine did not interest him and when he tried the other pillar of respectability of his time, the Church of England, that did not interest him either. What did interest him was something that others, most especially his father, considered quite useless— namely natural history. However, even then there were a few jobs for naturalists and one of them was on board H.M.S. *Beagle,* which was to make a voyage of exploration around the world.

The itinerary of the *Beagle* was stated in advance by George Peacock, a tutor at Cambridge (later professor of astronomy), to Professor Henslow in the opening sentence: "Captain Fitz-Roy is going out to survey the southern coast of Tierra del Fuego, and afterwards to visit many of the South Sea Islands, and to return by the Indian Archipelago." Pea-

---

* He did so in 1802; Lamarck advocated the use of the same term, with the same meaning, in the same year!

cock went on to say that the vessel had been fitted out specifically for scientific purposes (the emphasis was on geographical survey and the establishment of latitudes and longitudes of many points) and that a naturalist was wanted. He had hoped that one Leonard Jenyns would make the trip, but since Jenyns did not wish to be absent for several years running somebody else had to be found. Henslow recommended young Charles Darwin (who had just turned 22). Darwin was willing, but his father was not and had to be persuaded by a member of the Wedgwood family that the experience would be useful for Charles, whom he described as "a man of enlarged curiosity," probably the best five-word description of any good scientist.

In 1831 the *Beagle* weighed anchor, with Charles Darwin aboard. The voyage laid the foundation of Darwin's later fame; unfortunately it also was the cause of his lifelong ill health.* Of course he was asked later what his opinions had been when he started the voyage, but since this was many years later his recollection was uncertain. "When I was aboard the *Beagle,*" he wrote, "I believed in the permanence of species, but, as far as I can remember, vague doubts occasionally flitted across my mind." Apparently these doubts were not as vague as he thought later, for the captain of the *Beagle* (who became the governor of New Zealand and finally an admiral) stated strongly and with indignation that during the voyage he had often remonstrated with Darwin for expressing doubts about Genesis.

H.M.S. *Beagle* left England on December 27, 1831 and returned on October 2, 1836. The track chart as drawn up by Captain Robert Fitz-Roy shows that the east coast of South America was the first goal, with stopovers at the Canary and Cape Verde islands. Then the course was southward for Tierra del Fuego, with a side trip to the Falkland Islands, then northward along the South American west coast. The Galápagos Islands came next. After that the *Beagle* traveled almost due west to the Society Islands and made for the North Island of New Zealand. From there it went to Sydney, then south again around Tasmania. The last stop in Australia was King George Sound, near the southwestern tip of the island continent. Keeling Island to the south of Sumatra was the next stop, then Mauritius to the east of Madagascar. Madagascar was by-

---

* Darwin suffered from vague but disturbing symptoms for decades and it was only in his old age that, paradoxically, his health improved. A modern guess is that he might have suffered from trypanosomiasis, which contemporary medicine did not recognize and could not have cured if it had.

passed; the next landfall was the Cape of Good Hope. From there the voyage went to Ascension Island and from there once more to South America (Bahia) and finally home.

Darwin later wrote in his autobiography that "the voyage of the *Beagle* has been by far the most important event in my life and has determined my whole career." Looking at the track chart one might wonder how it could have been otherwise.

Practically everything he saw was new to him. Tropical forest with bright-colored birds and roving animals. The ostrichlike birds of the Pampas. The abundance of large fossil bones (Darwin bought a fossil skull of the extinct mammal *Toxodon* for 18 pence). Living armadillos. Fossil mammals like armadillos but much larger in size. On Tierra del Fuego he was impressed, almost shaken, by the sight of "naked savages" in a freezing rain to which they paid absolutely no attention. Darwin filled notebook after notebook with his observations. He saw worms living in a brine of such concentration that it would have killed any other worm Darwin had ever seen. The *Toxodon* skull he had bought would not fit into any classification of living mammals. The guanaco impressed him as "an elegant animal." The Chilean Andes with their snow-capped peaks under a deep blue sky caused the entry: "It was like watching a thunderstorm or hearing in full orchestra a chorus of the *Messiah*." He endlessly watched the condors wheeling overhead, marveling at the fact that they kept soaring for hours, apparently without moving a muscle.

Not every entry in his notebooks was strictly scientific. One might say that Darwin's "enlarged curiosity" extended to people, with the señoritas of Lima as a case in point:

> Their close elastic gowns fit the figure closely and oblige the ladies to walk with small steps which they do very elegantly and display very white silk stockings and very pretty feet. They wear a black silk veil, which is fixed around the waist behind, and is brought over the head and held by the hands before the face, allowing only one eye to remain uncovered. Then that one eye is so black and so brilliant and has such powers of motion and expression that its effect is very powerful.

Darwin himself said that notebooks are more reliable than recollections and for this reason the question of when he first wondered about the "fixity of species" during his side trips in South America cannot be answered. The notebooks for that period are silent on this point and "reconstructions" of what Darwin "must" have thought at a given moment

Sir Charles Darwin

may be entertaining but do not prove anything. After all the fixity of species was not an overwhelming dogma in Darwin's mind, he accepted it because that is what he had been taught. Moreover every day brought so many new impressions that it is unlikely that young Darwin had much time for concentrated thought. And there are even many early entries reading "felt feverish and sick," which is also not conducive to careful logical reasoning.

The next major stop in the voyage of the *Beagle* was a different story. This was the stopover in the Galápagos archipelago. This archipelago, about six hundred miles due west from the South American west coast under the equator, consists of half a dozen islands with ten times as many tiny islets, all of them volcanic in origin, as Darwin saw immediately. They had been given their name by Spanish speakers because of the gigantic tortoises that were abundant. Darwin noticed the tortoises of course and also the large black iguanas that swim out to sea. But he was most interested in the finchlike birds of the islands, now known as "Darwin's finches." There were at least fourteen species of them, none of them identical with mainland finches. One could say that the Lord had created fourteen species of finches just for the purpose of inhabiting this group of volcanic islands; one could not think about it at all; or one could remember the fact, which is what Darwin did. A full explanation, if there was one, would have to wait until later.

The trip went on across the Pacific Ocean. Darwin saw coral atolls and formulated a theory of the growth of coral reefs by a gradual build-up caused by the settling of living corals on the leftover accretions of former generations of now-dead corals.* It was the opposite of what Charles Lyell had said, but Lyell accepted Darwin's explanation as the superior one and the two became close friends.

About two years after his return to England, on January 29, 1839, Darwin married his cousin Emma Wedgwood. After 1836 Darwin did not travel any more; he was busy with what might be called laboratory work—but he did it at home—and with writing. His first publication was volume III of Captain FitzRoy's *Narrative of the Voyages,* which appeared in 1839. In 1845 Darwin's contribution to FitzRoy's work was reissued as a separate publication, and beginning with the third edition

* Later, when the thought of evolution had been formulated in his own mind, Darwin jotted down a sentence that should not be forgotten: "The tree of life should perhaps be called the coral of life—base of branches dead."

(1860) it bore the title under which it is now known: *A Naturalist's Voyage*.

The *Voyage* was followed by *Geological Observations* in three parts. Part I (1842) was *Coral Reefs,* Part II (1844) *Volcanic Islands,* Part III (1846) *Geological Observations on South America.* After the proofs of Part III had been returned to the printer, Darwin embarked on a specialized job, an investigation of the living and extinct *Cirripedia,* known to the layman as barnacles. The work took from 1846 to 1854 and resulted in two large books on living cirripeds and two smaller books on the extinct ones. Darwin realized that eight years spent on mere barnacles would strike an outsider as somewhat comical and wrote, "I do not doubt that Sir E. Lytton Bulwer had me in his mind when he introduced in one of his novels a Professor Long, who had written two huge volumes on limpets."

Darwin had a reason for sticking doggedly with barnacles for eight years. In 1842 he had made a pencil outline of his theory of evolution.* Two years later, in 1844, he had written a fairly complete sketch of his theory of natural selection, but had not published it. He not only wanted to collect much more material, which he did, but to clear up one thought in his mind. Since the conclusion of his reasoning had been that species are not constant but can change, he had to state just what the term "species" really meant. In retrospect the answer is simple: it means the form in which an animal or a plant appears at a given moment in geological time. But Darwin did not yet have such an answer. The concentration on ultrafine points in the classification of cirripeds no doubt helped.

In Darwin's opinion there were three qualifications that a naturalist has to have. These are patience, accuracy and devotion to his work. Work on cirripeds is an outstanding example; as to the third, his whole life is the example. As to the second, his advice to field collectors is worth reading:

> Let the collector's motto be, "Trust nothing to the memory," for the memory becomes a fickle guardian when one interesting object is succeeded by another one still more interesting. . . . Put a number on every specimen, and every fragment of a specimen; and during the very same minute let it be entered in the catalogue, so that if hereafter its locality

* For a long time it was thought that he had destroyed this first sketch after his main work on evolution had appeared, but it was found again in 1896.

be doubted, the collector may say in good truth, "Every specimen of mine was ticketed on the spot." Anything which is folded up in paper, or put into a separate box, ought to have a number on the outside (with the exception perhaps of geological specimens) but more *especially* a duplicate number on the inside attached to the specimen itself. A series of small numbers should be printed from 0 to 5,000; a stop must be added to those numbers that can be read upside down (as 699. or 86.). It is likewise convenient to have the different thousands printed on differently coloured paper, so that when unpacking, a single glance tells the approximate number.

From 1842, when he had put the first sketch of his concept of natural selection and evolution on paper, Darwin thought constantly about the book he was going to write. And although a rather complete outline existed in 1844, he let another one and a half decades go by until he published. He wanted to be absolutely certain himself. But that was not the only reason. Darwin's autobiography contains the key sentence: "I have steadily endeavoured to keep my mind free so as to give up any hypothesis, however much beloved (and I cannot resist forming one on every subject), as soon as facts are shown to be opposed to it."

Naturally he expected that others would have the same or at least a similar attitude. Hence, if only he amassed enough facts, his work would be convincing to others. He even harbored the idea that all resistance would be overcome and all controversy avoided if he did a good enough job in his presentation. When he finally published, he had facts enough— "where Lamarck had one or two facts, Darwin had a hundred," one historian of science wrote a century later—but resistance was overcome only slowly and controversy raged for decades to come. Darwin tended to think that this was largely because circumstances had "hurried" him into publishing before the work was really ready.

These circumstances took the shape of a manuscript by a younger British naturalist, Alfred Russel Wallace (1823–1913), whom Darwin knew personally. Wallace had traveled extensively in what were then called the Sunda Islands (now Indonesia). He had seen that the fauna on the islands to the west of the Strait of Macassar that separates Borneo from Celebes and the Strait of Lombok that separates Bali from Lombok was entirely different from the fauna to the east of these two straits. Some years later Wallace was to write a book *Island Life,* which is still worth reading.

In 1857 he had drawn the same conclusions as Darwin. The different animals of this multitude of large and small islands could not all be "special creations"; it was far more likely that species could change in the course of time. Competition among themselves and natural enemies would kill off the weaker individuals, so that this struggle actually "improved the race," as Wallace put it. Moreover those who survived did so because they were somehow different; in any group of animals you can find individuals that are faster, or stronger, or brighter. Wallace, who knew that Darwin was working on a book dealing with variation and species, wondered whether his thoughts were "worth considering" and sent his manuscript to his older friend for review and criticism.

Of course Darwin was surprised and no doubt dismayed to see his own thoughts in somebody else's handwriting—in many places even the sentences read alike. Sections of Wallace's treatise and portions of Darwin's work, when printed side by side, look like two drafts of the same manuscript. Darwin passed Wallace's work on to Charles Lyell and to Joseph Dalton Hooker and these two men discussed what should be done. Darwin was passive because he was grief-stricken over the very recent death of one of his children. Lyell and Hooker agreed that Wallace's treatise should be published as soon as possible but both also felt that something by Darwin should be published along with it since they knew from direct contact that Darwin could have published years earlier. Darwin agreed to let them publish the major part of his outline of 1844 even though it was, as he said, "written without care"—without intending it for publication. Lyell and Hooker also asked for a copy of a long letter that Darwin had previously written to the botanist Asa Gray in New England.

On July 1, 1858, the paper by Wallace, parts of Darwin's outline, and most of Darwin's letter to Gray were read at a meeting of the Linnaean Society of London. They caused astonishment but no immediate opposition, because both Lyell and Hooker had spoken briefly before the presentation, stressing the importance of what the members were about to hear and giving their tacit approval to the ideas to be presented. Thus, Darwin's first publication on evolution is not his book, but the issue of the journal of the Linnaean Society in which his paper was published.

The Origin of Species was finished ("in haste," in Darwin's opinion) in 1859, the corrected proofs went back to the printer in July of the same year, and the book was released for sale on November 24, 1859. All 1250 copies were sold on the first day. A second edition followed in 1860, a third in 1861, a fourth in 1866, a fifth in 1869, and a sixth in 1872—one year after the publication of Darwin's *The Descent of Man* which in spirit (*and* in Darwin's opinion) was the "second volume" of the original work.

The full title of that work was *The Origin of Species by Means of Natural Selection or the Preservation of Favoured Races in the Struggle for Life*. Thomas H. Huxley, after reading it, made a comment that has often been echoed since by other scientists when they read an outstanding work by a colleague. It was "How extremely stupid not to have thought of that."

The first chapter bore the innocent title: "Variation under Domestication." Darwin began with facts known to practically everybody— namely, that domesticated animals and plants show many varieties and that breeders take advantage of these varieties. This has been going on for so long that "we hardly know anything about the origin and history of domestic breeds." Then followed the second chapter, dealing with "Variation under Nature," leading up to chapter III, "Struggle for Existence," in which it is pointed out that competition in nature is so keen that even a slight advantage may be decisive. This, of course, leads straight into chapter IV, "Natural Selection and the Survival of the Fittest." Darwin has his main points together: variations occur all the time, a variation may be an advantage in the struggle for existence, and the fittest survive—at least in the sense that they are more likely than the less fit to produce offspring—and the "natural selection" that favors those better equipped also favors the ones that are somewhat different from their forbears, *if* the variation was useful. Being a careful man he did not claim that there were no other possibilities: "I am convinced that Natural Selection has been the main but not exclusive means of modification."

Chapter X has a title that is somewhat surprising to a modern reader. It is called "Imperfection of the Geological Records." One has to stop and remember that Darwin's book was written more than a hundred years ago, and that just those hundred years have brought all the geological, or rather paleontological, discoveries that are now cited as one of the proofs of the theory of evolution. On another point Darwin (no doubt with pleasure) had to change his mind between the first edition of his book and the final one of 1872. This point was one widely publicized by his German disciple Ernst von Haeckel, who condensed it into the three words: "ontogeny recapitulates phylogeny," meaning that the development of the individual from the fertilized ovum to birth (or hatching) goes quickly through the stages its species had gone through in the course of geological history. The recapitulation theory was not Haeckel's contribution, though he greatly enlarged on it, but had been mentioned by others before him. Darwin knew it mainly through the writings of Jean Louis Rodolphe Agassiz (1807–1873), a Swiss naturalist who went to the United States in 1846 for a series of lectures and stayed on until he died.

In the first edition of the *Origin of Species* Darwin wrote:

> Agassiz insists that ancient animals resemble to a certain extent the embryos of recent animals of the same class; or that the geological succession of extinct forms is in some degree parallel to the embryological development of recent forms. I must follow Pictet and Huxley in thinking that the truth of this doctrine is very far from proved. Yet I fully expect to see it hereafter confirmed . . . for this doctrine accords well with the theory of natural selection.

In the 1872 edition he could change this to read:

> Agassiz and several other highly competent judges insist that ancient animals resemble to a certain extent the embryos of recent animals belonging to the same classes; and that the geological succession of extinct forms is nearly parallel with the embryological development of existing forms. This view accords admirably well with our theory.

In the last chapter Darwin made his point admirably clear with a few sentences:

> Hereafter we shall be compelled to acknowledge that the only distinction between species and well-marked varieties is, that the latter are known, or believed, to be connected at the present day by intermediate gradations, whereas species were formerly thus connected. . . . In short we shall have to treat species in the same manner as those naturalists treat genera, who admit that genera are merely artificial combinations made for convenience. This may not be a cheering prospect; but we shall at least be free from the vain search for the undiscovered and undiscoverable essence of the term species.

By now the statement that species are not constant seems a minor matter but just this "minor matter" changed the description of living things to their explanation. The world of living animals is wonderfully diversified, the world of extinct animals fearfully so. If species could not change, a catalogue of animals of only one type for one locality—say the birds of Africa—would have all the charm of a telephone directory. But in the century that has gone by since the first publication of Darwin's most famous work, ten thousand items supporting the thought of the mutability of species have been found, and not a single one that contradicts the idea. And the knowledge of the multiple interconnections between species past and present has the result of changing the telephone directory into a list of people one knows. We now understand living nature much better—especially since we are a part of the whole.

Père David's deer or milu, drawn from life in 1900 by an unnamed Chinese artist.

Epilogue

W HEN the Baron de Cuvier was at the height of his career he made the remark that paleontology was all the more rewarding because the discovery of still unknown living animals had become highly unlikely. When Cuvier said that—in 1825 or 1826—the interiors of most of the continents had hardly been explored. Yet, by one of those coincidences which frequents the history of science, Cuvier's statement held true for a long time.

The first discovery of a "new" animal—at first glance not a very important one—was made by the British naturalist Hardwicke around the year 1850. The date is uncertain because Hardwicke was sloppy when it came to publishing his explorations and discoveries. The place of the discovery was in the mountains to the north of India. The British hunters who went after the animal called it either the Himalaya fox, because of its coloration, or the Himalaya raccoon, because of its face and its ringed tail. It is the animal now known as the Lesser Panda, with the scientific name of *Ailurus fulgens* (composed of the Greek word for "cat" and the Latin word for "shining" or "glossy"). Actually it is a relative of the North American raccoon.

Nobody then could have known that Hardwicke's minor discovery was to herald three major discoveries, all in inner Asia and all made by the same man—the French missionary Père Jean Pierre Armand David. Of course all three animals were known to the Chinese, but the Chinese of the mid-nineteenth century were not in the habit of writing zoological treatises.

Père David made his first discovery on forbidden territory—the Imperial Hunting Park outside of Peking, a park larger than the city itself. The park's Chinese name was Nan Hai-tzu and it had been walled in about the year 1400. Nobody was permitted to enter it, and especially no foreigners. But it was common knowledge that many game animals were kept in the park, even though the Emperor did not hunt any more, and that they were guarded by Tartar soldiers. Having learned that it was impossible to obtain a permit to enter the park, Père David, one day early in 1865, climbed the wall to look. There were the game animals he had expected to see, but he also saw numerous specimens of a large stag-like animal that had never been described by any naturalist.

The Chinese had a name for the animal. It was *sse-pu-hsiang,* which translates as "four dissimilarities," because the animal does *not* look like a goat, does *not* look like a donkey, does *not* look like a cow, and does *not* look like a stag. Presumably the name also implies that it does look a little bit like all four of these animals. Fortunately Père David learned that it was also called milu. The meaning of that name, if any, is not known, but it was certainly easier. The Chinese also said that the animal could be found only in the Imperial Hunting Park, a statement that was disbelieved at first but later proved to be correct.

Père David decided that science must learn about this animal via the Academy of Sciences in Paris. The guards were probably bribed through intermediaries; in any event Père David obtained two complete skins in January 1866. Apparently the Emperor himself did not feel as strongly about the animals in the park as did lesser dignitaries who obeyed old orders, for soon afterward the French Legation obtained permission to send three of the animals to Paris. They did not survive the trip, but the French naturalist Alphonse Milne-Edward was able to write a detailed description of the animal which was published in 1866 in the *Comptes rendus* of the Academy.

It is customary for the discoverer to propose the scientific name, but Père David, in his correspondence, had not done so. Instead he had used both Chinese names. Hence it was up to Milne-Edward to coin the scientific name. He chose *Elaphurus davidianus,* and the English appellation became "Père David's deer."

Of course everyone believed that there must be wild milus and this belief was strengthened, at first, by what seems to have been a simple mistake. Chinese hunters in the northern provinces were requested to capture *see-pu-hsiang* and they did. Or at least they thought they did. Not knowing the true *see-pu-hsiang* they fitted the name to another animal that qualified and brought in captured reindeer.

Originally the milu must have been wild, of course, and, as finds of bones at a much later date proved, it inhabited the swamps of the former province of Chihli. In time these swamps were drained and the milu was eradicated in the process. But it still existed when the Imperial Hunting Park was established and it survived there simply because the park, in spite of its name, was almost never used for hunting. The end of the Chinese milus came in 1895 when the Hun Ho river flooded, making thousands of peasants homeless and undermining the ancient wall of the park. Most of the park animals were eaten by the starving people, but some survived until 1900 when the park was thrown open. In 1901 only one milu, a female, was still alive—in China, that is. Before 1895 a number of specimens had been exported to various zoological gardens in Europe and the Duke of Bedford had bought a number of them and established them on his estate of Woburn Abbey.

Today the only existing herd of milus, over a hundred strong, lives at Woburn Abbey and many specimens from that herd have been distributed to various zoological gardens.

Père David, after shipping his two milu skins to Paris, had gone on to make more discoveries. One was a monkey in Szechwan province, which had been depicted on Chinese vases, but had not been believed to exist. The monkey was shown with gray fur on top, pure white farther down. Belly, chest, and the area around the face were depicted with a pattern of yellow and rusty red while the hairless face was a vivid blue-green. This fantastic monkey was depicted against a background of snowy mountains, "proving" that the whole was the invention of Chinese artists.

Père David found that the pictures on the vases were entirely correct, even to the snowy mountains. This time Père David coined the scientific name, *Rhinopithecus roxellanae;* in common parlance the Roxellana monkey, though German zoology books also use "snow monkey" as a common name.

Being in Szechwan, Père David took care to inquire about another animal that the Chinese talked about. The Chinese name was *bei-shun* or *peiss-yun,* both meaning "white bear," but Père David had learned that this bear was actually black and white. On March 11, 1869, he went, on invitation, to have tea with a local landowner named Li, and in Li's house he saw a black and white pelt. The animal was not a bear, however; it was what we now call the Giant Panda.* Its scientific name is *Ailuropoda melanoleucus*. The first part of the name really means "cat-footed" but is meant to indicate the relationship to *Ailurus,* the Lesser Panda. The specific name is composed of the Greek words for black and white.

The next discovery of a large, living, and up to then unknown, animal came about ten years later. The discoverer was a Russian cavalry officer of Polish descent, Nikolai Mikhailovitch Przevalski, and the animal was the Asiatic wild horse; its scientific name is *Equus przevalskii*. Specimens are kept in many zoological gardens and it breeds well in captivity. Quite recently (1966) it was found to be able to crossbreed with the domesticated horse.

But the discovery that really caused a stir in the scientific world was made in Africa in 1900. This was the short-necked giraffe okapi. Officially its discoverer was Sir Harry Johnston, but Johnston said that Sir Henry Stanley should receive the credit. Stanley, a year or two prior to 1890 (the year in which his book *In Darkest Africa* was published) had learned about an unknown animal which the Wambutti pygmies called *atti*. From a discussion with Stanley which took place after the animal had been scientifically described, Johnston concluded that Stanley had actually seen okapis without realizing that they were new to science.

The circumstance that is considered the actual discovery was Johnston's obtaining two strips of okapi skin from Belgian officials in the Congo. The Belgians told him that the animal was called "okhapi" by the natives, that it had a "drawn-out" muzzle, and that one had been killed recently. The skin was around and if Sir Harry wanted it, he could have it. But meanwhile native soldiers had cut up the skin for belts and bandoliers, and only two strips with zebralike markings could be found. These were sent to London. Johnston thought that the animal was an unknown species of zebra and Professor E. Ray Lankaster of the British Museum agreed tentatively, naming the animal *Equus (?) johnstoni*. The doubt expressed by the question mark was due mainly to the repeated mention of forests in descriptions of the animal; zebras avoid forests and prefer the open plain. In June 1901 Professor Lankaster could be pleased about his doubts. A complete skin and two skulls ar-

---

* The name panda is said to be a contraction of the native name *niyalya ponga,* which is supposed to mean "bamboo eater." I don't know whether the translation is correct, but the pandas are bamboo eaters.

rived in London, showing that the animal was not a zebra. The name then became *Okapia johnstoni*.

In the wake of the discovery of the okapi, European naturalists and animal dealers received a fairly steady stream of reports of other still unknown animals in Central Africa. Some of these reports sounded like fantasy, others were indubitably plain mistakes, but one was persistent. It referred to a wild hog of unusual size, and while the descriptions did not always tally they all agreed on the color: black. There also was one piece of evidence for this hog—a skull from the "Pepper Coast" that had been described by the American physician Dr. Samuel G. Morton in 1844 and had been given the name *Choeropsis*. The reports from Africa had also mentioned a native name for the wild hog; it was *nigbve*. Was the *nigbve* the same as Morton's *Choeropsis?*

The question seemed to be settled in 1904 when a Captain Meinertzhagen of The King's East African Rifles obtained a perfect skull of a black hog from a native and a somewhat damaged skin of another specimen from another native. The existence of an exceptionally large black hog was now an established fact and the animal was named *Hylochoerus meinertzhageni*. There was only one discrepancy. Captain Meinertzhagen's black hog had been killed in the Ituri forest while the rumors of the *nigbve* came from the west coast of Africa, centering more or less on Liberia. Moreover, the two skulls were so different that a small child, if shown pictures, would have seen that they did not belong to the same animal.

Meinertzhagen's discovery had been, so to speak, a side issue. Dr. Morton's *Choeropsis* was something else, possibly identical with the *nigbve* of the African natives but possibly extinct. Carl Hagenbeck, the animal dealer who ran his own zoological garden near Hamburg, heard more and more stories that made him believe that either *Choeropsis* or *nigbve* (if they were not the same animal) was not extinct and he finally decided to send Hans Schomburgk on a one-man expedition to Liberia. The local people in Monrovia, black and white alike, considered this a useless quest. But Schomburgk did not give up easily and on June 13, 1911 he saw a *nigbve* in the open. The onset of the rainy season prevented further exploration during that year, but in February 1913 Schomburgk was back on the scene. He shot a *nigbve* one day and captured another one alive the next day. The case was clear. *Choeropsis* and *nigbve* were the same and obviously the animal was not extinct. But it was not a hog either, but a fairly distant relative of the hippopotamus; it is now popularly known as the "pygmy hippo."

There were more rumors about unknown African animals but the next one that was discovered had not been rumored, mainly because it is taken for granted in its native habitat, the Congo forest.

In 1915 Dr. James P. Chapin of the American Museum of Natural History in New York had returned from Africa from an expedition mainly devoted to the okapi. Among the things he brought back were native headdresses, ornamented with bird feathers. As time went on, Dr. Chapin was able to classify all the feathers except one, which was very large. In size, shape, and coloration it did not fit any known African bird, but Chapin was understandably reluctant to announce the discovery of a new species of bird based on a single feather, with no information as to when and where it had been pulled out of a bird's carcass.

But in a Belgian museum in 1936 he found more evidence. There were two mounted birds labeled "young peacocks." They were not peacocks and, as was proved by the large spurs, they were not young. But what were they? The possibility that they might be hybrids of a peacock and some other bird was rejected by all the experts around the museum. Chapin then met people who had seen the bird in the Congo forest. He then was convinced that a relative of the Asian peacock lived in Africa and named it *Afropavo congensis,* the "African peacock from the Congo." In 1937 he went to the Congo to collect specimens. The natives needed only to be told that *itundu* were wanted; they knew the bird well because it is not especially rare.

The next discovery, scientifically more important than either okapi or Congo peacock, has some similarity with the Congo peacock story in the sense that the natives were not surprised—only the whites, and especially the white scientists. The discovery was a fish known to paleontologists and, because of the lack of fossils in the more recent geological layers, thought to have been extinct for at least 60 million years.

Its discovery was pure chance, but chance of a kind that caused confusion and a long search. In December 1938 a fishing vessel belonging to the firm of Irvin & Johnson of East London, South Africa, had come in with a large and unknown fish (that had been bright blue when alive) aboard. The manager of the company called Miss M. Courtenay-Latimer, curator of the local natural history museum, who had made friends with the trawler captains for the purpose of obtaining specimens. The fish, the manager said, was over 4½ feet long and weighed 127 pounds and the captain had never seen one like it before. Neither had Miss Latimer. Nor could she find it pictured in the reference books in her museum.

She wrote to Professor J. L. B. Smith of Rhodes University in Grahamstown, South Africa, who was the outstanding authority on the fishes of the Indian Ocean near the South African east coast, and enclosed a sketch. Smith did not believe his eyes. This sketch showed a coelacanth fish—a sheer impossibility, since that group of fishes had been extinct for sixty million years. Moreover, the fossil coelacanths were 5 inches or 8 inches long, not 4½ feet. By the time Professor Smith got to East London the fish had been mounted because it had begun to decompose in the heat of the southern hemisphere summer. But, he could see that it was a coelacanth and he named it *Latimeria chalumnae* (the Chalumna is a river near East London). Of course he wanted more specimens, preferably freshly caught specimens with all internal organs intact and in place.

The search lasted fourteen years—partly because the Second World War began the following year, but chiefly because of the incredible fact that the first specimen of *Latimeria* was a stray which had been caught far from its usual habitat. *Latimeria* normally lives around the Comores Islands to the north of Madagascar.

Other such stories could be added to the ones told here.

For example, the story of the discovery of another fish from the far past, *Neoceratodus,* a lungfish, in an Australian river in 1869. Or the story of the flightless bird *takahe,* rediscovered, after having been thought extinct, near Lake Te Anau on the South Island of New Zealand. Or the story of *Neopilina,* an invertebrate which is neither a snail nor a worm but apparently ancestral to both, and which was dredged, alive, from the ocean depth in 1952.

These stories all prove the same thing: zoology is not yet a static science and the days of discovery are not yet over.

Notes

Chapter I

[1] George Sarton, *A History of Science* (Cambridge, Mass.: Harvard University Press, 1952).

Chapter II

[1] Lyceum is one of the words for which the Latin form must be left alone; only a Greek scholar would know what I mean if I transliterated it as Lykeion. It received the name because it was situated next to the temple of Apollo Lykeios (Apollo the Wolf-God).

[2] Most of the writings of Aristotle from his teaching years in Assos, Pella, and Athens and from the Lyceum Period seem to have been preserved, but it is certain that the so-called *corpus* of Aristotelian writings contains sections by unknown pupils and even some definitely spurious material. True authorship will never be established and the *corpus* must be accepted as it stands. It was printed in the original Greek for the first time by Aldus Manutius in Venice in five folio volumes during the years 1495–1498. This is the *editio princeps*. A second edition of the Greek original appeared in Basel in 1531; the printing is not as fine as that of the Venetian work, but the text was prepared by two famous men, Erasmus of Rotterdam and Symon Grynaeus. The first edition of the collected works with Latin translation appeared in Lyons in 1590.

The most important modern editions are the one by Immanuel Bekker in five quarto volumes, with Latin translation, published by the Academy of Berlin 1831–1870 (the volumes appeared about eight years apart), and the English translation by W. D. Ross and associates. The latter appeared in eleven volumes (1908–1931) at Oxford. Since the chronological order of the works cannot be established—and, indeed, Aristotle may have worked on several books simultaneously—there is a kind of traditional arrangement that was made definite by Bekker and is also followed in the English edition. The arrangement is the following:

Vol. I. The Organon (overall title given to six books dealing with "pure" philosophy, categories, analysis, art of reasoning, etc.)

Vol. II.* Physics, On the Heavens; On Procreation and Corruption

Vol. III.* Meteorology; On the World; On the Soul; *Parva naturalia* (collective title of nine essays, including On the Senses, On Memory, On Sleep, On Breath, On Life and Death, etc.)

Vol. IV. Natural History of Animals

Vol. V. On the Parts, Motion, and Progression of Animals

Vol. VI.* On Colors; On Things Heard; Physiognomics; On Plants; On Marvellous Things Heard; Mechanica; On Indivisible Lines; The Situations and Names of the Winds; On Melissus, Xenophanes, and Gorgias.

Vol. VII. On Problems

Vol. VIII.* Metaphysics

Vol. IX.* The Nikomachean Ethics, Magna Moralia; the Eudemian Ethics

Vol. X.* Politics; Economics; On the Athenian Constitutions

Vol. XI.* On Rhetorics; Poetics

The volumes marked by an asterisk (*) are available in the Loeb Classical Library, original Greek on left-hand pages, English translation on right-hand pages. The arrangement in the Loeb Classical Library is not precisely the same as in the Oxford edition.

³ Table 3. The classes of the animals.

(Note: The following table is arranged for direct comparison with the classification by Aristotle. In current books the classification usually runs the other way, beginning with single-celled animals like the amoeba and ending with the mammals. For a more complete classification a handbook such as Professor Tracy I. Storer's *General Zoology* should be consulted.)

A. Vertebrates

I. *Mammalia*. Mammals, body usually covered with hair, lungs enclosed in pleurae, "warm-blooded," females with milk glands, normally four-limbed, though the number of limbs may be reduced in marine forms. The main subclasses are, in descending order: (1) the placentals (all higher mammals), (2) the marsupials or pouched mammals, like the kangaroo, (3) the egg-laying monotremes, of which platypus and echidna are the only two surviving forms.

II. *Aves*. Birds, body covered with feathers, "warm-blooded," four-chambered hearts (like mammals), paired lungs, egg-laying, fore-limbs changed into wings, in rare cases absent (New Zealand kiwi). Main subclasses are: (1) the ratite birds (like ostrich, emu, etc.), and (2) the carinates (all others).

III. *Reptilia*. Reptiles, body usually covered with scales, no skin glands, lungs, imperfectly four-chambered heart, normally egg-laying, body assumes temperature of the surroundings. Main subclasses are: (1) snakes, (2) lizards, (3) chelonians (turtles and tortoises), (4) armored reptiles (crocodiles and alligators), (5) the sphenodon or hatteria, a surviving form of primitive reptiles.

IV. *Amphibia*. Amphibians, body covered with soft skin with many skin glands, three-chambered heart, body assumes temperature of the surroundings, juvenile forms aquatic and breathing through gills, adult forms air-breathing through lungs, preferring moist surroundings if not actually aquatic. While aquatic reptiles are often marine, no marine amphibian, living or extinct, is known. Subdivided into tailless forms (frog) and tailed forms (salamander).

V. *Pisces*. Fishes, aquatic, breathing through gills, skin usually covered with scales, body assumes temperature of the surroundings. Subdivided into cartilaginous fishes (sharks, rays, etc.) and bony fishes (all others).

B. Invertebrates

   I. *Arthropoda*.
   (1) *Crustacea*. Lobsters, crabs, water fleas, barnacles, etc.
   (2) *Trilobita*. Trilobites, extinct.
   (3) *Insecta*. Insects, six-legged and with two or four wings.
   (4) *Arachnids*. Spiders, six pairs of appendages of which four pairs are walking legs, never winged. This class includes spiders, scorpions, mites, ticks, and the so-called horseshoe crab, a surviving ancient form.
   (5) *Centipedes*. One pair of antennae, body with 15 or more segments, each with one pair of walking legs, except the first and last.

(6) *Millipedes*. One pair of antennae, body with 20 to over 100 segments, each with *two* pairs of walking legs.

II. *Annelida*. Segmented worms, of which the common earthworm and the leech are examples.

III. *Mollusca*.

(1) *Amphineura*. Chitons.

(2) *Scaphopoda*. Tooth shells.

(3) *Gastropoda*. Univalve mollusks; the vineyard snail, the garden slug, and the limpet are typical gastropods.

(4) *Pelecypoda*. Bivalve mollusks, like oyster and clam.

(5) *Cephalopoda*. Octopus, squid, and relatives.

IV. *Echinodermata* (These are Cuvier's "radiates").

(1) *Crinoidea*. Crinoids, sea lilies, or feather stars; the most beautiful of them are unfortunately extinct.

(2) *Asteroidea*. Sea stars, 5 to 50 arms, roots of arms not sharply distinct from central disk.

(3) *Ophiuroidea*. Brittle stars; the very slender arms, usually five, sharply distinct from central disk.

(4) *Echinoidea*. Sea urchins.

(5) *Holothurioidea*. Sea cucumbers.

The very many distinct classes of smaller invertebrates do not need to be listed here; with the exception of sea anemones and jellyfishes, they were unknown to Aristotle. The majority of these are so small in size that they cannot be seen clearly without optical instruments.

Chapter III

[1] In the original: *Fortes fortuna juvat.*

[2] *Historia naturalis* was printed for the first time in Venice in 1469; this is the so-called *editio princeps* of Pliny's only extant work. The first English translation appeared in London in 1601. The quotations used in this chapter are from the annotated translation by John Bostok and H. T. Riley published in London in five volumes in 1855.

[3] The total number of names of Latin authors in *Historia naturalis* is 146; the names of non-Latin authors add up to a total of 327. Quite a number of the works mentioned are no longer extant, among them a book written in Greek by King Juba II of Numidia (who died in A.D. ca. 20), of which even Carus said that it is deplorable that we do not know the original.

[4] The opening sentence of chapter 16 in *Historia naturalis* is somewhat puzzling, because it states that "the north, too, produces herds of wild horses,

as Africa and Asia do of wild asses," and the problem is just what is meant by "the north." If it just means Europe north of the Alps, Pliny reported, second-hand of course, on a now extinct animal; if the term is also meant to embrace northern Asia, a still living animal might be meant.

The scientific facts are the following: at the end of the last glaciation the European area north of the Alps—present-day France and Germany and the smaller adjacent countries—was inhabited by at least two types of wild horses. One of them was discovered alive more than a century ago by the Russian Colonel Nikolai Mikhailovitch Przhevalski near Lob Nor in Asia, the place where the Chinese exploded their atomic bombs. Known as Przhevalski's horse, it is brown in color with a blackish tail and mane. The other wild horse, believed to have been gray in color, gradually became rare in northern Europe and, like Przhevalski's horse, seems to have migrated eastward, though it does not seem to have gone as far into Asia as the animal later found near Lob Nor. There is no way of telling just when, during historical times, these horses disappeared from northern Europe. That there were still herds of wild horses in Europe in Pliny's time is virtually certain, and it is too bad that Pliny's source did not mention the color.

[5] In book X of *Historia naturalis,* which is about the birds, Pliny began his chapter 70 with the words: "I look upon the birds as fabulous which are called 'pegasi' and are said to have a horse's head; as also the griffons, with long ears and a hooked beak."

[6] Pliny meant the Greek historian Ktesias, who was personal physician to the Persian King Artaxerxes II for a number of years and returned from Persia in 398 B.C. to write two books, one on Persia and one on India. The book on Persia survives only in a number of quotations; of the book on India we have a condensed abstract written by Photius, Patriarch of Constantinople, in about A.D. 900. The original is lost.

[7] The last of the zoological books of Pliny's *Historia naturalis* is book XI, on insects. It begins with a few general chapters in which Pliny defends ideas he has already mentioned earlier. Maybe the insects have no blood, but then they have something that takes the place of blood. Maybe insects have no lungs, but this does not mean that they don't breathe. The bee is the first insect to be discussed, because of its honey, but swarming bees are also quite often favorable omens. After the bee came wasps, hornets, and bumblebees, then the silkworm, after that the spiders, because they also spin. The spider is followed by the scorpion, by grasshoppers, beetles, and ants. These discussions take up the first 43 chapters. Chapters 44–119 are not about insects but are a discussion of the parts of bigger animals, limb by limb.

[8] The first printed edition, the *editio princeps,* of Aelianus' *De natura animalium* was prepared by Conrad Gesner of Zurich, who provided a parallel Latin translation. It appeared in Zurich in 1556. Almost two hundred years

later Abraham Gronovius revised Gesner's translation for the London edition which appeared in 1744. The first translation into a modern language, namely German, was that of C. F. W. Jacobs; it was published in Jena in 1832. An English translation by A. F. Scholfield of King's College, Cambridge, based on the critical edition of the original by Rudolf Hercher (published in Paris in 1858) became part of the Loeb Classical Library (1957). Entitled *Aelian on the Characteristics of Animals,* it is in three volumes, comprising the Greek text and Scholfield's translation.

[9] Scholars who undertook the task of tracing the sources utilized by Aelianus found to their surprise that he rarely used first-hand sources. That Aristotle was quoted via Aristophanes has already been mentioned. Aelianus' source for bird stories was one Athenaeus who, in turn, quoted the real bird expert of the time, Alexander the Myndian. His remarks on poisons and the like were based on Apollodorus, but via the poems of Nikander. The source for things Egyptian is not Herodotus, as one would expect, but one Apion, who during the first century A.D. was the head of the Alexandrian school.

[10] Book VII, section 2.

Chapter IV

[1] St. John Chrysostom was not born until A.D. 345 and there is much reason to believe that the book was already in existence at that time. For a variety of reasons the second century A.D. seems a likely time for its origin, though all the copies still in existence are of much more recent date.

The statement that the Greek Church Father Origenes (A.D. 185–245) mentioned the Physiologus is not necessarily correct. The piece of writing in question has been preserved only in Latin translation and the word physiologus in the Latin text might simply mean "naturalist" in the Aristotelian sense. Of course it *might* mean the book, but without the original Greek of Origenes that question cannot be decided. (And even the Greek original, if it were still extant, might permit both interpretations.)

[2] This version of the phoenix legend appears for the first time in the Physiologus. Herodotus, the first man to write about the phoenix, only said that every five hundred years a phoenix comes from Arabia to Heliopolis, carrying the body of its dead father in a ball of myrrh, in order to cremate it. That is the original version, devoid of self-cremation and mystic rebirth.

[3] One tends to assume that the translation into Latin was the first of the many translations of the Physiologus, but even if it was we don't know when it was made. Moreover, the Latin translation need not have been the first, for a literate Roman would read Greek as a matter of course, just as a literate Englishman or German of the seventeenth century would read Latin as a matter of course.

An Armenian translation which is known to linguists is believed to have been made some time during the fourth century, an Arabic translation was made soon after, and an Ethiopian translation followed during the fifth century. This Ethiopian translation is of much interest for several reasons. The translator did not know Greek very well, which, strangely enough, makes the translation valuable. To begin with, the translator took "Physiologus" to be a name, so that the book is claimed to have been written "by the blessed Fîsâlgôs." Because of the translator's poor Greek, the names are hardly changed; the *nyktikorax* appears as *nikitiko,* the phoenix as *fineks,* and the bird *charadrios* as *karadyon.* A fair number of Greek words which the translator evidently did not know appear almost as they are in Greek (except in a different alphabet). Because of all this we not only can be certain that the translation was made from a Greek manuscript, we can even reconstruct a number of the original sentences which sometimes differ from the traditional often-copied text.

Although again we do not know the date, the Old High German translation is believed to be the oldest of the European translations. It was followed by an Anglo-Saxon translation, an Old English translation, a Middle English translation, and another somewhat more recent German translation. There is one in Old French and one in Provençal and one in Icelandic; the last looks as if it were based on two manuscripts, one the Old High German and the other unknown.

All these were straight translations, which is to say that the writers expressed in their own language what the manuscript said in another language. Sometimes something is missing, in which case one may assume that the manuscript copy serving the translator was incomplete. Sometimes the order of the animals is different—in the Middle High German version, for example, the phoenix is last, not the ostrich—but that may be due to something as trivial as unnumbered manuscript pages.

[4] Tabulation: the animals of the *Physiologus.*

Name of Animal	Armenian and Greek	Syriac	Latin, 8th century	Late Latin and Old High German	Theobald	Old French	Icelandic
Panther	18	—	16	2	12	24	21
Sirens	15	28	—	5	9	12	2, 3, and 6
Antholops	2	3	6	11	—	2	—
Elephant	44B	—	10	10	10	34	22
Lion	1	—	—	1	1	1	—
Fox	17	4	22	18	5	15	—
Beaver	26	2	8	19	—	17	—

Stag	32	—	—	16	6	30	10
Hedgehog	16	10	15	21	—	13	—
Unicorn	25	—	18	3	—	16	—
Hyena	37B	1	12	6	—	18	—
Serra	4	32	19	12	—	4	—
Ibex	43B	—	—	17	—	20	16
Aspidochelone	19	30	4	—	8	25	4
Wild ass	11	—	—	8	—	21	17
Monkey	11B	—	—	9	—	22	18
Weasel	23	11	—	—	—	27	—
Eagle	8	14	2	22	2	8	—
Charadrius	5	15	7	29	—	5	—
Nyktikorax	7	21	—	24	—	7	14
Pelican	6	20	17	23	—	6	—
Phoenix	9	16	12	30	—	9	1
Fulica	46B	17	14	7/25	—	23	20
Grouse	21	23	—	26	—	26	5
Hoopoe	10	22	—	28	—	10	—
Crow	29	24	—	—	—	—	—
Turtle dove	30	25	—	—	11	29	9
Ostrich	49B	29	3	27	—	28	0
Vulture	20	19	—	—	—	—	12
Doves	41B	26	—	—	—	32, 33	—
Ibis	42B	18	—	—	—	14	—
Snakes	13	7	20	14	3	—	—
Viper	12	6	21	13	—	—	—
Aspis snake	—	—	5	—	—	in 27	8
Ant	14	13	11	20	4	11	—
"Ant-lion"	22	12	—	—	—	—	—
Lizard	36B	8	—	15	—	—	—
Ichneumon	27	5	—	—	—	—	—
Hydrus	24	31	—	4	—	19	15
Salamander	39B	9	—	—	—	31	11
Frog	38B	—	—	—	—	—	—

Note: The numbering in the Armenian translation and the Greek manuscript (published by Pitra) are alike, but numbers followed by a B appear in the Greek version only. Both list the following additional items: 31 Swallow, 33 "Zerahav," 34 Bee, 35 Tiger, 3 burning stones, and 28 the tree Peridexion. The Syriac Physiologus has the Swallow as no. 27. The eighth-century Latin translation has stones as numbers 1 and 9; no. 13 is lacking. Theobald has the Spider as no. 7. The Old French version has stones as numbers 3 and 35. The Icelandic version lists the wild boar as number 13.

[5] The Latin text of Theobald's poem on the lion is taken from the Cologne printed edition and the English from the translation by Lieutenant Colonel Alan Wood Rendell. Rendell, in addition to his military and diplomatic duties—he was honorary A.D.C. to the viceroy of India 1897–1901—seems to have been a lifelong student of the Physiologus, and certainly proved that he was a good Latinist. The title page of his translation reads: *Physiologus, a metrical Bestiary of Twelve Chapters by Bishop Theobald;* Translated by Alan Wood Rendell (London: John & Edward Bumpus, Ltd., 1928). The book contains a facsimile reprint of the Cologne edition, a rendering into English, a reprint in modern type of the Cologne edition, and the Latin texts

of two other and probably later metric Latin versions based on that of Theobald.

⁶ *Popular Treatises on Science written during the Middle Ages,* by Thomas Wright, Esq., London, 1841. This work was reprinted in 1965 for Dawsons of Pall Mall (London). It forms a part of a book called *Historical Society of Science 1841,* the first society specifically devoted to the history of science and founded in London during that year. Even though the Duke of Sussex was president, the society lasted for only about two years. The book issued by Dawsons of Pall Mall comprises all the material originally printed for this society.

⁷ The *Etymologiarum* was printed for the first time in Augsburg in 1472. A complete edition of St. Isidore's known works was edited by F. Arevalo and published in seven volumes in Rome in 1797–1803. Two important studies of the works are: *An Encyclopedist of the Dark Ages, Isidore of Seville* by Dr. Ernest Brehant in Columbia University Studies in History, Economics and Public Law, vol. 48, no. 1 (whole no. 120) and *Die historisch-geographischen Quellen in den Etymologiae des Isidorus von Sevilla,* by Dr. Hans Philipp (2 vols., Berlin, 1912).

Chapter V

¹ St. Hildegard's complete writings were printed for the first time by J. P. Migne as *S. Hildegardis abbatissae opera omnia* (in *Patrologia latina,* vol. 197; Paris, 1855). The *Physica* had been printed separately at an earlier date, in Strasbourg in 1533. All translations that have been made are in German, as is virtually everything written about St. Hildegard. The only major article in English is Charles Singer's "The Scientific Views and Visions of Hildegard (in *Studies in the History of Science,* vol. I, pp. 1–55, Oxford, 1917). I have not seen *The Life and Visions of Hildegard* by Francesca Maria Steele, published in London in 1914, but I have heard unenthusiastic appraisals of it.

² Frederick's German designation is *Friedrich (II) der Staufer,* to distinguish him from other rulers called Frederick II, for example Frederick II (the Great) von Hohenzollern.

³ From *Studies in the History of Mediaeval Science* by Charles Homer Haskins (Cambridge: Harvard University Press, 1924). The book also contains a fine treatise on the book on hunting by Frederick II.

⁴ The first printed edition of "The Art of Hunting with Birds" was that of Markus Welser (Velser) of Augsburg in 1596; the text by Frederick II, with Manfred's additions, forms pp. 1–358 of the book; the other pages (359–414) contain the treatise on falcons by Albertus Magnus. A reprint of this work in two volumes appeared in Leipzig in 1788–89, arranged by the zoologist Johann Gottlieb Schneider who added a zoological commentary. The first

German translation of the two-book version was made by Johann Erhard Pacius (Ansbach, 1756), and the second by Hans Schöpffer, who added a list of the specialized terms used by falconers. This appeared in Berlin in 1896. A French translation of the two-book version was made around the year 1300 for Jean de Dampierre and his daughter Isabel. The manuscript is in the Bibliothèque nationale in Paris. It was never printed, but a French treatise on falconry by Guillaume Tardif, published in Geneva in 1560, contains sections of Frederick's work.

[5] Actually, the accomplishments of the thirteenth-century encyclopedists were made possible by the labors of a man who had lived one century earlier, the Italian Gerard of Cremona (1114–1187). Gerard was "only" a translator, but no translator in all history has ever been so important. Greek science was readily accessible in Gerard's time but it was obscured by a language barrier: all the manuscripts were in Arabic and were, of course, in the possession of Arabs. But in 1085 the Spaniards had reconquered Toledo, which had been an important center of Moslem learning; hence Arabic manuscripts in large numbers became available. And there were learned Arabs willing to teach their own language. Gerard either learned Arabic and then went to Toledo or else went to Toledo, and learned Arabic there. In any case he spent many years in the "college of translators" that flourished in Toledo under Archbishop Raymond. Apparently he did not return to Cremona, where he died, until late in his life. In the meantime he had translated from the Arabic not less than 92 works, among them the whole *Almagest* of Ptolemy, a number of the works of Aristotle, the *Elements* and *Data* of Euclid, the extant works of Hippocrates and of Galen, the *Algebra* of al-Khwārizmi, the Arabic version of Pliny, and countless Arabic commentaries and original works. It was a nearly impossible feat, even for someone completely fluent in both Arabic and Latin.

After Gerard had done the linguistic work, copyists could provide the libraries of the bishoprics and, somewhat later, of the larger monasteries, with copies of the works, thus laying the foundations for the advancement of learning.

[6] *De sphaera* by the English scholar Iohannes de Sacrobosco (John of Holy-Wood) was a short but very influential book on the astronomy of Ptolemy. For more detail see my *Watchers of the Skies* (New York: Viking, 1963), pages 56ff. Little is known about the life of its author.

[7] According to Professor Heinrich Balss, Pliny is mentioned by Albertus 65 times and criticized 11 times; Solinus is mentioned 22 times and criticized 5 times, while Jorach fared worst, being mentioned 13 times and criticized 6 times (*Albertus Magnus als Zoologe,* Munich, 1928).

[8] The whole *Speculum* of Vincent of Beauvais was printed in Strasbourg by Johannes Mentelin during the years 1473–1476; it is divided into seven folio

volumes but often bound into ten volumes because of the large number of pages. It was reprinted in Nuremberg in 1483–1486 and in Venice three times, 1484, 1493–94, and 1591. One more complete edition appeared at Douay in 1624. Only one portion, the *Speculum historiale,* has ever been translated, namely into French, appearing in 1495–96.

The *Collected Works* of Albertus Magnus were first published by Peter Jammy in Lyon in 1651 in 21 folio volumes; another *Collected Works* (slightly different in arrangement), prepared by Auguste Borgnet with the help of Emile Borgnet for the later volumes, appeared in Paris in 38 volumes in 1890–99. The latest complete edition was prepared over many years by the Albertus Magnus Institute of Cologne; it was finished in 1955 and contains a few treatises that had never been printed before.

The books on the animals are, of course, contained in these editions. The first separate edition of *De animalibus* appeared in Rome in 1478, published by Simon Chardella. Later printings were by Paul von Butzbach in Mantua in 1479, by Johannes and Gregorius de Gregoriis in Venice in 1495, and by Veter Scoti's heirs in Venice in 1519.

The best edition appeared during the years 1916–1920 under the title *De animalibus libri XXVI* in *Beiträge zur Geschichte der Philosophie des Mittelalters,* published in Münster in Westfalen. The edition was prepared by Hermann Stadler from the Cologne manuscript which is in all probability the author's original!

A reasonably complete German translation appeared in Frankfurt am Main in 1545 under the title *Thierbuch / Alberti Magni / Von Art Natur / und Eygenschafft der Thierer / . . . Durch Waltherum Ryff verteutscht.* A German translation of a few parts of the work, made by Heinrich Mynsinger in about 1450, was not printed until 1863 (Stuttgart, edited by K. D. Hassler).

[9] The second part, the *Speculum doctrinale,* somewhat belies its title—doctrine, theology, religious mythology, Holy Scripture, and the Fathers of the Church are only part of it. Its 17 books (with a total of 2,374 chapters) include discussions of the mechanical arts and statements about the duties of a prince, about the calling of the scholar, and about tactics in battle. It deals, under the general heading of "mathematics," with geometry, weights and measures, astronomy and astrology, music and metaphysics. It is one of the first European books in which the so-called Arabic numerals were explained.

The third part, the *Speculum historiale,* consists of 31 books, divided into 3,793 chapters, comprising all history from the creation to the Crusade of St. Louis.

The later printed versions of the *Speculum majus* show a fourth part, called *Speculum morale,* which was written by an unknown author sometime between 1310 and 1325. But the very large size of the *Majus* was a disadvantage. It could constitute a whole library for a man who wanted a general work of reference but seems to have been worthless for the specialist. In the field of zoology it is the least quoted of all medieval works.

[10] Bartholomaeus Anglicus' *De proprietatis rerum* was printed for the first time in Basel in about the year 1470. Reprints of this edition appeared in Cologne (1472, 1481, and 1483), in Lyon (1480 and 1482), in Nuremberg (1483, 1492, and 1519), in Strasbourg (1485, 1491, 1505, and 1575), in Heidelberg (1488), in Venice (1571), in Paris (1574), and in Frankfurt-am-Main (1601 and 1609)—evidently it was a book that the printers could sell. A French translation made by Jean Corbechon appeared in Lyon (first in 1482, with reprints in 1485, 1486, 1487, 1491, and 1500), in Paris (first in 1493, with reprints in 1510, 1518, 1525, 1528, 1530, 1539, and 1556—the last-mentioned year saw four different printings!), and in Rouen in 1512. A Dutch translation appeared in Haarlem in 1485. The Spanish translation by Vicente of Burgos was first printed in Toulouse (1494) and Batman appeared in London in 1582. A condensed version by Robert Steele in Westminster in 1495 and in London in 1535; a rearrangement by Stephen reprinted in Toledo (1529). The English version by John of Trevisa appeared (called Medieval Lore. . . , etc.) appeared in London in 1893 and was re-issued in 1907.

[11] Though Jakob van Maerlant was famous in his own lifetime and exerted a great influence on Dutch and Flemish letters, very little is known about him as a person. The year of his birth was probably 1235; the place was Damme near Bruges. Later he was sexton in Maerlant; hence, since sexton is *koster* in Dutch, he is sometimes called Jakob de Koster van Maerlant. Of his works, most of them translations, six are known by title, but only four have survived. The translation of Thomas of Cantimpré is one of them; another is a free translation of Vincent of Beauvais' *Speculum historiale* under the title *Spieghel historiael*. At about the time he finished the translation of Thomas he returned to Damme where he died in 1299.

Since Dutch is the language of a small area only, it is easy to understand why the early printers preferred books written in the universal Latin. *Der Naturen Bloeme* survived in manuscript form but was never printed until the middle of the nineteenth century, when J. H. Bormans prepared the first four books (books I, III, IV, and V of Thomas) for the printer as a memorial edition. It appeared in Brussels in 1857; a complete edition prepared by E. Verwijs appeared in Groningen in 1878.

[12] Conrat von Megenberg's version of Thomas of Cantimpré's work is not merely a translation, and for that very reason it is a treasure trove of incidental information, including a number of facts about Conrat's own life which would otherwise be unknown. Most important, Conrat's asides provide the date that the translation was made or else finished. He mentions that an "earthquake" (more likely a mountain slide) took place near Villach in Carinthia

in 1348, and also that the astrologers had prophesied an end of the Black Death at a certain time "but the dying still continues in this, the 1349th year." Elsewhere he says that "in the year 1349 since the birth of Christ some people arose who are called the *geissler,* who beat each other with whips until they fell to the ground," and then mentions the pastoral letter of Pope Clement VI to the bishop of Augsburg, condemning this practice. Since no later dates are given, Conrat must have concluded his work in 1349; otherwise he would have mentioned, for example, that Pope Clement died in 1352.

[13] The first printed edition of *Puoch der Natur* by Conrat von Megenberg was brought out by Hans Bämler of Augsburg in 1475. The same printer reprinted it in 1478 and 1481. A fourth printing was made by Hans Schönsperger, also of Augsburg, in 1482, and a fifth printing by Anton Sorg was made in the same city in the same year. Hans Schönsperger printed it again in 1499. By that time the language used by Conrat was becoming unfamiliar to German-speakers and the next edition shows a modernized language. Strangely enough the author's name had also been changed, for the title page reads *Conrad Mengelbergers Naturbuch.* This edition was published in Frankfurt-am-Main by the printer Christian Egenolff in 1536, with a reprint in 1540. An annotated reprint of the original was published by Dr. Franz Pfeiffer in Stuttgart in 1861 under the title *Das Buch der Natur von Conrad von Megenberg.* A few decades later a professor of German language and history, Dr. Hugo Schulz, translated it into modern High German. His translation was published in Greifswald in 1897.

[14] The Pope's prohibition against eating the Tree-geese refers only to fast times (and any Friday). It had been argued that these were not really birds but vegetables.

[15] Book IV of Conrat von Megenberg's work is about the trees and is in two sections: A, about "the trees," and B, about "the savory trees." The division corresponds loosely to trees and other plants that are native to northern Europe and trees that are not. But the use of classical sources has disturbed this scheme, for laurel, olive tree, pomegranate, and "the palm" (meaning the date palm) all appear in section A, though they don't grow in northern Europe. Section A consists of 55 chapters and section B of 29 chapters. Book V deals with herbs, in 89 chapters. Book VI consists of 85 chapters on "noble stones"—precious stones, semiprecious stones, and unusual minerals. The diamond and the lodestone were, as was then customary, both called *adamas;* the chapter contains a description of the mariner's compass. The book concludes with a chapter (no. 86 in most editions) consisting mainly of a Latin prayer to be said by a priest after mass for the purpose of restoring the "virtue" to gems that may have lost it for some reason. The introduction to the book on stones contains a very interesting passage: "The opinion of the Latin book cannot be right and it is a childish concept

to think that God gave the stones their virtues without using natural influences, and that He did it differently with trees and herbs. . . . I say that the herbs have virtues just as wonderful as those of the stones . . . and *therefore I, the Megenberger, say that I doubt that magnus Albertus has written the Latin book* [Author's italics], because in other works he speaks far differently about things than our book says. . . ."

Book VII, about the metals, has 10 chapters, beginning with gold (*aurum*). Silver comes next, then quicksilver, then *auripigmentum* (this name meant different things in different authors; Conrat's seems to be the yellow compound of sulfur and arsenic), then *electrum* (an alloy of gold and silver which appears under the strange name of *Gunderfai* in Conrat's German version), then copper, iron, tin, sulfur, and finally lead.

The final book, "On Wonderful Springs," is quite short and a collection of the type of the pseudo-Aristotelian "Of Marvellous Things Heard."

Conrat's version of *De natura rerum* has been treated at some length for several reasons, one of them being that it is virtually unknown in the Western world (except in Germany), but mainly because it is typical of all the encyclopedias of the thirteenth and early fourteenth centuries. In describing the *Puoch der Natur* they have all been described, at least as far as their zoological sections are concerned.

Just for the sake of completeness it must be stated that Jakob van Maerlant and Conrat von Megenberg were not the only translators of the work of Thomas of Cantimpré. A third translation exists. Georg, Baron of Waldburg, had obtained a copy of Thomas' work in about 1470, but feeling that his own Latin was not adequate, he requested one Peter Königschlaher, schoolmaster and city chronicler of Waldsee, to translate it into German for him. Schoolmaster Königschlaher complied, but his translation lacked Conrat's knowledge and common sense. German medievalists who examined the manuscript in the Royal Library of the King of Württemberg in Stuttgart, said that it "translated every word of the original with slavish obedience." It was never printed.

Chapter VI

[1] Not much has been written in English about Conrad Gesner. There is a biography in Sir W. Jardine's Naturalist's Library (in the volume on *Horses* by C. Hamilton Smith, published in Edinburgh in 1841) and an article "Conrad Gesner, the Father of Bibliography" by J. C. Bay in *Papers of the Bibliographical Society of America,* vol. X (Chicago, 1916).

[2] Both Conrad Gesner's first name and his surname present difficulties. The last name has been misspelled literally for centuries. Swiss, Germans, Frenchmen, and Englishmen were fairly unanimous in spelling it Gessner. The mistake was aided and abetted by the fact that the Swiss artist and poet

Salomon Gessner (1730–1788), who belonged to the same family, did spell his name with a double s, a German letter looking like a beta. As regards the first name, the reason one can find several versions in print is that several forms of it did exist in his time. In the sixteenth century the Germans spoke a number of dialects, as they still do. But nowadays the spelling of words is fixed regardless of dialect, while during the sixteenth century everybody wrote the words in a manner that looked right to him. Thus we find Conrad, Konrat, Künrat, Cunrat, Chuonrat, and Chünrad.

Whenever such a situation prevails there is only one way out, namely to discover if possible what the bearer of the name wrote himself. Fortunately a large number of Gesner's papers have been preserved and they show that he signed his letters as Conradus Gesnerus (the Gesnerus with a long s) and sometimes Con. Gesnerus; evidently the non-Latin version would be Conrad Gesner. In Gesner's last will and testament, which is in Swiss-German, the name appears as Cunrat Gessner, but we do not have his own handwritten original, only copies made by city clerks who obviously spelled it as they pronounced it.

[3] The printing history of Gesner's zoological work is as follows:

The original Latin edition

(Vol. I)   Conradi Gesneri Medici Tigurini *Historia animalium,* liber primus, qui est de quadrupedibus viviparis, cum figuris . . . , etc. etc. Zurich, 1551; new editions in 1603 and 1620.

(Vol. II)   Conradi Gesneri Medici Tigurini *Historia animalium* liber secundus, de quadrupedibus oviparis . . . , etc. etc. Zurich, 1554; new editions in 1586 and 1617.

(Vol. III)   Conradi Gesneri Medici Tigurini *Historia animalium* liber tertius, qui est de Avium natura . . . , etc. etc. Zurich, 1555; second enlarged edition, edited by Robert Cambier (using Gesner's notes found among his papers after his death), Frankfurt-am-Main 1585; reprint of the latter edition in 1617.

(Vol. IV)   Conradi Gesneri Medici Tigurini *Historia animalium* liber quartus, qui est de Piscium and aquatilium animantium natura. Cum iconibus . . . , etc. etc. Zurich, 1558, new editions in 1604 and 1620.

(Vol. V)   Conradi Gesneri Medici Tigurini *Historia animalium* liber quintus, qui est de Serpentum natura . . . , etc. etc. Zurich, 1587; second edition in 1621 (compiled from Gesner's papers by Jacobus Carronus of Frankfurt, with an added section on the natural history of the scorpion by Dr. Caspar Wolf of Zurich, from Gesner's papers for a planned sixth volume on insects).

The books are of greatly differing lengths. Not counting title pages, dedications, prefaces, tables of contents, etc., Vol. I. has a length of 1,110 pages; Vol. II. only 137 pages; Vol. III. 779 pages; Vol. IV. 1,297 pages, and Vol. V. 170 pages plus 22 pages on the scorpion.

The shortened Latin edition

(Vol. I) Icones Animalium quadrupedum viviparorum et oviparorum quae primo et secundo Historiae Animalium libris a CONRADO GESNERO describuntur, cum nomenclaturis lat. ital. Gall. & germ. Zurich, 1553, in folio, 68 pages, containing the illustrations from Vols. I and II of the main edition, plus names in four languages, etc.; second edition, Zurich, 1560, 135 pages in folio, dedicated to Queen Elizabeth of England.

(Vol. II) Icones Avium omnium quae in Avium Historia describuntur . . . , etc.
Zurich, 1555, 135 pages, folio. Second edition Zurich, 1560, 247 pages.

(Vol. III) Icones Animalium aquatilium in mari et dulcibus aquis degentium. . . . Zurich, 1560, folio, 374 pages.

The German edition

(Vol. I) *Thierbuch* (Book of Animals), translated by Dr. Conrad Forer. Zurich, 1563, 343 pages; second edition, 1583. This comprises Vols. I and II of the main edition.

(Vol. II) *Vogelbuch* (Book of Birds), translated by Dr. Rudolf Heusslin. Zurich, 1557, 522 pages; second edition, 1582, reprinted in 1600.

(Vol. III) *Fischbuch* (Book of Fishes), translated by Dr. Conrad Forer. Zurich, 1563, 404 pages; second edition, 1575, third edition, Frankfurt-am-Main, 1598.

(Vol. IV) *Schlangenbuch* (Book of Snakes), anonymous translator. Zurich, 1589, reprints in 1613 and in 1662 *or* 1671—it is believed that the date MDCLXII should read MDCLXXI.

Gesnerus redivivus. A reprint of the four German volumes with minor changes, published by G. Horst in 1669–70. Strangely enough, this late reprint is rarer than either the main Latin or the first German edition.

The English version of Edward Topsell

The Historie of Fovre-footed Beastes. Describing the true and liuely figure of euery Beast, with a discourse of their seuerall Names, Conditions, Kindes, Vertues (both naturall and medicinall), Countries of their breed, their loue and hate to Mankinde, and the wonderfull worke of God in their Creation,

Preseruation and Destruction . . . collected out of all the Volumes of Con-
radvs Gesner . . . by Edward Topsell. London, 1607, 700 pages, small folio.

In spite of the statement on the title page, Topsell utilized only the first
volume of the main Latin edition for his work. It is dedicated to "the reverend
and right worshipfull Richard Neile, D. of Divinity, Deane of Westminster";
Topsell signed his dedicatory preface as "Your Chaplaine in the Church of
Saint Buttolphe Aldergate." Apparently he intended to translate the other
volumes too, if the first one was a success, but only Vol. V of the main edition
was published, appearing in 1608 under the title *The Historie of Serpents*.
Both volumes were reprinted in 1658, along with an English translation of
Thomas Mouffet's book on insects, originally published in Latin in London,
1634.

In 1967 the Da Capo Press in New York City issued a facsimile edition of
the 1658 edition in three volumes. The overall title is *The History of Four-
Footed Beasts and Serpents and Insects*. The size has been slightly reduced;
the first volume of 586 numbered pages contains the four-footed beasts, the
second volume (227 numbered pages) the serpents, and the third (of 251
numbered pages) the insects.

Other books by and about Gesner

Conradi Gesneri Opera Botanica, Nuremberg, 1753, two volumes, extra-large
folio, edited by Dr. Casimir Christopher Schmiedel. The botanical papers of
Gesner with many illustrations which he had collected. The first volume contains a long biography by Gesner by Schmiedel, which also exists as a separate
book. Other biographies of Gesner are: *Vita Conradi Gesneri* by Josias Simm-
ler, Zurich, 1566, in two parts: part I being the biography, part II a list of
Gesner's works. A German translation of this book by David Richter appeared
in Leipzig in 1711 under the title *Des Welt-berühmten Medici, Physici &
Polyhistoris Conradi Gesneri Leben und Schrifften*. A valuable work based
on archival sources, etc., is Johannes Hanhart's *Conrad Gessner,* published in
Winterthur in 1824.

[4] Traditionally Gesner considered Hebrew to be the "first language" which
has remained pure and unchanged. All other languages were divided into two
groups, the classical languages on the one hand and the "barbarian" languages
on the other. The classical ones were Greek and Latin; a subdivision of the
classical languages was the "flawed languages"—French, Italian, and Spanish.
Among the barbarian languages the languages of Scandinavia formed a family,
closely allied to Saxon. He was especially interested in what is now called the
"vowel shift" of English, by which the letter *a* came to express the sound that
e has in Latin, Italian, and French, while the letter *e* expresses the *sound i*
in those languages. To give an example of the languages discussed Gesner

published the Lord's Prayer in 22 different languages, throwing in a metric German version he had written himself.

⁵ One of Gesner's ingratiating habits was always to inform his readers why he did what he did. Thus he explained his scheme of treating the material about a certain animal. Each, if possible, would have eight subdivisions, which were to be numbered A, B, C, D, and so forth. "I did not choose numbers because in some cases nothing may be known and leaving out a letter is less annoying to the eye than leaving out a number." Section A listed all the names in various languages, including the various German dialects. Section B included area of occurrence, whether frequent or rare, description of the animal, and, if available, its internal organs. Section C dealt with the motion of the animal and with the diseases it was known to have. Section D describes the habits and instincts. Section E deals with its usefulness, either as game or for domestication. Section F deals with the animal as food (if edible), section G with its medicinal value (if any). The last section, H, might be called the literary section, for it quotes poetic names, with their etymology, poetic allusions, proverbs about the animal, places named after the animal, and the fables told about it.

Dr. Rudolf Heusslin, the translator of the volume on birds, was just as careful: "Know then that under A I have left out the foreign names but retained the German names, one, two, three or how many there may be. To this I have added B . . . have made one German chapter out of two in Latin. Then I have grouped C and D and those facts about food and medicine, as much as is needed, under a separate heading. The last chapter, the one called H, I left out since it may be useful in other languages but is unnecessary in German, considering that it deals with the word and not with knowledge and history. A few short chapters, which have no pictures and about which there might be some doubt, I have left out. And I have done all this so that it may be more pleasing to the reader."

⁶ An excellent account of the literary history of the unicorn is Dr. Odell Shepard's *The Lore of the Unicorn* (Boston: Houghton Mifflin, 1930).

⁷ Harteret's article on the *Waldrapp* appeared in *Novitates zoologicae,* vol. IV, p. 371. The scientific name used was *Comatibis eremita,* a name proposed by Linnaeus after he himself had begun to doubt that the *Waldrapp* was a hoopoe and had tentatively moved it to the ibises.

⁸ The titles of Pierre Belon's two main works are: *Histoire de la Nature des Oyseaux* and *Histoire Naturelle des Étranges Poissons marines;* the latter is the work used by Gesner.

⁹ A good biography of Aldrovandi has yet to be written. An Italian zoologist living in or near Bologna with access to the city archives would be the logical candidate for the job. Recent Italian writings on Aldrovandi's books contain a

number of biographical items, but the only straight biography of any length is that by Giovanni Fantuzzi, included in his *Notizie degli Scrittori Bolognesi* (Vol. I), published in 1781. The only substantial article in English that I know of is a biographical chapter preceding the main body of the book *British Quadrupeds* by William Macgillivray, published in Edinburgh in 1843. The book *Aldrovandi on Chickens,* a translation of the sections on chickens in the second volume of Aldrovandi's *Ornithologia,* contains a short biography by L. R. Lind, who also did the translation. This book also lists bibliographical material. It was published by the University of Oklahoma Press, Norman, Oklahoma, in 1963.

[10] The printing history of Aldrovandi's work is as follows:

Vol. I.   *Ornithologia,* first part, Bologna, 1599; Frankfurt-am-Main, 1610.

Vol. II.   *Ornithologia,* second part, Bologna, 1600; Frankfurt-am-Main, 1629.

Vol. III.   *Ornithologia,* third part, Bologna, 1603; Frankfurt-am-Main, 1621. Reprints: Bologna, 1637, 1646, 1652, and 1681.

Vol. IV.   *De animalibus insectis . . . ,* etc. Bologna, 1602; reprints 1620 and 1638; Frankfurt-am-Main, 1623.

Vol. V.   *De reliquis animalibus exanguibus . . . De Mollibus, Crustaceis, Testaceis & Zoophytis.* Bologna, 1606 and 1646; Frankfurt-am-Main, 1623.

Vol. VI.   *De Piscibus libri V et De Cetos liber unus,* edited by Iohannes Cornelius Uterverius and Hieronymus Tambrinus. Bologna, 1613, 1638, and 1661; Frankfurt-am-Main, 1623, 1629, and 1640.

Vol. VII.   *De Quadrupedibus solidipedibus,* edited by Uterverius and Tambrinus. Bologna, 1616, 1639, and 1648; Frankfurt-am-Main, 1623.

Vol. VIII.   *Quadrupedum omnium bisulcornum historia,* edited by Uterverius and Thomas Dempsterus. Bologna, 1621 and 1653; Frankfurt-am-Main, 1647.

Vol. IX.   *De quadrupedibus digitatis viviparis libri tres, et, De quadrupedibus digitatis oviparis libri duo.* Edited by Bartholomaeus Ambrosinus. Bologna, 1637, 1645, and 1663.

Vol. X.   *Serpentum, et draconem historiae libri duo,* edited by Ambrosinus. Bologna, 1640.

Vol. XI.   *Monstrorum historia,* edited by Ambrosinus. Bologna, 1642 and 1658.

Vol. XII.   *Musaeum metallicum in libros IIII.* Bologna, 1648. (An abbreviation of this volume appeared in Leipzig in 1701 with the title *Synopsis Museai Metallici.*)

Vol. XIII.   *Dentrologiae naturalis . . . ,* etc. Bologna, 1668.

Chapter VII

[1] Such delays were all too common, unfortunately, as is shown by the case of the Venetian Prosper Alpinus (1553–1617). In 1578, after having obtained his medical doctorate, he went to Egypt to serve the Venetian colony there as resident physician. While in Egypt he collected material on the snakes of the area, on African monkeys, and especially on the hippopotamus and wrote a good book about his personal observations. But it was not printed until 1735, by which time it no longer contained much that was "new."

[2] A careful discussion of which animals were meant by the forty four-footed animals in José d'Acosta's book was not published until 1827, as a historical study by the German zoologist Lichtenstein.

[3] Like Gesner, John Ray thought that Hebrew was "the original tongue" and he made vain attempts to derive Greek, Latin, and even English words from Hebrew.

[4] Publications by John Ray:

1660   *Catalogus Cantabrigiam*

1663   Appendix to the *Catalogus;* second appendix in 1685

1670   *Catalogus Angliae;* second ed. 1677
       Collection of English Proverbs; second ed. 1678

1673   *Observationes et Catalogus Exteris*
       Collection of English Words; second ed. 1691

1675   *Dictionariolum;* second ed., retitled *Nomenclator Classicus,* 1689; third ed. 1696; fourth ed. 1703; more editions after Ray's death, the eighth (and last?) in 1736

1676   Willughby's *Ornithologia* in Latin; English version in 1678

1682   *Methodus Plantarum*

1686   Willughby's *Historia Piscium*
       Historia Plantarum, Vol. I

1688   *Historia Plantarum,* Vol. II
       Fasciculus Britannicarum; second ed. 1696

1691   *Wisdom of God;* second ed. 1692; third ed. 1701; fourth ed. 1704

1692   *Miscellaneous Discourses*

1693   *Synopsis Quadrupedum*
       Collection of Curious Travels
       Three Physico-Theological Discourses; second ed. same year; third ed. 1713

1696   *Dissertatio de Methodis*
       Persuasive to a Holy Life

1704   *Historia Plantarum,* Vol. III
       Methodus Insectorum

1710   (posthumous) *Historia Insectorum*
1713   (posthumous) *Synopsis Avium et Piscium*
1718   (posthumous) *Philosophical Letters*

An excellent biography of Ray was published by the Cambridge (England) University Press in 1942, reprint 1950. The title of the book is *John Ray, Naturalist* and its author is Charles E. Raven, D.D. and D. Sc.

Chapter VIII

[1] Fossil fishes had also been mentioned by Xenophanes. The subject of antique reports on fossil fishes received a thorough going-over in the journal *Isis,* vol. XXXIII (1941), pp. 56–58, and p. 335; vol. XXXIV (1942), pp. 24 and 363; and vol. XXXVI (1946), p. 155.

[2] The translation of *De re metallica* first appeared in *The Mining Magazine* (London), 1912; it was published in book form with most of the original illustrations by Dover Publications, New York, in 1950. One of Agricola's other works, *De natura fossilium,* originally published in 1546, also has been translated. The translators were Mark Chance Bandy and Jean A. Bandy, and their translation was published as Special Paper 63 by The Geological Society of America in November 1955.

[3] A small book by Gesner's friend Johann Kentmann, physician in Torgau (in Agricola's mining district), which was published along with Gesner's *De natura fossilium,* is much less ambitious and much better. Under the title *Nomenclaturae rerum fossilium,* Kentmann published a list of the 1,600 mineralogical specimens in his collection, with short descriptions in both Latin and in German.

Another book from this period, though it did not contribute to science, must be mentioned. Its title is *Sarepta* (Nuremberg, 1571) and the author was Johann Matthesius, Lutheran pastor of Joachimsthal. "It was a collection of sermons for miners, all the geological and mineralogical statements of the Holy Writ being explained, illuminated and moralized. It shows that the good pastor was very familiar with the mining lore and customs of his parishioners." (George Sarton in *Six Wings,* p. 160.)

[4] Latin reprints of Nicolaus Sten's *Prodromus* were made in Leyden (1679) and Pistoja (1743); an English translation appeared in London in 1671 (Henry Oldenburg). In 1904 Junk in Berlin published a facsimile reprint of the original; a Danish translation by August Krogh and Wilhelm Maar (1902) was followed by another Latin reprint (Copenhagen, 1910). An English version by John Garrett Winter appeared as Vol. XI of the Humanistic Series of the University of Michigan Studies (published by Macmillan, New York, 1916) and a German translation was published as No. 209 of *Ostwald's Klassiker* in 1923.

[5] *Writings of Thomas Jefferson,* 1904 edition, Vol. II, p. 71.

[6] Leibniz died on November 14, 1716, at Hanover. The manuscript of the *Protagaea* existed in two copies, known as A and B. Manuscript B was printed in 1748 in Latin; a German translation of it by Christian L. Scheid appeared a year later. Manuscript A, which shows corrections in Leibniz' hand, was published as Vol. I of his *Collected Works* in 1949, with a German translation by W. von Engelhardt. There is a French translation, but none into English. Manuscript B was destroyed by fire during the Second World War; Manuscript A is still preserved.

Chapter IX

[1] The introduction to Cuvier's *Recherches* . . . was later printed separately, literally by public demand, as *Discours sur les révolutions de la surface du globe.*

[2] Charles Darwin, a number of years after the first publication of his fundamental *Origin of Species,* was asked whom he himself considered to have been his precursors and Darwin, always willing to please, listed them in the introduction to the third edition of his work. Lamarck heads the list, of course, along with his successor Geoffroy Saint-Hilaire. Darwin also listed one Robert E. Grant of Edinburgh, S. S. Haldemann of Philadelphia, C. S. Rafinesque (of Sicily, but working in America), the German geologist Christian Leopold von Buch and the French geologist Jean-Jacques Omalius d'Halloy, the Rev. William Herbert (an ardent horticulturist), Charles Wells, an American physician—and it must be said that Darwin's list was not complete. He left out scientists writing in German and untranslated at the time—it took Darwin hours to read just two pages of German—such as the German zoologist Johann Jakob Kaup and the Swiss botanist Karl Wilhelm von Nägeli. All of these had voiced a belief in "mutability" at some time, the Reverend Herbert as a result of his studies in plant breeding, and Dr. Wells had studied skin pigmentation in humans in relation to the climate in which they lived, with resulting ideas remarkably similar to Darwin's principle of natural selection.

[3] The story of Robert Chambers, of *Vestiges,* and of the reaction to the book has been well told in *Just Before Darwin, Robert Chambers and Vestiges* by Milton Millhauser (Middletown, Conn., Wesleyan University Press, 1959).

[4] Crosse seems to have been trying to make pure silicon when his little animals appeared unexpectedly. He gave them the name *Acarus electricus;* the drawing he made strongly resembles the well-known *Acarus horridus.*

Index

Numbers in italics refer to pictures.